Assessment Sourcebook

UCSMP Secondary Component

THE UNIVERSITY OF CHICAGO SCHOOL MATHEMATICS PROJECT

ADVANCED ALGEBRA

INTEGRATED MATHEMATICS

About Assessment
Assessment Forms

Chapter Tests, Forms A, B, C, and D
Chapter Tests, Cumulative Form
Answers
Evaluation Guides

Scott Foresman
Addison Wesley

Editorial Offices: Glenview, Illinois • Menlo Park, California
Sales Offices: Reading, Massachusetts • Atlanta, Georgia • Glenview, Illinois
Carrollton, Texas • Menlo Park, California

http://www.sf.aw.com

Contents

Pages	Contents
iv	Assessing Student Performance in Mathematics
vi	Portfolios and Notebooks
vii	Using Free-Response and Multiple-Choice Tests
viii	Using Performance Assessment
x	Using Assessment Forms

Student-Completed Forms

Pages	Contents
xi	Student Survey
xii	Student Self-Assessment
xiii	Cooperative Groups Self-Assessment
xiv	About My Portfolio

Teacher-Completed Forms

Pages	Contents
xv	Portfolio Assessment
xvi	Notebooks *Individual Assessment*
xvii	Notebooks *Class Checklist*
xviii	Problem Solving *Individual Assessment*
xix	Problem Solving *Class Checklist*
xx	Observation *Individual Assessment*
xxi	Observation *Class Checklist*
xxii	Cooperative Groups *Class Checklist*
xxiii	Projects *Individual Assessment*
xxiv	Overall Student Assessment *Class Checklist*

Tests

Pages	Contents
1	Quiz Lessons 1-1 Through 1-3
2	Quiz Lessons 1-4 Through 1-6
3–5	Chapter 1 Test, Form A
6–8	Chapter 1 Test, Form B
9	Chapter 1 Test, Form C
10	Chapter 1 Test, Form D
11	Quiz Lessons 2-1 Through 2-3
12	Quiz Lessons 2-4 Through 2-6
13–15	Chapter 2 Test, Form A
16–18	Chapter 2 Test, Form B
19	Chapter 2 Test, Form C
20	Chapter 2 Test, Form D
21–24	Chapter 2 Test, Cumulative Form
25	Quiz Lessons 3-1 Through 3-3
26	Quiz Lessons 3-4 Through 3-6
27–29	Chapter 3 Test, Form A
30–32	Chapter 3 Test, Form B
33	Chapter 3 Test, Form C
34	Chapter 3 Test, Form D
35–38	Chapter 3 Test, Cumulative Form
39–42	Comprehensive Test, Chapters 1–3
43	Quiz Lessons 4-1 Through 4-3
44	Quiz Lessons 4-4 Through 4-7
45–47	Chapter 4 Test, Form A
48–50	Chapter 4 Test, Form B
51	Chapter 4 Test, Form C
52	Chapter 4 Test, Form D
53–56	Chapter 4 Test, Cumulative Form
57	Quiz Lessons 5-1 Through 5-4
58	Quiz Lessons 5-5 Through 5-7
59–61	Chapter 5 Test, Form A
62–64	Chapter 5 Test, Form B
65	Chapter 5 Test, Form C
66	Chapter 5 Test, Form D
67–70	Chapter 5 Test, Cumulative Form
71	Quiz Lessons 6-1 Through 6-4
72	Quiz Lessons 6-5 Through 6-7
73–75	Chapter 6 Test, Form A
76–78	Chapter 6 Test, Form B
79	Chapter 6 Test, Form C
80	Chapter 6 Test, Form D
81–83	Chapter 6 Test, Cumulative Form
84–88	Comprehensive Test, Chapters 1–6

ISBN: 0-673-45811-3

5 6 7 8 9 10 11 - DBH - 04 03 02 01

Pages	Contents
Tests	
89	Quiz Lessons 7-1 Through 7-3
90	Quiz Lessons 7-4 Through 7-6
91–93	Chapter 7 Test, Form A
94–96	Chapter 7 Test, Form B
97	Chapter 7 Test, Form C
98	Chapter 7 Test, Form D
99–101	Chapter 7 Test, Cumulative Form
102	Quiz Lessons 8-1 Through 8-3
103	Quiz Lessons 8-4 Through 8-6
104–106	Chapter 8 Test, Form A
107–109	Chapter 8 Test, Form B
110	Chapter 8 Test, Form C
111	Chapter 8 Test, Form D
112–114	Chapter 8 Test, Cumulative Form
115	Quiz Lessons 9-1 Through 9-3
116	Quiz Lessons 9-4 Through 9-7
117–119	Chapter 9 Test, Form A
120–122	Chapter 9 Test, Form B
123	Chapter 9 Test, Form C
124	Chapter 9 Test, Form D
125–128	Chapter 9 Test, Cumulative Form
129–133	Comprehensive Test, Chapters 1–9
134	Quiz Lessons 10-1 Through 10-3
135	Quiz Lessons 10-4 Through 10-7
136–138	Chapter 10 Test, Form A
139–141	Chapter 10 Test, Form B
142	Chapter 10 Test, Form C
143	Chapter 10 Test, Form D
144–146	Chapter 10 Test, Cumulative Form
147	Quiz Lessons 11-1 Through 11-3
148	Quiz Lessons 11-4 Through 11-7
149–151	Chapter 11 Test, Form A
152–154	Chapter 11 Test, Form B
155	Chapter 11 Test, Form C
156	Chapter 11 Test, Form D
157–159	Chapter 11 Test, Cumulative Form
160	Quiz Lessons 12-1 Through 12-3
161	Quiz Lessons 12-4 Through 12-7
162–164	Chapter 12 Test, Form A
165–167	Chapter 12 Test, Form B
168	Chapter 12 Test, Form C
169	Chapter 12 Test, Form D
170–172	Chapter 12 Test, Cumulative Form
173	Quiz Lessons 13-1 Through 13-3
174	Quiz Lessons 13-4 Through 13-7
175–177	Chapter 13 Test, Form A
178–180	Chapter 13 Test, Form B
181	Chapter 13 Test, Form C
182	Chapter 13 Test, Form D
183–185	Chapter 13 Test, Cumulative Form
186–189	Comprehensive Test, Chapters 1–13

Pages	Contents
Answers	
Quizzes; Tests, Forms A and B, Cumulative Forms; Comprehensive Tests	
190	Chapter 1
191	Chapter 2
193	Chapter 3
196	Chapter 4
199	Chapter 5
201	Chapter 6
204	Chapter 7
206	Chapter 8
207	Chapter 9
210	Chapter 10
211	Chapter 11
214	Chapter 12
216	Chapter 13
Evaluation Guides	
Tests, Forms C and D	
219	Chapter 1
221	Chapter 2
223	Chapter 3
225	Chapter 4
227	Chapter 5
229	Chapter 6
231	Chapter 7
233	Chapter 8
235	Chapter 9
237	Chapter 10
239	Chapter 11
241	Chapter 12
243	Chapter 13

Assessing Student Performance in Mathematics

The Changing Face of Mathematics Instruction and Assessment

In the past decade, the National Council of Teachers of Mathematics and other mathematics education organizations and professionals have examined the methods teachers use to instruct students in mathematics and have recommended ways to improve this instruction. Their recommendations stress the importance of providing more diverse methods of instruction including activities, open-ended investigations, and long-term projects, many of which utilize cooperative learning. They challenge us to make the goal of mathematics the acquisition of the dynamic processes of critical thinking and problem solving, rather than merely the mastery of a static body of facts and procedures.

Instruction and assessment are closely linked. As instructional methods change, the methods of evaluation need to change. New forms of assessment being proposed provide a more authentic way of evaluating the depth of our students' knowledge of mathematics rather than their ability to memorize facts and procedures. These alternative methods of assessment offer students the opportunity to display how they approach problem situations, collect and organize information, formulate and test conjectures, and communicate their mathematical insights.

An authentic assessment program contains tasks that are appropriate to the topics the students are learning and that provide outcomes that are valuable to the students. Such an assessment program allows for such highly individual factors as a school's curriculum objectives, a teacher's style of instruction, and a student's maturity level and preferred learning style. Each individual teacher determines the assessment program best suited to the needs of his or her students.

In an instructional environment that demands a deeper understanding of mathematics, testing instruments that call for only identification of single correct responses no longer suffice. Instead, our instruments must reflect the scope and intent of our instructional program to have students solve problems, reason, and communicate.

NCTM Standards

To help a teacher select the most appropriate evaluation tools for his or her classroom, this *Assessment Sourcebook* provides the following materials. (See pre-chapter pages in UCSMP **Advanced Algebra** Teacher's Edition for correlation of test items to chapter objectives.)

Assessment Forms

- student-completed forms
- teacher-completed forms for individual, group, and class activities

Assessment Instruments

- **Chapter Quizzes,** two per chapter, which cover three or four lessons and which contain mostly free-response items
- **Chapter Tests, Forms A and B,** which are alternate versions of each other and which test every chapter objective in primarily free-response format
- **Chapter Tests, Form C,** which consist of 4 to 6 performance-based, open-ended items, many of which assess several chapter objectives
- **Chapter Tests, Form D,** which are performance based and which often assess 5 or more chapter objectives as applied to a single larger task
- **Chapter Tests, Cumulative Form,** which contain mostly free-response items
- **Comprehensive Tests,** every three or four chapters, which are cumulative in nature and consist primarily of multiple-choice items

To assess development of a student's mathematical power, a teacher needs to use a mixture of means: essays, homework, projects, short answers, quizzes, blackboard work, journals, oral interviews, and group projects.

Everybody Counts: A Report to the Nation on the Future of Mathematics Education

Guidelines for Developing an Authentic Assessment Program

Developing an authentic program of assessment is an ongoing process. Some assessment instruments will seem perfectly suited to the teacher and his or her students from the start. Others may be effective only after the teacher has had a chance to experiment, and refine them. Still others may be inappropriate for a given class or instructional situation. The following are some guidelines that may be helpful when choosing the types of assessment for a particular program.

Assessment serves many purposes.

- For the teacher, assessment yields feedback on the appropriateness of instructional methods and offers some clues as to how the content or pace of instruction could be modified.
- For the students, assessment should not only identify areas for improvement, but it should also affirm their successes.
- Traditional forms of assessment yield a tangible score.

Make the assessment process a positive experience for students.

- Use a variety of assessment techniques.
- Provide opportunities for students to demonstrate their mathematical capabilities in an atmosphere that encourages maximum performance.
- Emphasize what students *do* know and *can* do, not what they do not know and cannot do.
- Motivate students to achieve by using tasks that reflect the value of their efforts.

Authentic assessment focuses on higher-order thinking skills.

- Provides a picture of the student as a critical thinker and problem solver
- Identifies *how* the student does mathematics, not just what answer he or she gets

Provide assessment activities that resemble day-to-day tasks.

- Use activities similar to instructional activities to assess.
- Use assessment activities to further instruction.
- Give students the immediate and detailed feedback they need to further the learning process.
- Encourage students to explore how the mathematics they are learning applies to real situations.

Include each student as a partner in the assessment process.

- Encourage students to reflect on what they have done.
- Encourage students to share their goals.

Portfolios and Notebooks

A portfolio is a collection of a student's work—projects, reports, drawings, reflections, representative assignments, assessment instruments—that displays the student's mathematical accomplishments over an extended period. The following suggestions for use should be adapted to the needs and organizational style of each situation.

A student notebook should reflect the student's day-to-day activities related to the mathematics class. It may include a section for journal entries as well as sections for homework, tests, and notes.

Getting Started

- Provide file folders labeled *Portfolio.*
- Provide guidelines for notebook format.

The Portfolio

- The Portfolio can be used as the basis for assessing a student's achievements. The focus of the Portfolio should be on student thinking, growth in understanding over time, making mathematical connections, positive attitudes about mathematics, and the problem-solving process.

The Notebook

- The notebook is for "work in progress." The student should keep in it all class and reading notes, group work, homework, reports and projects, and various student assessment forms, such as *Student Self-Assessment.*
- Every two to six weeks students review their notebooks to determine the materials they would like to transfer to their Portfolios.
- The teacher also selects student materials for the Portfolio and includes any appropriate assessment instruments.
- The student completes the *About My Portfolio* form.

The opportunity to share mathematical ideas through portfolios can mark a real turning point in student attitudes.

Mathematics Assessment (NCTM Publication)

- Portfolios may include:
  student selected items from the notebook; a letter from the student about the work; a math autobiography; other work selected by the teacher including math surveys; various assessment documents.

Evaluating a Portfolio

- Keep in mind that portfolio evaluation is a matter of ongoing discussion.
- Set aside time to discuss the Portfolio with the student.
- Use the Portfolio when discussing the student's progress with his or her family.
- Use it as a basis for identifying strengths and weaknesses and for setting goals for the next block of work.
- Consider developing your own criteria for evaluating portfolios, for example, numeric scales.

Evaluating a Notebook

- Notebooks should be evaluated based on agreed-upon guidelines.
- Notebooks should be evaluated for organization and neatness, completeness, and timeliness.
- Notebooks may be evaluated every week, every chapter, or any time you feel is appropriate.
- You may choose to evaluate notebooks by checking items or by assigning numeric values to specific items.

Using Free-Response and Multiple-Choice Tests

Teachers use written tests for many purposes. Particularly when it is objective-referenced, a test can be a relatively quick and efficient method of diagnosing the scope of a student's mathematical knowledge. Tests can also provide valuable instructional feedback. And, of course, grades are a traditional instrument for reporting student achievement to parents, administrators, and the community. This *Sourcebook* provides a large number of both free-response and multiple-choice items.

Free-Response Tests

A free-response test, sometimes called a completion test, is a collection of items for which a student must supply requested information. While free-response tests are generally designed for written responses, they may also be used orally with individual students, especially those with limited English proficiency.

Multiple-choice Tests

A multiple-choice test consists of many well-defined problems or questions. The student is given a set of four or five possible answers for each item and is asked to select the correct or best answer. The other choices, often called distractors, usually reflect common misconceptions or errors.

This *Sourcebook* contains:

- Quizzes covering three or four lessons in each chapter. The quizzes are primarily free response in nature.
- Chapter Tests, Forms A and B, which are alternate forms of each other and which test every chapter objective. The tests contain primarily free-response items, but they may also include several multiple-choice items. These tests can be used as chapter pretests and posttests to help implement needed individualized instruction
- Chapter Tests, Cumulative Form, for Chapters 2-13, which are basically free-response assessment
- Comprehensive Tests for Chapters 1-3, 1-6, 1-9, and 1-13, which consist of mostly multiple-choice items and are cumulative in nature

Using Performance Assessment

In order to provide more authentic forms of assessment, this *Sourcebook* provides two forms of chapter tests that focus on students' ability to demonstrate their understanding of mathematical concepts.

Chapter Tests, Form C

The Form C Chapter Test items help you make a judgment of the students' understanding of mathematical concepts and their ability to interpret information, make generalizations, and communicate their ideas. Each assessment contains four to six open-ended questions, each of which is keyed to several chapter objectives.

Administering Form C Tests

The tests can be administered in a way that is best suited for the students. Provide manipulatives, extra paper, and other tools as needed. The use of calculators is assumed.

- Use all the assessment items.
- Use only one or two, along with a free-response or a multiple-choice test.
- Use the assessment items to interview each student.
- Have students give the explanations orally, and then write the answers.

Evaluating Form C Tests

Each test item is accompanied by a list of two or more evaluation criteria that can be used as a basis for judging student responses.

To rate how well students meet each criterion, a simple scale such as this may be used.

+ excellent
✓ satisfactory
− inadequate

Evaluation Guides for these tests are found starting on page 219 of this *Sourcebook.*

Comparison of Form C Tests and Free-Response Tests

	Form C Tests	Free Response Tests
Number of items	4–6	15–35
Sample Format	○ Draw 3 different rectangles that each have an area of 12 square centimeters.	○ Find the area of a rectangle that is 4 centimeters long and 3 centimeters wide.
Mode of administration	○ Interview ○ Written response ○ Combination of interview and written responses	○ Written response
Answers	○ May have more than one ○ May require an explanation by student	○ Single, short
Scoring	○ 2–4 evaluation criteria given ○ Use of simple rating scale	○ One correct answer for each item
Benefits	○ More accurate determination of instructional needs and strengths of students	○ Easy to score

Chapter Tests, Form D

The Form D Chapter Tests in this *Sourcebook* are composed of large mathematical tasks which allow students to demonstrate a broad spectrum of their abilities:

- how they reason through difficult problems;
- how they make and test conjectures;
- how their number sense helps them give reasonable answers;
- how they utilize alternative strategies.

These performance tasks also give teachers a means of assessing qualities of imagination, creativity, and perseverance.

Administering Form D Tests

Some Classroom Management Tips

Whenever possible, use Form D Tests as cooperative group activities, listening as students interact in their groups.	Have any needed mathematical tools or manipulatives readily available. The use of calculators is assumed.
Ask students questions that will give you information about their thought processes.	Be sure all students understand the purpose of the task. Offer assistance as needed.

Evaluating Performance Assessments

For each assessment, a set of task-specific performance standards provides a means for judging the quality of the students' work. These standards identify five levels of performance related to the particular task. The specific standards were created using the following characteristics of student performance as general guidelines.

Level 5: Accomplishes and extends the task; displays in-depth understanding; communicates effectively and completely.

Level 4: Accomplishes the task competently; displays clear understanding of key concepts; communicates effectively.

Level 3: Substantially completes the task; displays minor flaws in understanding or technique; communicates successfully.

Level 2: Only partially completes the task; displays one or more major errors in understanding or technique; communicates unclear or incomplete information.

Level 1: Attempts the task, but fails to complete it in any substantive way; displays only fragmented understanding; attempts communication, but is not successful.

Each test is accompanied by a set of teacher notes that identifies the chapter objectives being assessed, as well as the mathematical concepts and skills involved in the performance task. The notes also list any materials that are needed and provide answers where appropriate. Questions to guide students as they seek solutions are provided, along with ideas for extending the activity. These notes, along with the performance standards as described at the left, are found in the Evaluation Guides starting on page 220 of this *Sourcebook.*

Since performance tasks are open-ended, student responses are as varied and individual as the students themselves. For this reason, it may be helpful to use these general guidelines as well as the task-specific standards when determining the level of each student's performance.

Using Assessment Forms

Using Student-Completed Forms

To do meaningful work in our fast-paced and ever-changing technological world, students must learn to assess their own progress. This *Sourcebook* provides four forms that can be used to help students with self-assessment. Use one or more depending on the needs of your students.

Using Teacher-Completed Forms

This *Sourcebook* also provides ten assessment forms that are designed to help you keep a record of authentic assessments. Some forms are for use with individual students, while others are for use with groups of students. Determine which would be best suited for use in your classroom.

	Form	Purpose	Suggested Uses
Student-Completed	*Student Survey*	Checklist of student attitudes toward various math activities	○ Periodically monitor the change in student attitudes toward math
	Student Self-Assessment	Checklist of student awareness of how well he or she works independently	○ Monitor student progress in working independently
	Cooperative Groups Self-Assessment	Form for students to describe their attitudes and interaction with other students in a cooperative-learning situation	○ Completed at the conclusion of group learning activities ○ Completed by individual students or groups of students
	About My Portfolio	Form for student to describe the contents of his or her portfolio	○ Completed when student transfers work from the notebook to the *Portfolio*
Teacher-Completed	*Portfolio Assessment*	Form to assess student's mathematical accomplishments over time	○ Use to discuss student's progress in discussions with family
	Notebooks, Individual Assessment	Form to record student's organizational skills and completeness of assignments	○ Describe student's attention to specified daily tasks
	Notebooks, Class Checklist	Checklist to record students' notebook maintenance	○ Use when setting goals for improving study skills
	Problem Solving, Individual Assessment	Form to assess each student in a problem-solving situation	○ Describe level of student performance ○ Modify the level to meet individual needs
	Problem Solving, Class Checklist	Checklist to assess groups of students in problem-solving situations	○ Assess the entire class ○ Assess small groups over time
	Observation, Individual Assessment	Form to determine the student's thought processes, performances, and attitudes	○ Record observation of student in classroom
	Observation, Class Checklist	Checklist for observing several students at one time	○ Provide a mathematical profile of the entire class ○ Identify common strengths and weaknesses ○ Help in modifying content or pace and in determining appropriate groupings
	Cooperative Groups, Class Checklist	Checklist to assess students' abilities to work constructively in groups	○ Assess one or more cooperative groups
	Project Assessment	Form for evaluating extended projects or oral presentations	○ Evaluate an individual or group project or presentation ○ Prepare students for presentations or projects
	Overall Student Assessment, Class Checklist	Checklist summary of students' overall performance	○ Evaluate student performance over an entire instructional period

Name ____________________ Date ____________________

Student Survey

Answer the following questions using the rating scale provided.

5 Always
4 Usually
3 Sometimes
2 Rarely
1 Never

______ **1.** I read material more than once if I don't understand it.

______ **2.** I use the reading heads and bold terms to help me preview the material.

______ **3.** I review for a test more than one day before it is given.

______ **4.** I concentrate when I study.

______ **5.** I try all the examples.

______ **6.** I do all of my assigned homework.

______ **7.** I pay attention in class.

______ **8.** I take notes and keep my notebook up-to-date and neat.

______ **9.** I bring the required materials to class.

______ **10.** I really try to get good grades.

______ **11.** I ask questions and try to get help when I need it.

______ **12.** I use the Progress Self-Test and Chapter Review to prepare for tests.

______ **13.** I make up work when I have been absent.

______ **14.** I look for uses of math in real life.

______ **15.** I can solve most problems.

______ **16.** I like to try new strategies.

______ **17.** I give up too easily.

______ **18.** I work cooperatively.

My favorite kind of math is ______________________________

because ______________________________

List some activities in which you have used math.

____

____

____

Name ____________________ Date ____________________

Student Self-Assessment

Assignment ____________________

Complete the following sentences to describe your learning experience.

I was supposed to learn ____________________

I started the work by ____________________

As a group member, I contributed ____________________

I learned ____________________

I am still confused by ____________________

I enjoyed the assignment because ____________________

I think the assignment was worthwhile because ____________________

Check the sentences that describe your work on this assignment.

☐ I was able to do the work.
☐ I did not understand the directions.
☐ I followed the directions but got wrong answers.
☐ I can explain how to do this assignment to someone else.
☐ The assignment was easier than I thought it would be.
☐ The assignment was harder than I thought it would be.

Name ______________________________ *Date* ______________

Cooperative Groups Self-Assessment

Assignment ______________________________

Reader: ______________________ *Writer:* ______________________

Materials handler: ______________________ *Checker:* ______________________

Others in group: ______________________________

Materials: ______________________________

Check the sentences that describe your work.

- ☐ We had a new idea or made a suggestion.
- ☐ We asked for more information.
- ☐ We shared the information we found.
- ☐ We tried different ways to solve the problem.
- ☐ We helped others explain their ideas better.
- ☐ We pulled our ideas together.
- ☐ We were reminded to work together.
- ☐ We demonstrated a knowledge of the mathematical concept.
- ☐ We encouraged those who did not understand.

Complete each sentence.

We learned ______________________________

____

____

We found an answer by ______________________________

____

____

After we found an answer, we ______________________________

____

____

By working together, we ______________________________

____

____

Name _______________________________ Date _______________

About My Portfolio

Complete the following sentences about the work you are putting into your portfolio.

Describe the assignment.

____

____

____

I chose this work as part of my portfolio because

____

____

____

I began my work by

____

____

____

Doing this work helped me

____

____

____

The work was ☐ too easy ☐ easy ☐ just right ☐ hard ☐ too hard

because ____

____

____

Name *Date*

Portfolio Assessment

The work in this portfolio:

shows growth in the student's mathematical understanding.

exhibits the student's ability to reason mathematically.

makes connections within mathematics.

makes connections to other disciplines.

shows that the student is able to work on mathematical tasks in cooperative groups.

illustrates the appropriate use of a variety of tools.

Name ______________________ Date ______________

Notebooks

Individual Assessment

Rate items, based upon your requirements, as follows:

+ if excellent
✓ if satisfactory
- if needs improvement
NA if not applicable

Written Assignments **Comments**

______ **1.** Assignment sheet
______ **2.** Daily homework
______ **3.** Lesson Warm-ups
______ **4.** Lesson Masters
______ **5.** Activities
______ **6.** Projects

Reading and Class Notes **Comments**

______ **7.** Definitions
______ **8.** Properties
______ **9.** Examples
______ **10.** Class notes, handouts

Assessment **Comments**

______ **11.** Chapter Quizzes
______ **12.** Chapter Progress Self-Test
______ **13.** Chapter Review
______ **14.** Chapter Tests
______ **15.** Cumulative Chapter Test
______ **16.** Comprehensive Test

Other **Comments**

______ **17.**
______ **18.**
______ **19.**
______ **20.**

Overall Rating/Comments

____

____

Notebooks

Class ____

Rate each item as follows:

+ if excellent
✓ if satisfactory
- if needs improvement
NA if not applicable

Students	Date	Written Assignments			Reading/Class Notes			Assessment			
1.											
2.											
3.											
4.											
5.											
6.											
7.											
8.											
9.											
10.											
11.											
12.											
13.											
14.											
15.											
16.											
17.											
18.											
19.											
20.											
21.											
22.											
23.											
24.											
25.											
26.											
27.											
28.											
29.											
30.											

Name Date

Problem Solving

Individual Assessment

Check each statement below that accurately describes the student's work. This list includes suggested student behaviors to consider. Feel free to modify it to suit your needs.

Reads carefully **Comments**

☐ Looks up unfamiliar words
☐ Understands lesson concepts and can apply them
☐ Rereads
☐ Finds/uses information appropriately
☐
☐

Creates a plan **Comments**

☐ Chooses an appropriate strategy
☐ Estimates the answer
☐
☐
☐

Carries out the plan **Comments**

☐ Works systematically and with care
☐ Shows work in an organized fashion
☐ Computes correctly
☐ Rereads the problem if the first attempt is unsuccessful
☐ Rereads the problem and interprets the solution
☐ States the answer in required format
☐
☐
☐

Checks the work **Comments**

☐ Checks by estimating
☐ Tries alternate approaches
☐
☐
☐

Problem Solving

Class ______________________

Rate each item as follows:

+	if excellent
✓	if satisfactory
-	if needs improvement
NA	if not applicable

Students	Date	Looks up unfamiliar words	Understands the question/task	Uses information appropriately	Chooses an appropriate strategy	Estimates the answer	Is systematic and careful	Computes correctly	Rereads the problem if necessary	States answer in required format	Tries alternate approaches
1.											
2.											
3.											
4.											
5.											
6.											
7.											
8.											
9.											
10.											
11.											
12.											
13.											
14.											
15.											
16.											
17.											
18.											
19.											
20.											
21.											
22.											
23.											
24.											
25.											
26.											
27.											
28.											
29.											
30.											

Name _______________ Date _______________

Observation

Individual Assessment

	Usually	Sometimes	Rarely
Understanding			
Demonstrates knowledge of skills	☐	☐	☐
Understands concepts	☐	☐	☐
Selects appropriate solution strategies	☐	☐	☐
Solves problems accurately	☐	☐	☐
Work Habits			
Works in an organized manner	☐	☐	☐
Works neatly	☐	☐	☐
Submits work on time	☐	☐	☐
Works well with others	☐	☐	☐
Uses time productively	☐	☐	☐
Asks for help when needed	☐	☐	☐
Confidence			
Initiates questions	☐	☐	☐
Displays positive attitude	☐	☐	☐
Helps others	☐	☐	☐
Flexibility			
Tries alternative approaches	☐	☐	☐
Considers and uses ideas of others	☐	☐	☐
Likes to try alternative methods	☐	☐	☐
Perseverance			
Shows patience and perseverance	☐	☐	☐
Works systematically	☐	☐	☐
Is willing to try	☐	☐	☐
Checks work regularly	☐	☐	☐
Other			
_______________	☐	☐	☐
_______________	☐	☐	☐
_______________	☐	☐	☐

Observation

Class Checklist

Class ______________________

Rate each item as follows:

+ if excellent
✓ if satisfactory
- if needs improvement
NA if not applicable

Students	Date	Demonstrates knowledge of skills	Understands concepts	Works neatly and systematically	Works well with others	Asks for help when needed	Uses time productively	Displays positive attitude	Tries alternative approaches	Considers and uses ideas of others	Shows patience and perseverance
1.											
2.											
3.											
4.											
5.											
6.											
7.											
8.											
9.											
10.											
11.											
12.											
13.											
14.											
15.											
16.											
17.											
18.											
19.											
20.											
21.											
22.											
23.											
24.											
25.											
26.											
27.											
28.											
29.											
30.											

Cooperative Groups

Class Checklist

Class ______________________

Rate each item as follows:

+ if excellent
✓ if satisfactory
\- if needs improvement
NA if not applicable

Students	Date	Works with others in the group	Considers and uses ideas of others	Tutors and helps others	Has a positive attitude	Disagrees but is not disagreeable	Shows patience and perseverance	Works systematically	Initiates questions		
1.											
2.											
3.											
4.											
5.											
6.											
7.											
8.											
9.											
10.											
11.											
12.											
13.											
14.											
15.											
16.											
17.											
18.											
19.											
20.											
21.											
22.											
23.											
24.											
25.											
26.											
27.											
28.											
29.											
30.											

Name ____ Date _______________

Project Assessment

Project ____

Rate each item as follows:

+ if excellent
✓ if satisfactory
- if needs improvement
NA if not applicable

The Project

______ Demonstrates mathematical concepts properly

______ Communicates ideas clearly

______ Shows connection to another subject

______ Shows evidence of time spent in planning and preparation

______ Is original and creative

______ Includes charts, tables, and/or graphs where appropriate

______ Uses available technology effectively

______ Stimulates further investigation of the topic

______ Includes a short written report if the project is a model or demonstration

______ Lists resources used

The Oral Presentation

______ Is organized (includes an introduction, main section, and conclusion)

______ Uses audio-visual materials where appropriate

______ Speaks clearly and paces presentation properly

______ Answers questions and stimulates further interest among classmates

______ Holds audience's attention

Overall Project Rating/Comments

____

____

____

____

Overall Student Assessment

Class Checklist

Class ____________________

Rate each item as follows:

+ if excellent
✓ if satisfactory
- if needs improvement
NA if not applicable

Students	**Date**	Class Work	Discussion	Cooperative Groups	Problem Solving	Homework	Notebooks	Projects	Tests		
1.											
2.											
3.											
4.											
5.											
6.											
7.											
8.											
9.											
10.											
11.											
12.											
13.											
14.											
15.											
16.											
17.											
18.											
19.											
20.											
21.											
22.											
23.											
24.											
25.											
26.											
27.											
28.											
29.											
30.											

Name

QUIZ

Lessons 1-1 Through 1-3

1. Consider the expression $4 - 24 \div 6 + 10 \cdot 5$. According to the rules for the order of operations, what is the first step that you should complete when evaluating this expression? 1. ______

2. There are c classrooms in a school. Each classroom can hold s students. How many students would be in the school if all the classrooms were full? 2. ______

3. Evaluate $3t^2 + 4t - 7$ when $t = -5$. 3. ______

In 4 and 5, use the table of values below.

n	-1	1	-2	2	-3	3
v	1	1	2	2	3	3

4. Is n a function of v? Why or why not?

______

______

5. a. Suppose that n is the independent variable. Find the domain of the relation. 5. a. ______

b. Find the range. b. ______

6. What real numbers are *not* in the domain of $f(x) = \dfrac{3x}{x^2 - 49}$? Justify your answer.

______

______

7. Given the function g defined by $g(y) = y^3 + 11$, find $g(4)$. 7. ______

8. Use the function r defined by $r: t \rightarrow -3t + 9$. Find $r: -7 \rightarrow$ __?__. 8. ______

9. When Carlita bought her new car, she made a down payment of \$1000 and agreed to make monthly payments of \$358. The function $C(n) = 1000 + 358n$ gives the total amount she has paid as a function of the number n of monthly payments made. Find the total amount Carlita will pay for the car if she makes payments for 5 years (60 months). 9. 

Name ______________________

QUIZ

Lessons 1-4 Through 1-6

In 1 and 2, use the graph at the right.

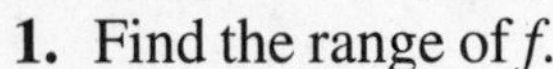

1. Find the range of f. **1.** ________

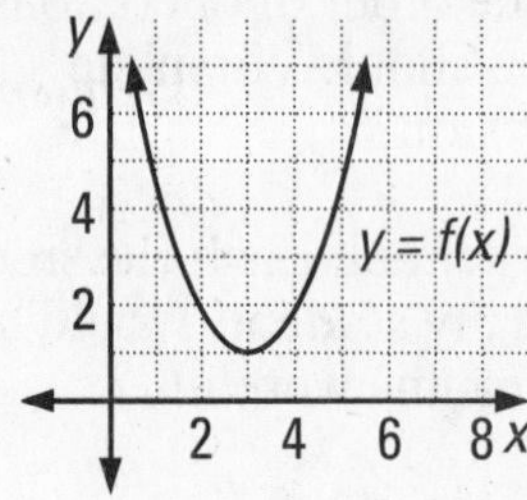

2. What is $f(4)$? **2.** ________

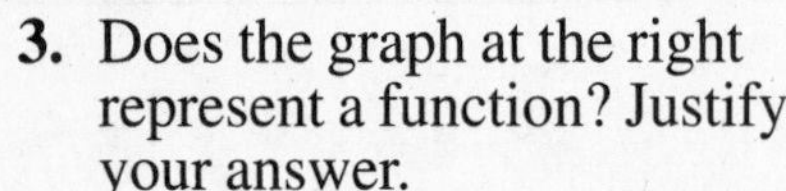

3. Does the graph at the right represent a function? Justify your answer.

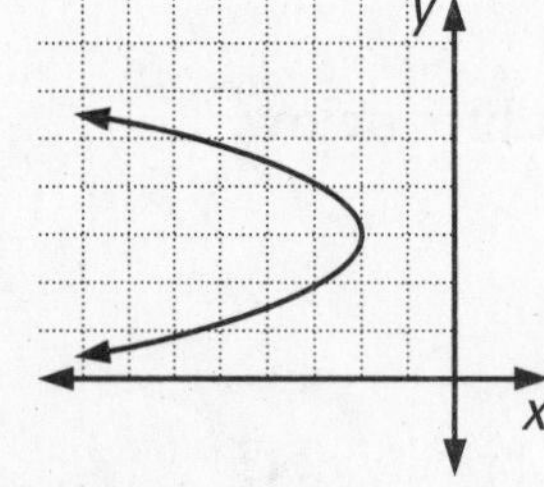

____

____

4. Solve $\frac{4}{5}(x - 15) = 8$. **4.** ________

5. Solve $38 = 22 - (8 - 6t)$. **5.** ________

6. At a local high school, $\frac{3}{8}$ of the students are freshmen, $\frac{1}{4}$ are sophomores, $\frac{1}{5}$ are juniors, and 245 are seniors. Find the total number of students in the school. **6.** ________

7. Darnel has \$5000 to invest. He plans to put some in a savings account paying 4% interest and the rest in a CD paying 5.5% interest. If d dollars are invested at 4%, then **7.** ________

$$I = .04d + .055(5000 - d)$$

represents the interest earned in one year from the two accounts. How much should Darnel put into each account to earn a total of \$245 interest in one year?

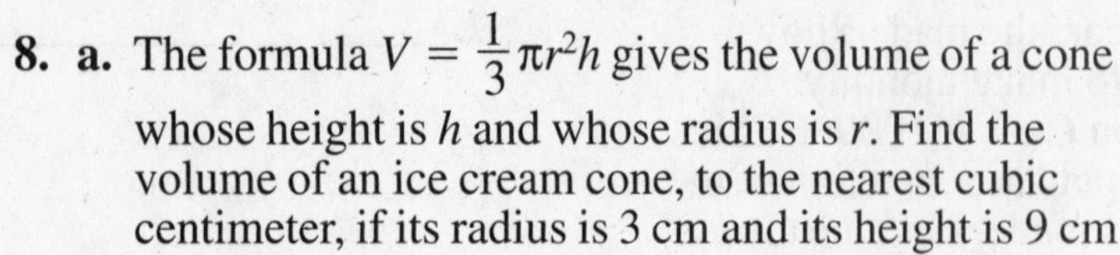

8. a. The formula $V = \frac{1}{3}\pi r^2 h$ gives the volume of a cone whose height is h and whose radius is r. Find the volume of an ice cream cone, to the nearest cubic centimeter, if its radius is 3 cm and its height is 9 cm. **8. a.** ________

b. Rewrite the formula for h in terms of r and V. **b.** ________

Name

CHAPTER 1 TEST, Form A

In 1–3, sequences *A* and *B* are defined as follows.

Sequence A

$r_n = 4n^2 + 9$, for integers $n \geq 1$

Sequence B

$\begin{cases} c_1 = 6 \\ c_n = 3c_{n-1} - 4, \text{ for integers } n \geq 2 \end{cases}$

1. Write the first four terms of sequence *A*. **1.** ________

2. Write the first four terms of sequence *B*. **2.** ________

3. Suppose you need to find the 80th term of each sequence. In which sequence would the 80th term be easier to find? Justify your answer.

____

____

4. Consider the sequence 8, 13, 18, 23, 28, ... Write a recursive definition for this sequence. **4.** ________

5. If $p(x) = 2x^3 + 7x^2 - 4x$, find $p(5)$. **5.** ________

6. Suppose $Z: w \rightarrow \dfrac{w(w+1)(w+2)}{6}$. Then $Z: 10 \rightarrow$ ___?___. **6.** ________

7. Solve for b_1 in the formula $2A = h(b_1 + b_2)$. **7.** ________

8. Suppose 32 ounces of stewed tomatoes cost *c* cents. Write an expression that represents the unit cost. **8.** ________

In 9–11, use the formula $V = \pi r^2 h$ for the volume of a cylinder.

9. Find the volume of the cylinder at the right to the nearest cubic centimeter. **9.** ________

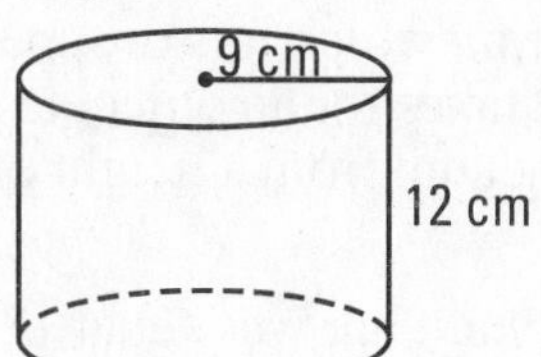

10. What is a reasonable domain for the height *h*? **10.** ________

11. Rewrite the formula for *h* in terms of *r* and *V*. **11.** ________

Name ____________________

12. Consider the following function.
{(256, 4), (-256, 4), (81, 3), (-81, 3), (16, 2), (-16, 2), (1, 1), (-1, 1)}

a. Identify its domain. **12. a.** ____________

b. Identify its range. **b.** ____________

13. Consider the relation defined by the table below.

x	0	1	2	3	4	5
y	0	2	4	6	8	10

Is y a function of x? Justify your answer.

____

____

In 14 and 15, solve the equation. Show your work.

14. $5(9x + 2) = 145$ **14.** ____________

15. $\frac{2}{3}z + \frac{4}{5} = \frac{7}{15}z$ **15.** ____________

16. If an object is dropped in a vacuum near the surface of Earth, then the function $t(h) = \sqrt{\frac{2h}{g}}$, with $g = 32$ ft/sec^2, gives the time it takes for the object to reach the ground as a function of the height h from which it is dropped. Find to the nearest second the time it takes for an object to reach the ground when it is dropped in a vacuum from a height of 1000 feet. **16.** ____________

17. At a track meet, the pole-vault bar was set at 12 feet (144 inches) for the first round of competition. At the beginning of each new round, the bar was raised 1 inch. Let h_n = height of the bar in inches at the beginning of round n of competition.

a. Write a recursive formula to describe this situation. **17. a.** ____________

b. Find h_4. **b.** ____________

Name

18. A youth choir won a state-level competition and decided to raise money to attend the national competition. One fund-raising project involved selling Vidalia onions. For each 25-pound bag of onions sold, the choir raised \$1.75. How many bags must the choir sell to raise \$341.25? **18.** ________

In 19 and 20, refer to the graph below, which shows the number of army and air force personnel of the United States for the years 1980 to 1993. Let $A(x)$ = the number of army personnel in year x and $F(x)$ = the number of air force personnel in year x.

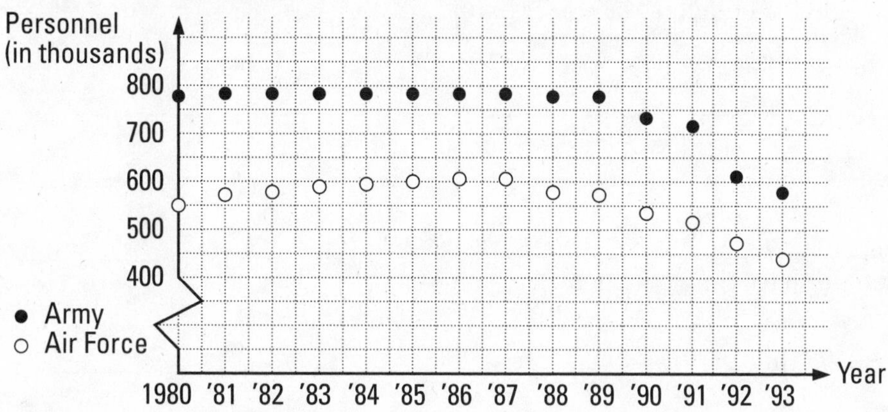

19. Estimate $F(1989)$. **19.** ________

20. Estimate $A(1993) - A(1980)$ and explain what the result means.

____

____

21. On the grid at the right, sketch a graph that does *not* represent a function. **21.** ________

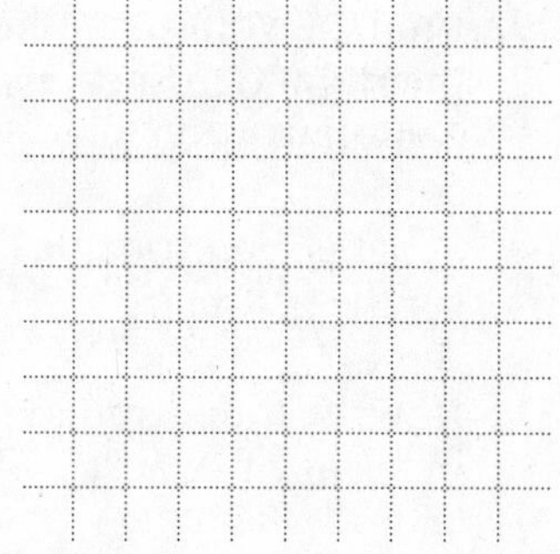

Check all your work carefully.

Name

CHAPTER 1 TEST, Form B

In 1–3, sequences *A* and *B* are defined as follows.

Sequence A

$r_n = 5n^2 - 11$, for integers $n \geq 1$

Sequence B

$$\begin{cases} c_1 = 7 \\ c_n = 4c_{n-1} + 3, \text{ for integers } n \geq 2 \end{cases}$$

1. Write the first four terms of sequence *A*. **1.** ______

2. Write the first four terms of sequence *B*. **2.** ______

3. Suppose you need to find the 80th term of each sequence. In which sequence would the 80th term be easier to find? Justify your answer.

______

______

4. Consider the sequence 11, 17, 23, 29, 35, ... Write a recursive definition for this sequence. **4.** ______

5. If $g(x) = 4x^3 - 11x^2 + 7x$, find $g(-5)$. **5.** ______

6. Suppose $W: u \rightarrow \frac{(u-1)u(u+1)}{6}$.
Then $W: 12 \rightarrow$ ___?___. **6.** ______

7. Solve for V in the formula $3V = 4\pi r^3$. **7.** ______

8. Suppose 20 tea bags cost d cents. Write an expression that represents the cost of each tea bag. **8.** ______

In 9–11, use the formula $V = \frac{1}{3}\pi r^2 h$ for the volume of a cone.

9. Find the volume of the cone at the right to the nearest cubic centimeter. **9.** 

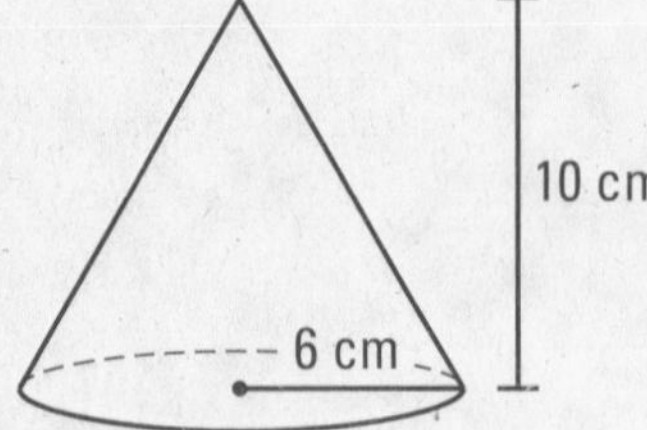

10. What is a reasonable domain for the height h? **10.** 

11. Rewrite the formula for h in terms of r and V. **11.** ______

Name

12. Consider the following function.
{(4, 256), (-4, 256), (3, 81), (-3, 81), (2, 16), (-2, 16), (1, 1), (-1, 1)}

a. Identify its domain. **12. a.** ________

b. Identify its range. **b.** ________

13. Consider the relation defined by the table below.

x	0	4	4	9	16	25
y	0	-4	4	-6	8	10

Is y a function of x? Justify your answer.

____

____

In 14 and 15, solve the equation. Show your work.

14. $7(8x + 1) = 231$ **14.** ________

15. $\frac{3}{4}y - \frac{5}{6} = \frac{7}{12}y$ **15.** ________

16. If you are standing at the top of a tall building on a clear day, then the function $d(h) = \sqrt{\frac{3h}{2}}$ gives an excellent approximation of the distance d that you can see to the horizon (in miles) as a function of the height h of the building (in feet). Find to the nearest mile the distance you can see to the horizon on a clear day from a height of 500 feet. **16.** ________

17. George's parents gave him $500.00 to open a savings account. After that, he is supposed to deposit $100.00 into this account each month. Let S_n = the amount of money George has in his savings account after n months. Assume no other deposits or withdrawals are made, and interest is ignored.

a. Write a recursive formula to describe this situation. **17. a.** ________

b. Find S_{11}. **b.** ________

Name

18. Lupita earns $.25 for each *Healthwise* magazine she sells. How many magazines must Lupita sell to earn $10.75?

18. ____________

In 19 and 20, refer to the graph below, which shows the motor vehicle production in the United States and Japan for the years 1980 to 1992. Let $A(x)$ = the number of motor vehicles produced in the United States in year x and $J(x)$ = the number of motor vehicles produced in Japan in year x.

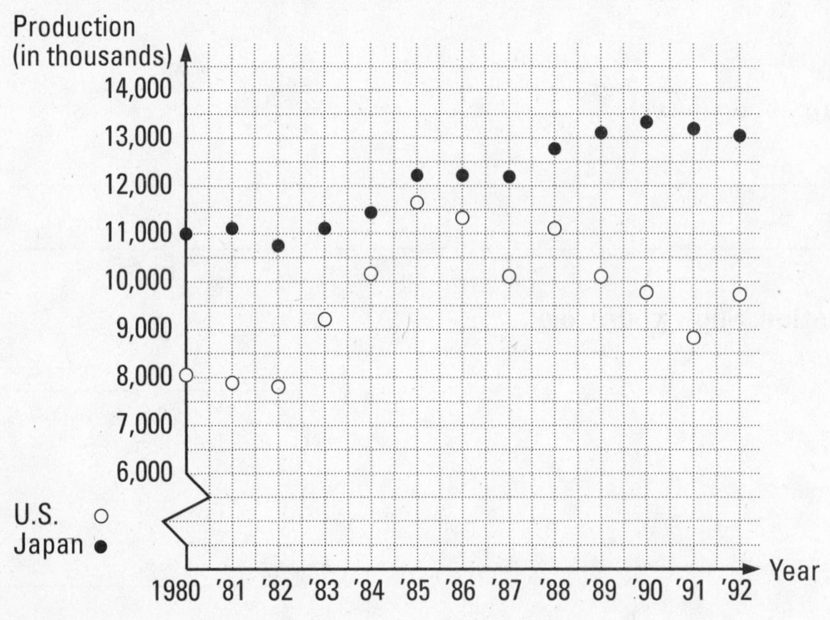

19. Estimate $J(1989)$.

19. ____________

20. Estimate $A(1992) - A(1980)$ and explain what the result means.

____

____

21. Explain how to tell whether or not a graph represents a function.

____

____

Check all your work carefully.

Name

CHAPTER 1 TEST, Form C

1. a. Describe a real-world situation that might be modeled by the expression $80 + 5n$.

   b. Evaluate the expression when $n = 3$, when $n = -3$, and when $n = 3.25$.

   c. Indicate the real-world meaning of the values of the expression for at least one value of n.

2. Given $I = prt$, the following are equivalent.

   $p = \frac{I}{rt}$ $\quad r = \frac{I}{pt}$ $\quad t = \frac{I}{pr}$

   Leah thinks she sees a pattern in these formulas. So, given $A = p(1 + rt)$, she says that the following are all equivalent.

   $p = \frac{A}{1 + rt}$ $\quad r = \frac{A}{1 + pt}$ $\quad t = \frac{A}{1 + pr}$

   Do you agree or disagree with Leah? Explain why or why not.

3. If $f(x) = \frac{1}{2}x - \frac{2}{3}x$, how is $f(-24)$ different from $f(x) = -24$?

4. Explain the difference between an explicit formula and a recursive formula for a sequence. Give an example of each.

5. Explain how you know from the graph that the relation at the right is a function. Then tell as many facts as you can about the function, its domain, and its range.

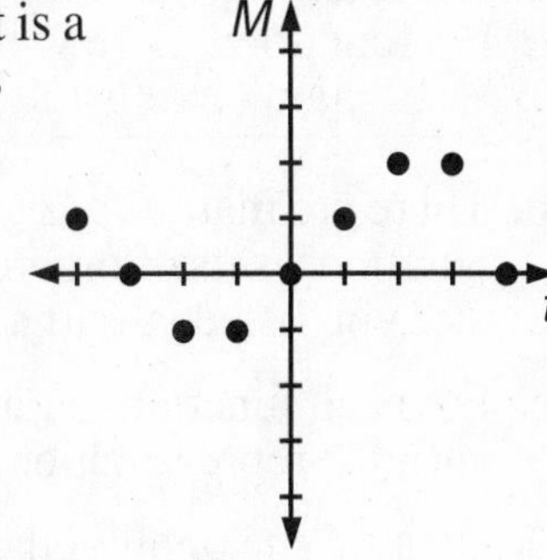

Name

CHAPTER 1 TEST, Form D

Suppose that there recently was a major fire in a nearby town. It generated a lot of interest in fires, fire fighting, and fire prevention. A reporter for a local newspaper gathered the following facts.

Many experts recommend that you insure your home against fire and other perils for an amount that is four fifths of the assessed value of your home.

There are more than 300 different ways a fire can start in the home.

In a multi-story home, place one smoke detector on each level, including the basement.

In a single-story home, place one smoke detector near each separate sleeping area and at the bottom of each basement stairway.

Facts for Fire Fighters

To quickly figure how many feet from a wall to place the base of a ladder, divide the length of the ladder (in feet) by five and add two.

To quickly figure the amount of water flow (gal/min) needed to knock down a fire, divide the number of square feet that are fully involved in the fire by three.

The underwriter's formula,

$$F = 2q^2 + q$$

gives the amount of flow (gal/min) lost every 100 feet due to friction as water flows through a 2.5-inch hose. In this formula, q is the initial flow in hundreds of gallons per minute, and the value of q must be greater than 100. If q is less than 100, the formula is:

$$F = 2q^2 + .5q$$

One gallon of water weighs about 8.35 pounds and produces about 200 cubic feet of steam.

Amount of United States Fire Losses

Year	Total	Per capita
1970	$2,328,000,000	$11.41
1975	3,190,000,000	14.81
1980	5,579,000,000	24.55
1985	7,753,000,000	32.47
1990	9,495,000,000	38.18

From 1977 through 1984, the number of fires in the United States averaged 2,752,100 annually; 36% involved structures, 17% involved vehicles, and 47% involved outside combustibles and other categories. Of the fires in structures, 71% were in residential properties.

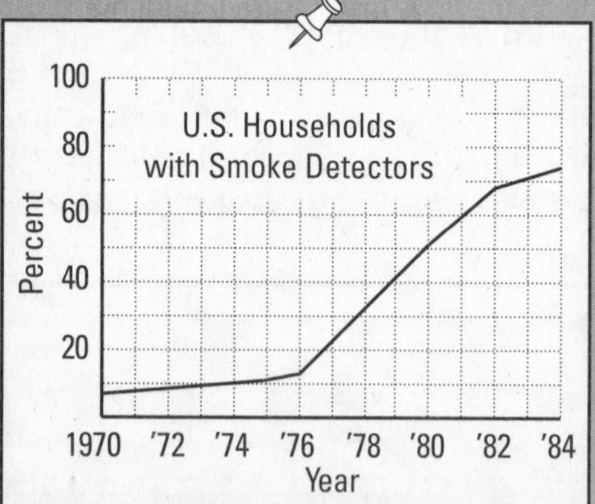

a. Refer to the information above. List as many relations as you can that are functions. Give your answers in the following form.

____________ is a function of ____________.

b. There are many ways to represent functions, such as graphs, function notations, sets of ordered pairs, and tables. Choose three of the functions that you listed in Part a. Represent each in as many ways as you can.

c. For each function in Part b, identify the domain and the range. If there is a variable representation, name the independent and dependent variables.

d. Using some or all of the information above, write a newspaper article (or articles) about fires, fire fighting, and fire prevention. Be sure to represent the information in the way you think most appropriate. That is, you might represent some information graphically, some as formulas, and so on.

Name

QUIZ

Lessons 2-1 Through 2-3

In 1–3, refer to the following equations.

(a) $r = \frac{100}{t}$ (b) $y = 7x$ (c) $I = \frac{\pi}{m^2}$ (d) $a_n = 5n^2 + 3$

1. Which equation or equations represent a direct-variation function? 1. ________

2. Which equation or equations represent an inverse-variation function? 2. ________

3. Which equation or equations are not variation equations? 3. ________

4. Give an example of an equation for a variation function in which multiplying the independent variable x by c results in the dependent variable y being multiplied by c^2. 4. ________

In 5 and 6, describe the change in the y-value when the x-value is doubled.

5. $y = 4x$ 5. ________

6. $y = \frac{4}{x^2}$ 6. ________

In 7 and 8, suppose the weight w of a bass (in pounds) varies directly with the cube of its length, ℓ (in inches).

7. If an 18-inch bass weighs 4 lb, write a specific equation relating w and ℓ. 7. ________

8. Use your answer to Question 7. Estimate the weight of a 20-inch bass. 8. ________

9. The volume of a gas varies inversely with the pressure (while temperature is held constant). If the pressure was 20 psi while the volume was 83 ft^3, what will the volume be when the pressure is 60 psi? 9. ________

Name

QUIZ

Lessons 2-4 Through 2-6

1. What is a *default window* on a graphics calculator?

2. What is the slope of the line with equation $y = \frac{2}{3}x$? **2.**

3. Graph $y = \frac{8}{x^2}$ using the grid at the right. **3.**

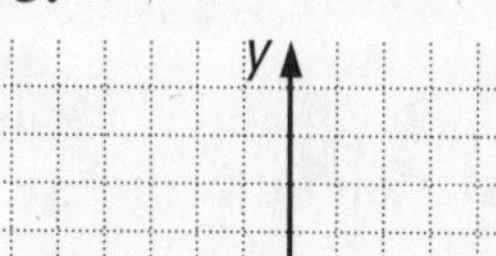

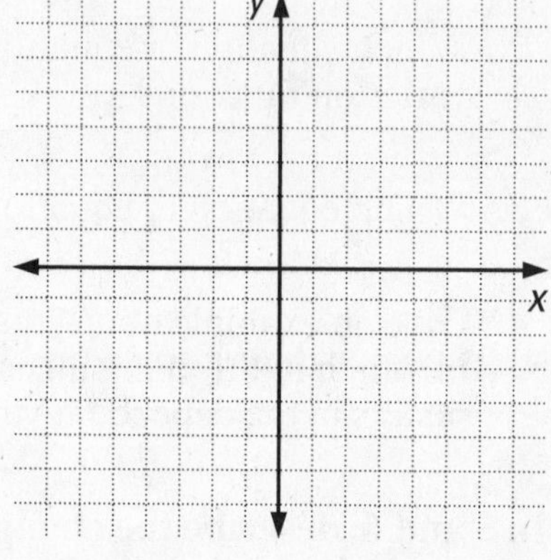

In 4–6, consider $y = 2x^2$.

4. Find the rate of change from $x = 1$ to $x = 2$. **4.**

5. Find the rate of change from $x = 2$ to $x = 3$. **5.**

6. Explain why the answers to Questions 4 and 5 are not equal.

7. In which quadrants are the branches of the graph of $y = -\frac{4}{x}$? **7.**

8. Below is the graph of $y = 2x$ on the window $-6 \le x \le 6$, $-24 \le y \le 24$. **8.**

24

-6 6

-24

x-scale = 1
y-scale = 3

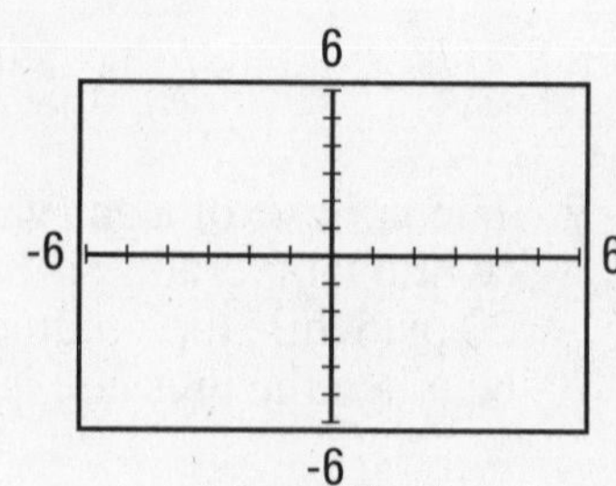

x-scale = 1
y-scale = 1

Sketch a graph of $y = 2x$ on the window at the right.

Name

CHAPTER 2 TEST, Form A

1. Write the variation equation $L = kd^2$ in words.

In 2-3, use this information: *c* varies inversely as the square of *d*. If $d = 4$, then $c = 25$.

2. Find the constant of variation. 2. ____

3. Find c when $d = 12$. 3. ____

In 4–6, use this information: The volume of a gas varies directly as its temperature measured in degrees Kelvin (°K) and inversely as its pressure. When the temperature of a certain gas is 250°K and its pressure is 76.2 cm of mercury, its volume is 750 cm^3.

4. Find the constant of variation. 4. ____

5. Write a variation equation that models the situation. 5. ____

6. What would be the volume of this gas to the nearest cubic centimeter if its temperature were 300°K and its pressure were 73.66 cm of mercury? 6. ____

In 7 and 8, consider the equation $s = 16d^2$.

7. How does the value of s change if d is doubled? 7. ____

8. How does the value of s change if d is divided by 3? 8. ____

In 9 and 10, complete with "directly," "inversely," or "neither directly nor inversely."

9. When a seesaw is in balance, the distance a person is from the fulcrum varies __?__ as the weight of that person. 9. ____

10. The weight of a stack of paper varies __?__ as the number of pieces of paper in the stack. 10. ____

Name

In 11–13, consider the equation $y = \frac{4}{x}$.

11. Find the rate of change from $x = 1$ to $x = 2$. **11.** ______

12. Find the rate of change from $x = 2$ to $x = 3$. **12.** ______

13. Explain why the answers in Questions 11 and 12 are *not* equal.

______

______

14. Given the equation $y = \frac{k}{x^3}$, suppose that $y = 2$ when $x = 2$. Find y when $x = 4$. **14.** ______

15. *Multiple choice.* Which could be the graph of $y = \frac{4}{x^2}$? **15.** ______

(a)
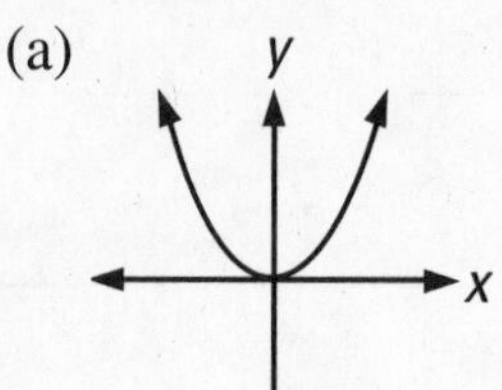

(b)
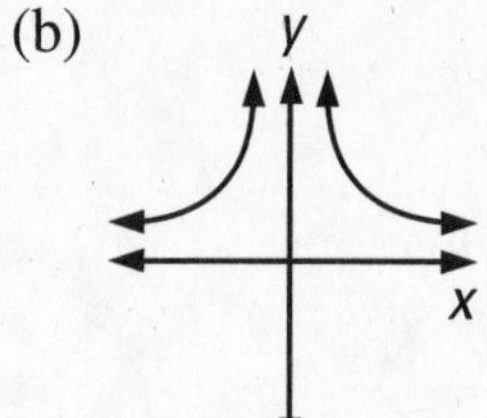

(c)
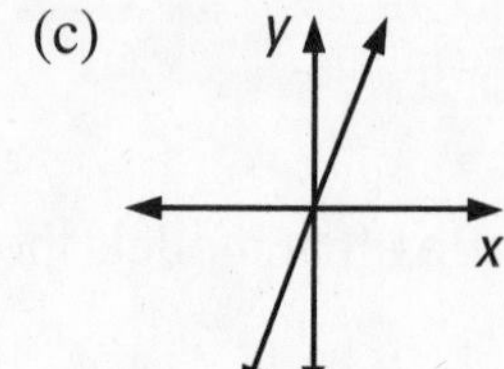

(d)
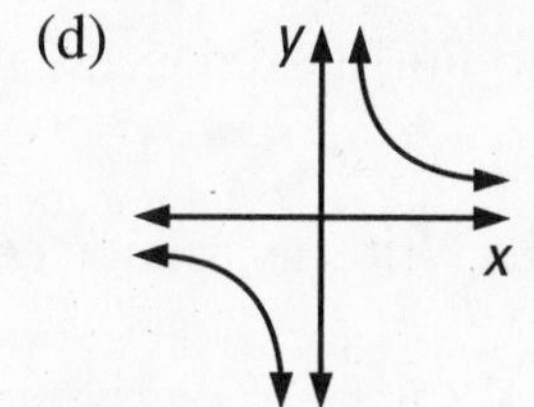

In 16-18, consider the equation $y = -3x$.

16. Make a table of values for the equation. **16.**

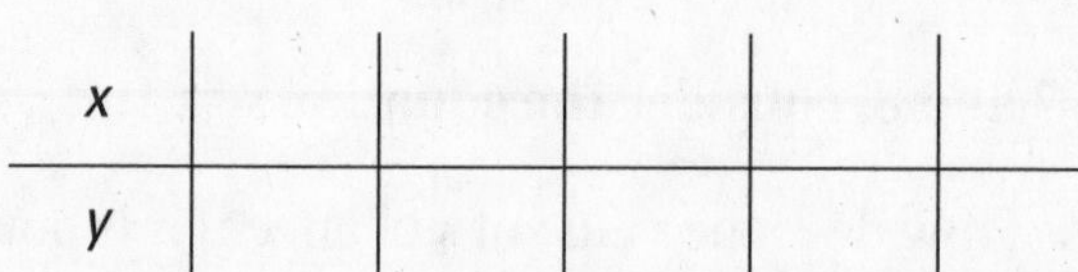

17. Graph the equation on the grid at the right. **17.**

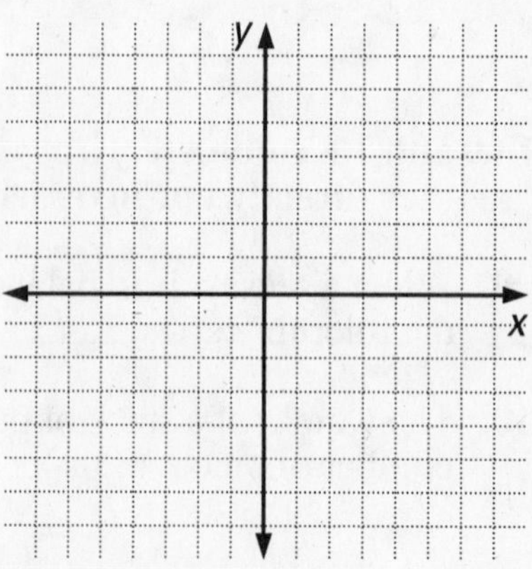

18. Find the slope of the graph of the equation. **18.** ______

Name

19. At the right is the graph of $y = \frac{3}{x}$ on the window $0 \le x \le 10, 0 \le y \le 10$.

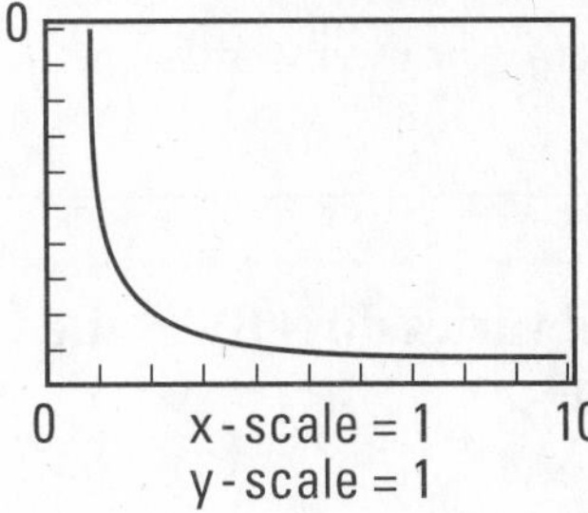

a. Give the dimensions of a window that would show both branches of the graph.

19. a. ______________

b. Identify two asymptotes to the graph.

b. ______________

20. Suppose that variables *w, n, R,* and *L* are related as illustrated in the graphs below. The points on the graph in the middle lie on or near a parabola. The points on the other two graphs lie on a line through the origin. Write a general equation approximating the relationship between *w, n, R,* and *L*.

20. ______________

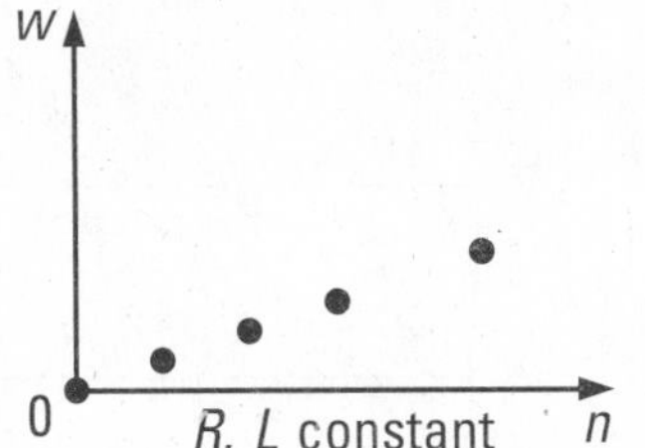

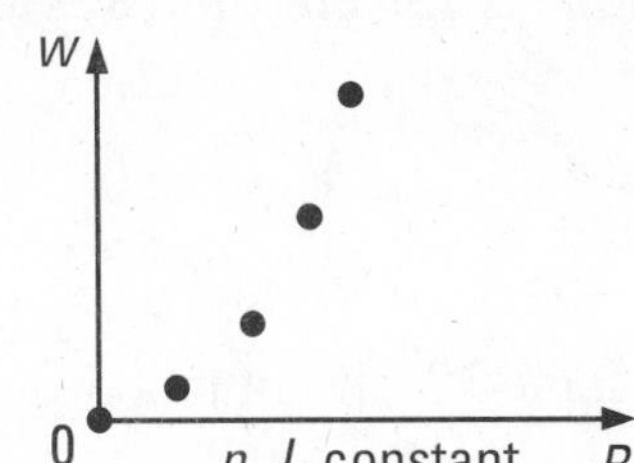

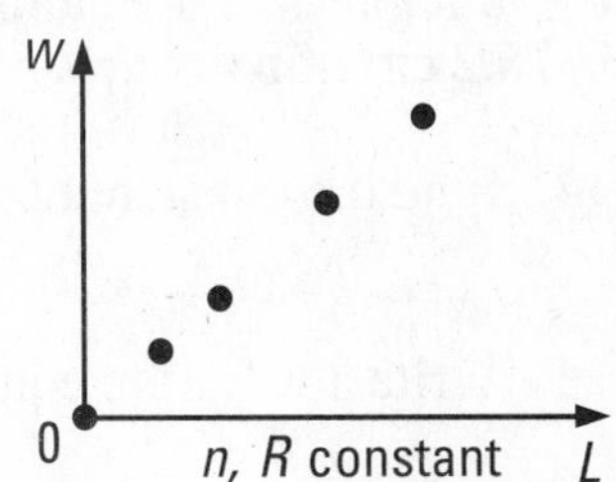

In 21 and 22, refer to the data in the table below, which relate the braking distance of a car to its speed at the time the brakes are applied.

Speed (km/hr)	s	10	20	30	40	50	60
Braking Distance (m)	d	.6	2.4	5.3	9.4	14.7	21.2

21. Let the speed *s* be the independent variable and the braking distance *d* be the dependent variable. Graph the data on the grid at the right.

21.

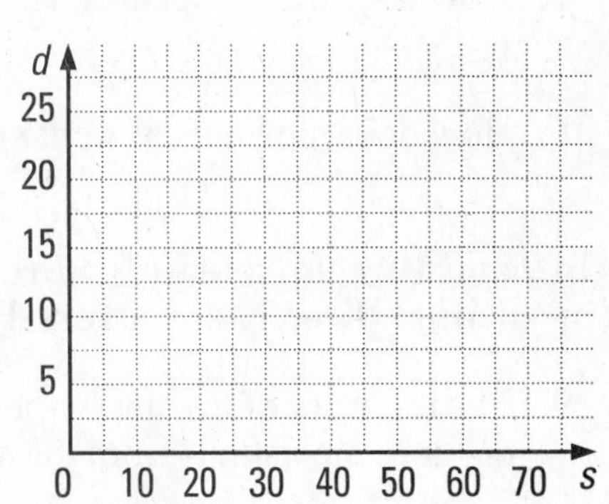

22. *Multiple choice.* Which equation best models the data?

22. ______________

(a) $d = ks$ (b) $s = kd$ (c) $d = ks^2$ (d) $s = kd^2$

Check all your work carefully.

Name

CHAPTER 2 TEST, Form B

1. Write the variation equation $y = kx^4$ in words.

____

In 2–3, use this information: d varies directly as the square of t. If $t = 2$, then $d = 64$.

2. Find the constant of variation. 2. ______

3. Find d when $t = 6$. 3. ______

In 4–6, use this information: The pressure of a gas varies directly as its temperature measured in degrees Kelvin (°K) and inversely as its volume. When the temperature of a certain gas is 250°K and its volume is 750 cm^3, its pressure is 76.2 cm of mercury.

4. Find the constant of variation. 4. ______

5. Write a variation equation that models the situation. 5. ______

6. What would be the pressure of this gas to the nearest tenth of a centimeter of mercury if its temperature were 275°K and its volume were 1000 cm^3? 6. ______

In 7 and 8, consider the equation $s = \frac{16}{d^2}$.

7. How does the value of s change if d is multiplied by 4? 7. ______

8. How does the value of s change if d is divided by 3? 8. ______

In 9 and 10, complete with "directly," "inversely," or "neither directly nor inversely."

9. The intensity of a sound varies __?__ as the square of the distance a person is from the source of the sound. 9. ______

10. The price you pay for notebooks varies __?__ as the number of notebooks you buy. 10. ______

Name

In 11–13, consider the equation $y = \frac{8}{x^2}$.

11. Find the rate of change from $x = 1$ to $x = 2$. **11.** ____________

12. Find the rate of change from $x = 2$ to $x = 3$. **12.** ____________

13. Explain why the answers in Questions 11 and 12 are *not* equal.

____

____

14. Given the equation $y = kx^3$, suppose that $y = -40$ when $x = 2$. Find y when $x = 6$. **14.** ____________

15. *Multiple choice.* Which could be the graph of $y = \frac{4}{x}$? **15.** ____________

(a)

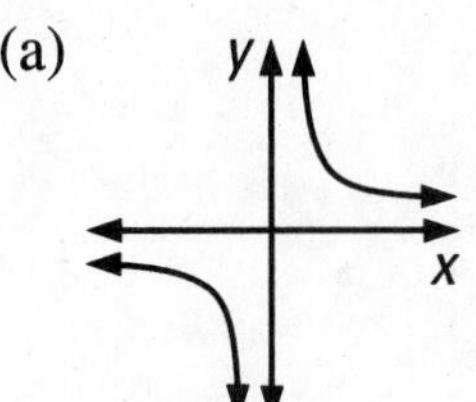

(b)

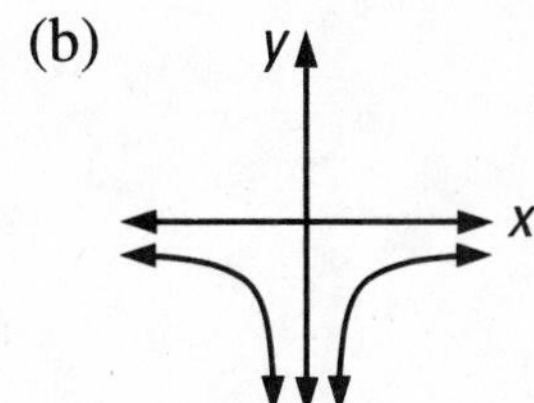

(c)

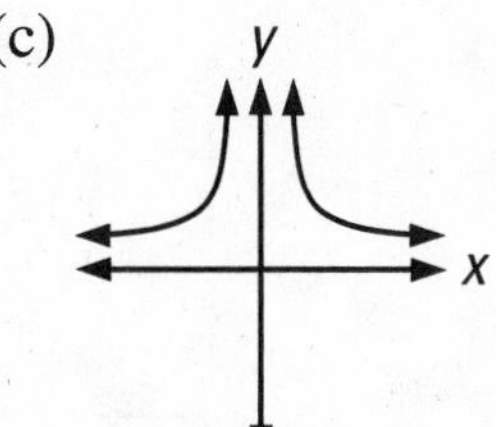

(d)

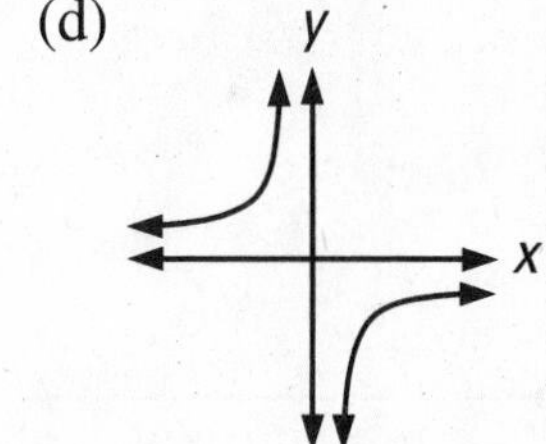

In 16–18, consider the equation $y = 5x$.

16. Make a table of values for the equation. **16.**

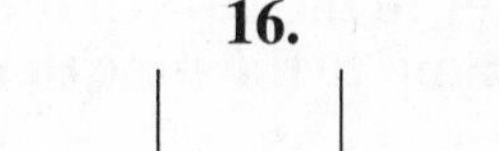

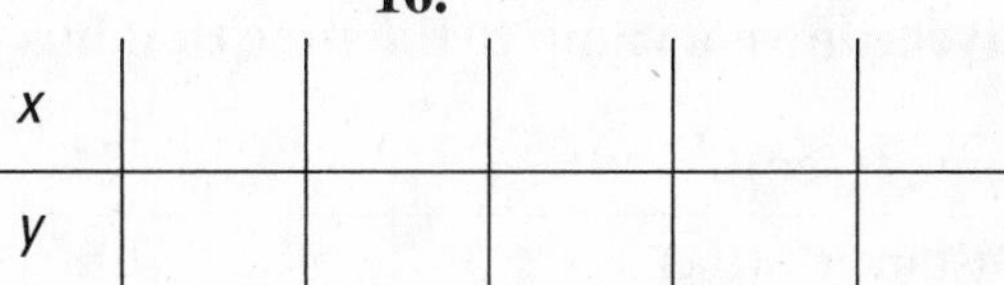

17. Graph the equation on the grid at the right. **17.**

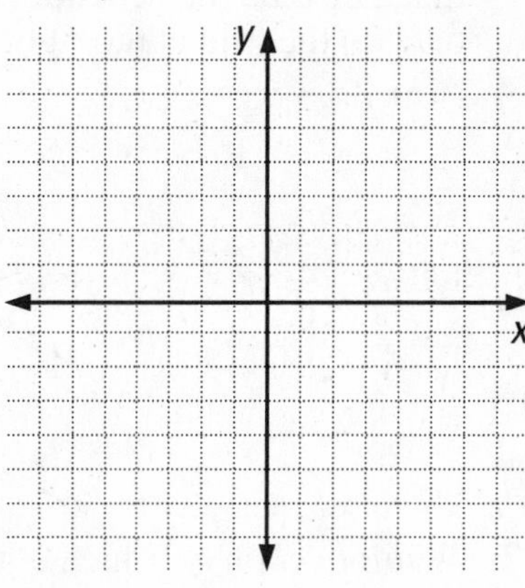

18. Find the slope of the graph of the equation. **18.** ____________

Name

19. At the right is the graph of $y = \frac{4}{x^2}$ on the window $0 \le x \le 10, 0 \le y \le 10$.

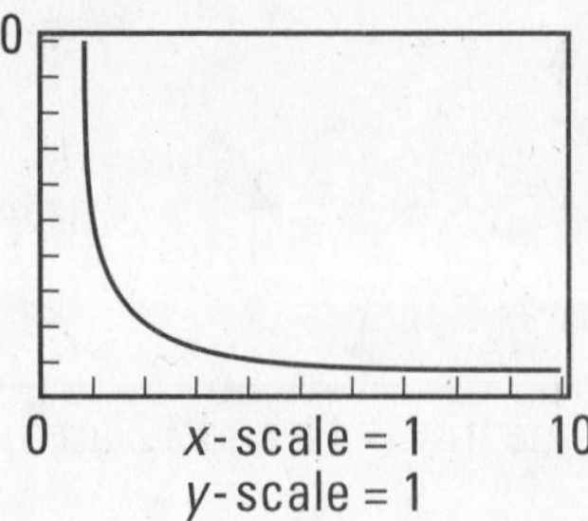

a. Give the dimensions of a window that would show both branches of the graph. **19. a.** ________

b. Identify two asymptotes to the graph. **b.** ________

20. Suppose that variables *L, m, d,* and *x* are related as illustrated in the graphs below. The points on the graph at the right lie on a line through the origin. The points on the other two graphs lie on or near a parabola. Write a general equation approximating the relationship between *L, m, d,* and *x*. **20.** ________

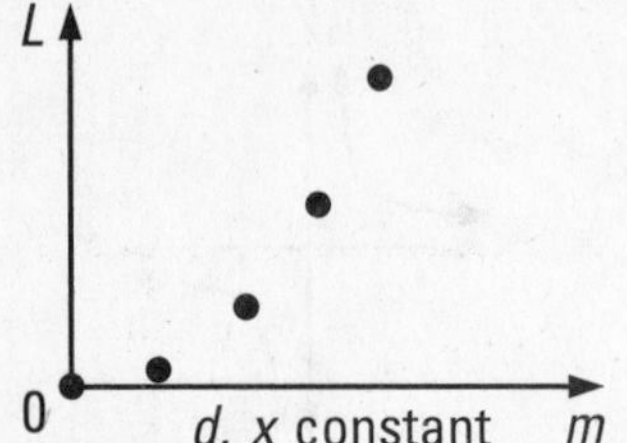

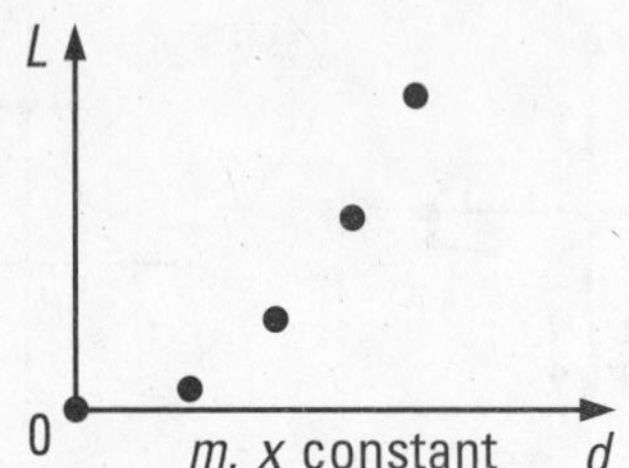

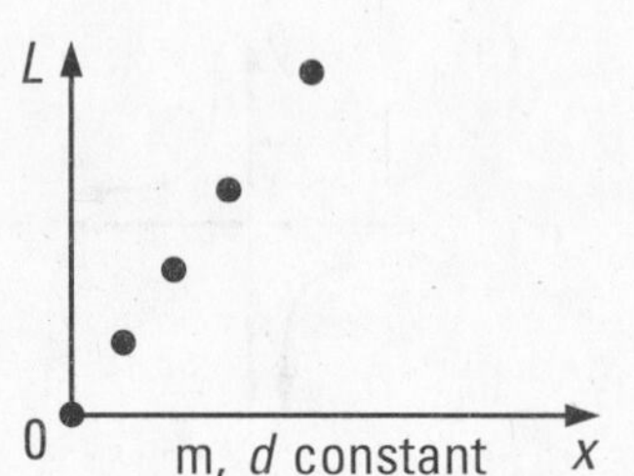

In 21 and 22, refer to the data in the table below, which relate the distance a ball travels down a ramp to the time that has passed since it was released.

Time t (sec)	0	1	2	3	4	5
Distance d (in.)	0	.4	1.6	3.6	6.4	10.0

21. Let the time t be the independent variable and the distance d be the dependent variable. Graph the data on the grid at the right. **21.**

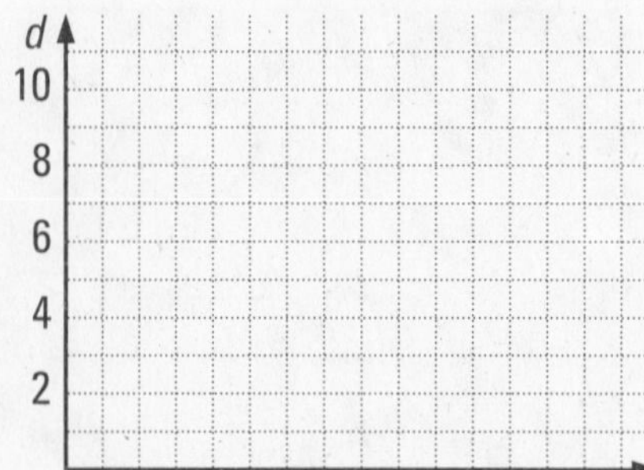

22. *Multiple choice.* Which equation best models the data? **22.** ________

(a) $d = kt$ (b) $d = kt^2$ (c) $t = kd$ (d) $t = kd^2$

Check all your work carefully.

Name

CHAPTER 2 TEST, Form C

1. Suppose that y varies inversely as the cube of x, and $y = 54$ when $x = 2$. Show how to use the constant of variation and an equation to find the value of y when $x = 6$. Explain how your result illustrates the Fundamental Theorem of Variation.

2. In the formula $d = rt$, d is distance traveled, r is a constant rate of travel, and t is time spent traveling at that rate. Suppose you must travel exactly 120 miles. What type of variation exists in the relationship between r and t? Write a variation equation that represents the situation and give two examples of how you might use it.

3. Use rates of change to demonstrate that the graph of $y = \frac{48}{x}$ is not a line.

4. State as many facts as you can about the graph of an equation of the form $y = \frac{k}{x^2}$.

5. Len and Mai each graphed $y = \frac{1}{2}x^2$ using an automatic grapher. Their graphs are shown at the right. Which graph do you think gives a better picture of the function? How could you adjust it in any way to improve the picture?

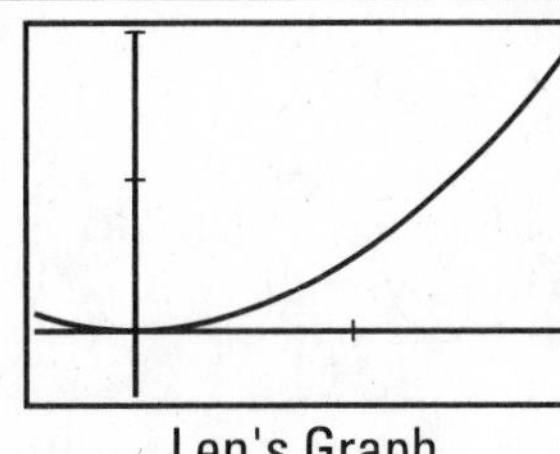
Len's Graph

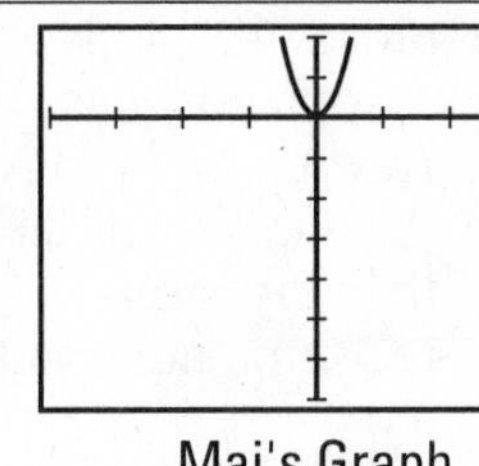
Mai's Graph

CHAPTER 2 TEST, Form D

Imagine you are an urban planner for a large city. You are planning a small fountain on a 40-foot square plot of land. At the right is a proposed design for a 3-layered fountain to be built on the plot.

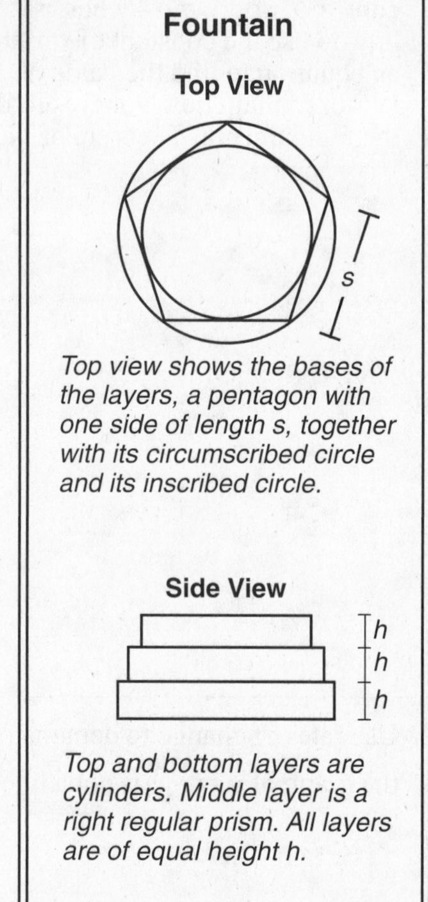

Top view shows the bases of the layers, a pentagon with one side of length s, together with its circumscribed circle and its inscribed circle.

Top and bottom layers are cylinders. Middle layer is a right regular prism. All layers are of equal height h.

a. Suppose that the base of the middle layer of the fountain is a regular pentagon, as shown in the sketch. Suppose further that $s = 30$ feet and $h = 1$ foot.

A formula for the volume of a cylinder or prism is $V = Bh$, where B is the area of the base and h is the height. Use this formula and the chart at the bottom of the page to find the volume of granite that will be needed for the top, middle, and bottom layers and for the entire fountain. Round your results to the nearest whole number.

b. As s increases, does the volume of each layer and of the entire fountain decrease or increase? Are the relationships between the volumes and s variation relations? If so, what are the constants of variation?

c. The area of the plot of land not covered by the fountain will be used for walkways. As s increases, does this area increase or decrease? Is the relationship between this area and s a variation relation? If so, what is the constant of variation?

d. The person who must make the final decision about the size of the fountain is the mayor. The granite is expensive – \$225 per cubic foot – and the budget is limited. So the mayor's decision will almost certainly be based on the cost of the granite. Write a report that will give the mayor sufficient information on which to base the decision. Your report should include the following information.

i. Your recommendations for s and h, given that the length of each side of the plot is 40 feet long

ii. A total cost based on your recommendations

iii. An analysis of the effect on cost should the mayor choose to alter your recommendation for either s or h

Your report should include at least one graph.

Regular Pentagon with Sides of Length s		
Area of Inscribed Circle	Area of Pentagon	Area of Circumscribed Circle
$1.488s^2$	$1.720s^2$	$2.273s^2$

Name

CHAPTER 2 TEST, Cumulative Form

In 1–9, refer to the following equations.

(a) $A = \frac{\pi d^2}{4}$ (b) $I = \frac{3}{10}mr^2$ (c) $\begin{cases} t_1 = -3 \\ t_n = t_{n-1} + 2, \text{ for integers } n \geq 2 \end{cases}$

(d) $f(x) = 3x^2 + 5$ (e) $L = \frac{36}{W}$ (f) $S_n = \frac{180(n-2)}{n}$

1. Which equation represents an inverse variation? 1. ______

2. Which equation represents a joint variation? 2. ______

3. Give the first four terms of the sequence represented by the set of equations in (c). 3. ______

4. Which equation is an explicit formula for a sequence? 4. ______

5. Which equation has a graph that is a hyperbola? 5. ______

6. In equation (a), how does the value of A change if d is multiplied by 6? 6. ______

7. Using equation (f), find S_{10}. 7. ______

8. Using equation (d), find $f(-4)$. 8. ______

9. Solve for m in equation (b). 9. ______

In 10 and 11, use the following information: It costs $2 to enter a taxi. Then it costs $4.00 to travel every mile.

10. Write a formula that gives the cost c of traveling n miles. 10. ______

11. You need to travel 6 miles, but you have only $20. Can you afford to ride in the taxi? Explain.

______

______

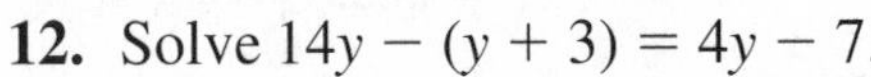

12. Solve $14y - (y + 3) = 4y - 7$. 12. ______

Name

▶ CHAPTER 2 TEST, Cumulative Form *page 2*

In 13 and 14, graph the equation on the grid at the right.

13. $y = 4x^2$

13.

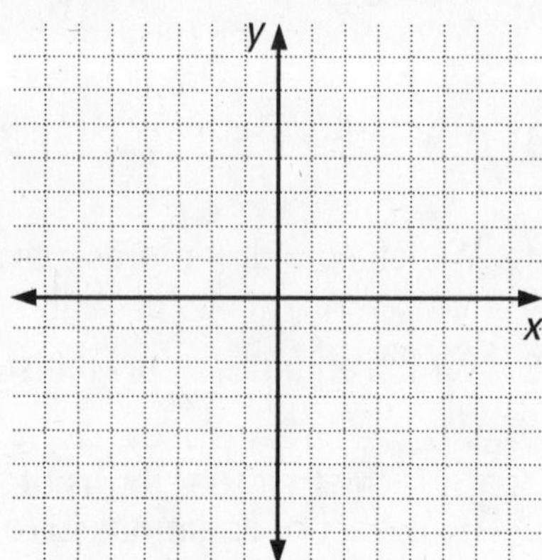

14. $y = -\frac{8}{x}$

14.

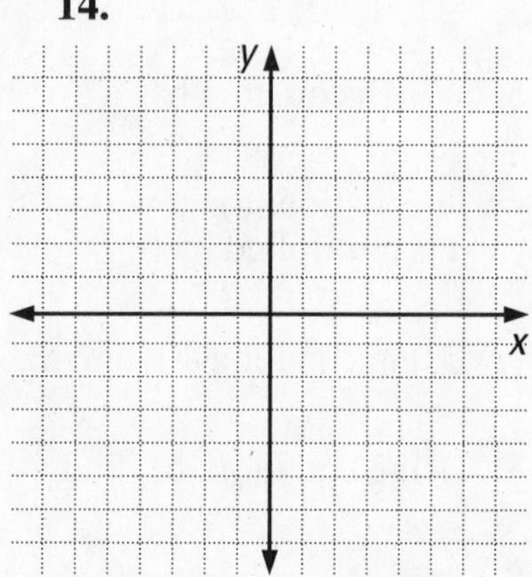

15. Below is the graph of $y = 2x$ on the window $-7 \le x \le 7$, $-7 \le y \le 7$.

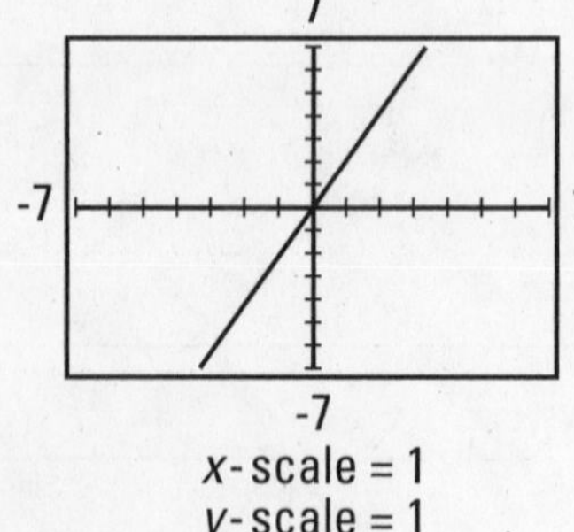

x-scale = 1
y-scale = 1

Sketch a graph of $y = 2x$ on the window at the right.

15.

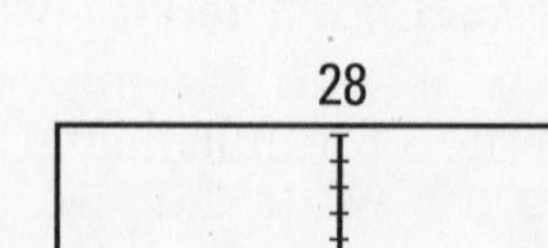

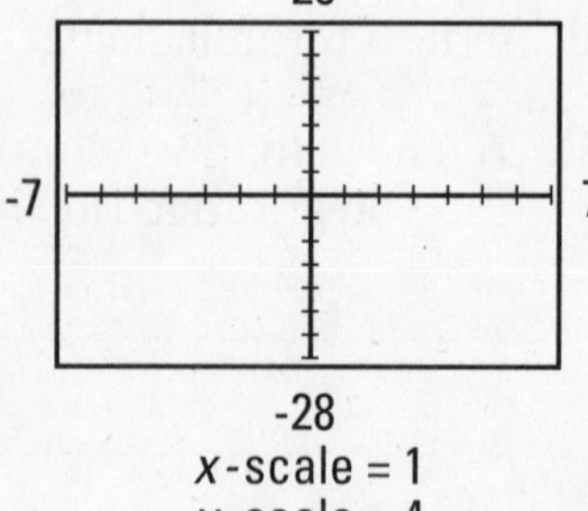

x-scale = 1
y-scale = 4

Name

16. The depth to which a given amount of water fills a cylindrical storage tank varies inversely with the square of the radius of the tank. A cylindrical tank with radius 65 feet is filled with water to a depth of 26 feet. What is the depth to the nearest foot to which the same amount of water will fill a cylindrical tank with radius 45 feet?

16. ____________

In 17–20, refer to the data in the table below, which relate the number of people seated at a kitchen table doing homework and the amount of space available to each person.

Number of People n	2	4	6	8	10
Space per Person s (ft^2)	10	5	$3\frac{1}{3}$	$2\frac{1}{2}$	2

17. Let the number of people n be the independent variable and the space per person s be the dependent variable. Draw a graph of the data on the grid at the right.

17.

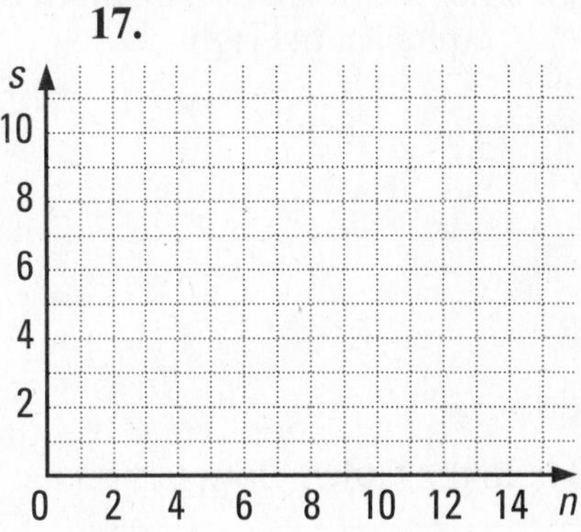

18. Write a general equation of variation relating n and s.

18. ____________

19. Find the constant of variation, and write a specific variation equation relating n and s.

19. ____________

20. Determine the amount of space each person would have if twelve people were seated at the table.

20. ____________

21. a. Describe the sequence π, -3π, 9π, -27π, . . . in words.

____

____

b. Write a recursive definition for the sequence.

____

Name

22. Does the graph at the right represent a function? Why or why not?

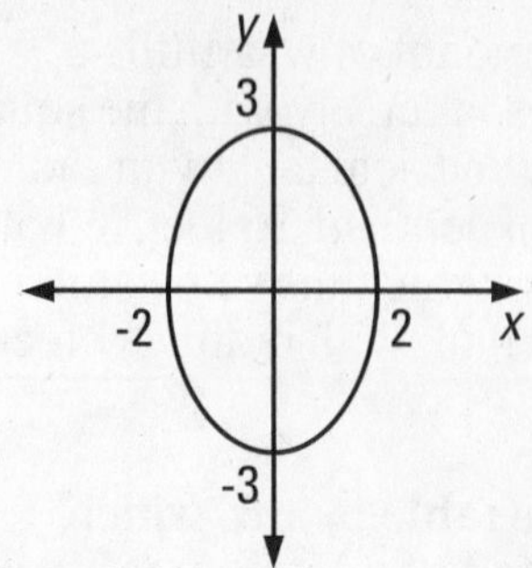

23. Find the range of the function graphed at the right.

23. ______________

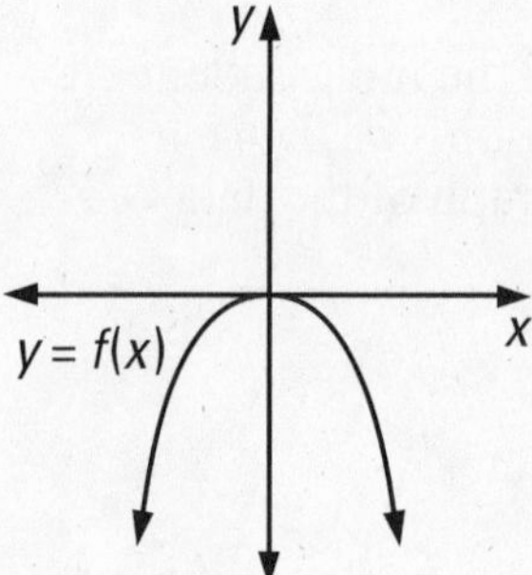

24. In the table below, is y a function of x? Justify your answer.

x	-3	3	-1	1	0
y	3	3	1	1	0

25. *Multiple choice.* Select the equation whose graph is most like that shown at the right. Assume the scales on the axes are equal.

(a) $y = 5x$ (b) $y = 5x^2$

(c) $y = \frac{5}{x}$ (d) $y = -\frac{5}{x}$

25. ______________

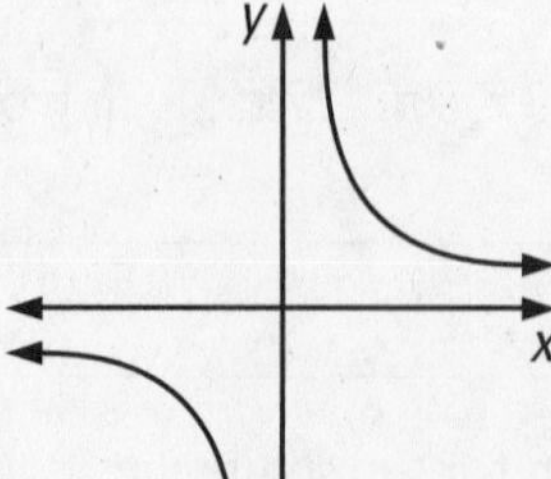

Check all your work carefully.

Name

QUIZ

Lessons 3-1 Through 3-3

1. Graph the line $y = -\frac{4}{3}x + 4$ on the coordinate axes at the right.

1.

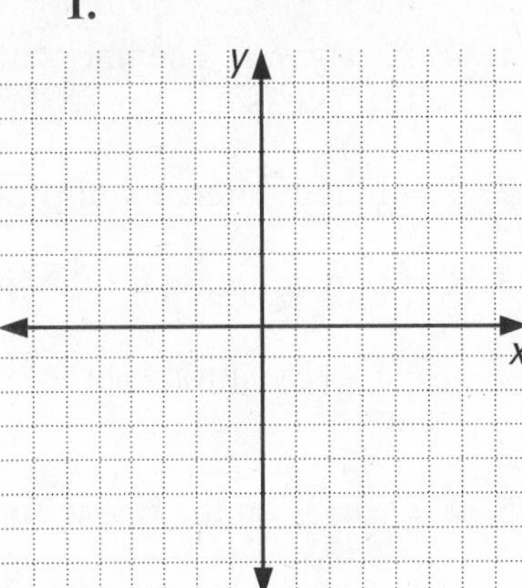

In 2–4, consider the line $y = -3$.

2. Give the coordinates of two points that lie on the line. 2. ____________

3. Identify the slope and the y-intercept of the line. 3. ____________

4. Identify the range of the function represented by the line. 4. ____________

5. *Multiple choice.* Which is an equation of a line parallel to $y = \frac{1}{3}x - 8$? 5. ____________

   (a) $y = -8$ (b) $x = 8$ (c) $x + 3y = 8$ (d) $x - 3y = 8$

In 6 and 7, refer to the following situation: A tank has left a military base and is traveling to a second base that is 288 miles away. The tank maintains a constant speed of 45 mi/h.

6. Write an equation that relates the tank's distance d from the second base as a function of the number of hours h it has traveled. 6. ____________

7. After how many hours will the tank be 135 miles from the second base? 7. ____________

In 8 and 9, refer to the following situation: A fertilizer company mixes x pounds of a fertilizer that is 30% nitrate with y pounds of a fertilizer that is 10% nitrate.

8. Suppose the company wants 45 pounds of nitrate in the final mixture. Write an equation that relates x, y, and the 45 total pounds of nitrate. 8. ____________

9. How many pounds of the 10%-nitrate fertilizer must be added to 75 pounds of the 30%-nitrate fertilizer to get 45 pounds of nitrate in the final mixture? 9. ____________

Name

QUIZ

Lessons 3-4 Through 3-6

1. *True or false.* The line with equation $x = -4$ is parallel to the x-axis. **1.** ____________

2. Find the x-intercept of the line with equation $4x - 5y = 40$. **2.** ____________

3. Give an equation for the line through (-1, 9) and (12, -6). **3.** ____________

4. Give an equation for the line parallel to $8x + 3y = 10$ that contains (7, -2). **4.** ____________

5. If $(3, n)$ is on the line with equation $y - 5 = 2(x - 4)$, find n. **5.** ____________

6. A service technician charges $36.25 for 5 hours of work and $65.25 for 9 hours of work. Assuming a linear relationship between the charge and the number of hours worked, what will be the charge for 15 hours of work? **6.** ____________

In 7–10, use the table below, which shows the winning times for the Women's 100-meter run in eight recent Olympic games.

Year	1964	1968	1972	1976	1980	1984	1988	1992
Time (Seconds)	11.4	11.0	11.07	11.08	11.6	10.97	10.54	10.82

7. Make a scatterplot of the data on the coordinate axes at the right. **7.**

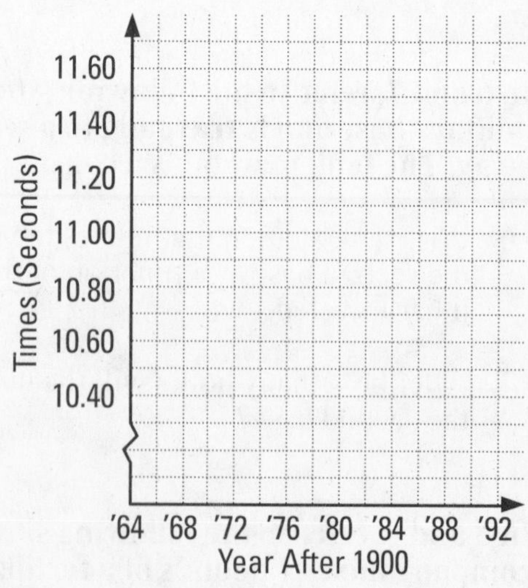

8. Find an equation of the line of best fit to these data. **8.** ____________

9. Find the correlation coefficient. **9.** ____________

10. Is a linear equation a reasonable model for these data? Why or why not?

____

____

Name

CHAPTER 3 TEST, Form A

In 1 and 2, use the arithmetic sequence 11, 19, 27, 35, ...

1. Write an explicit formula for the sequence. **1.** ____________

2. Write a recursive formula for the sequence. **2.** ____________

3. a. Elizabeth borrowed $5500 from her parents to buy a car. She is paying them back at the rate of $75 a month. Write an equation that relates the amount *A* that she still owes to the number of payments *m*. **3. a.** ____________

b. How much will Elizabeth owe after 18 payments? **b.** ____________

4. Evaluate $\lfloor -\pi - 1 \rfloor$. **4.** ____________

In 5–8, consider the line with equation $4x + 6y = 12$.

5. What is the slope of the line? **5.** ____________

6. What is the *y*-intercept of the line? **6.** ____________

7. What is the *x*-intercept of the line? **7.** ____________

8. Graph the line on the coordinate axes at the right. **8.**

y

x

9. Give an equation for the line parallel to $y = 6x + 5$ that contains (-8, 10). **9.** ____________

10. Give an equation for a line with undefined slope. **10.** ____________

11. Tickets to tour a country farm cost A dollars for adults and C dollars for children. A day-camp group consists of 30 children and 5 adults. Write a linear combination to find the total cost of tour tickets for this group. **11.** ______

12. Does the formula $a_n = 3n + 8$ generate an arithmetic sequence? Explain why or why not.

______

______

13. What is an equation for the line graphed at the right? **13.** ______

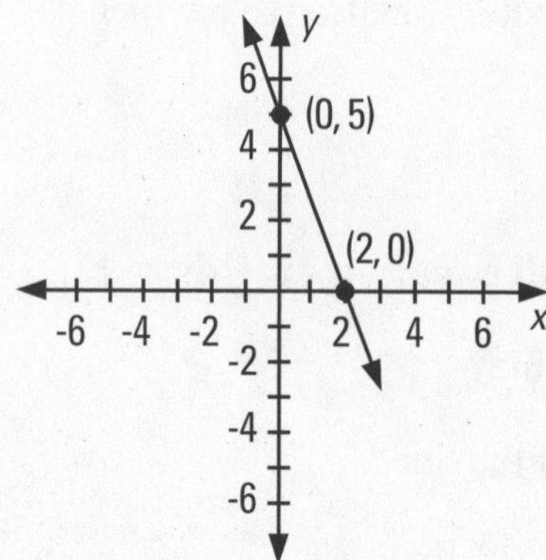

14. *Multiple choice.* A manufacturer produces c cans of tea each day. The tea is packed in cases that each contain 24 cans. Which of the following represents the number of full cases of tea produced each day? **14.** ______

(a) $\left\lfloor \frac{24}{c} \right\rfloor$ (b) $\lfloor 24c \rfloor$ (c) $\left\lfloor \frac{c}{24} \right\rfloor$ (d) $\frac{c}{24}$

In 15–17, refer to the lines graphed below. Match each equation with the line that could be its graph.

(a)

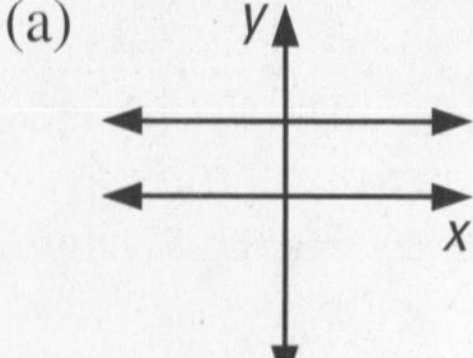

(b)

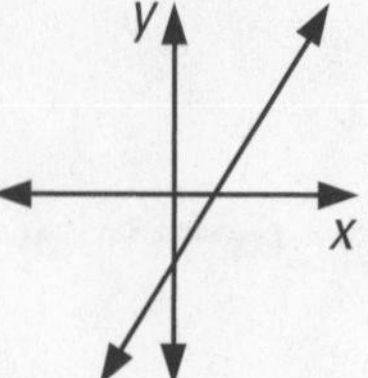

(c)

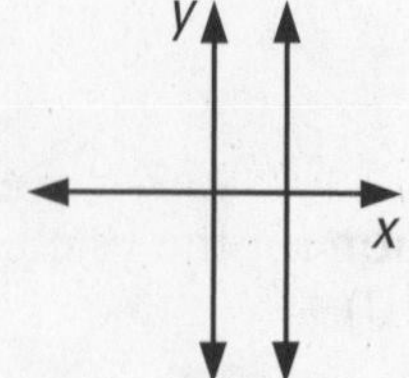

15. $Ax + By = C$, where $A = 0, B \neq 0, C \neq 0$ **15.** ______

16. $Ax + By = C$, where $A \neq 0, B = 0, C \neq 0$ **16.** ______

17. $Ax + By = C$, where $A \neq 0, B \neq 0, C \neq 0$ **17.** ______

18. To organize a closet, Hoa bought wire shelving that was 12 inches wide. The cost was $4.20 for 60 inches of the shelving and $2.80 for 40 inches. Assuming a linear relationship between the cost of the shelving and the length, what would be the cost of 84 inches of shelving?

18. ____________

19. a. Graph the function f defined by $f(x) = \lfloor x \rfloor + 2$ on the coordinate axes at the right.

19. a.

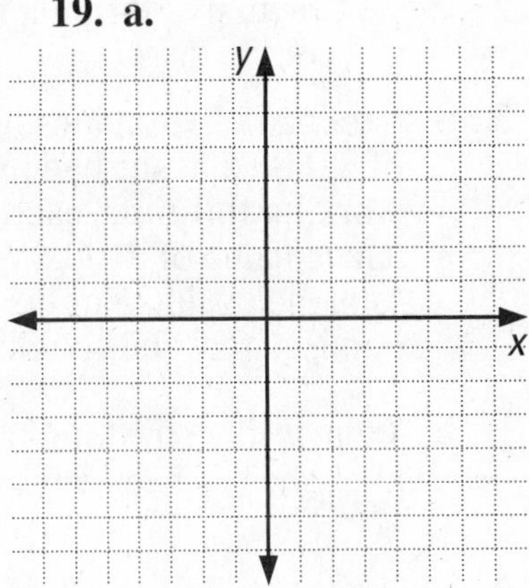

b. Find the domain and the range of f.

b. ____________

____

20. a. The table below gives the percent of 13-year-old students who say "I am good at mathematics" and their average math score on a proficiency test. Make a scatterplot of the data on the coordinate axes at the right.

Country	Percent Who Say They're Good at Math	Average Math Score
United States	68	473.9
Canada	61	522.8
Spain	60	511.7
Ireland	49	504.3
United Kingdom	47	509.9
South Korea	23	567.8

20. a.

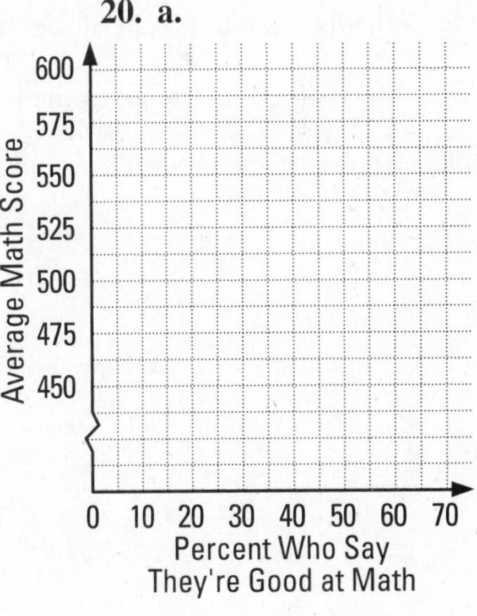

b. Find an equation of the regression line.

b. ____________

c. Find the correlation coefficient.

c. ____________

d. Use your equation for the regression line to predict the average math score in a country where 33% of the 13-year-old students say they are good at math.

d. ____________

Check all your work carefully.

Name

CHAPTER 3 TEST, Form B

In 1 and 2, use the arithmetic sequence -7, -5, -3, -1, 1, ...

1. Write an explicit formula for the sequence. **1.** ______________

2. Write a recursive formula for the sequence. **2.** ______________

3. a. Sara had U.S. savings bonds with a total face value of \$2800 that she had received as gifts. Now that she is working full-time, each month she buys a bond with a face value of \$100. Write an equation that relates the total face value *F* of her savings bonds to the number of bonds *m* that she bought. **3. a.** ______________

b. What will be the total face value of Sara's bonds after she has been buying them for 3 years? **b.** ______________

4. Evaluate $\lfloor -\pi + 1 \rfloor$. **4.** ______________

In 5–8, consider the line with equation $9x + 6y = 18$.

5. What is the slope of the line? **5.** ______________

6. What is the *y*-intercept of the line? **6.** ______________

7. What is the *x*-intercept of the line? **7.** ______________

8. Graph the line on the coordinate axes at the right. **8.**

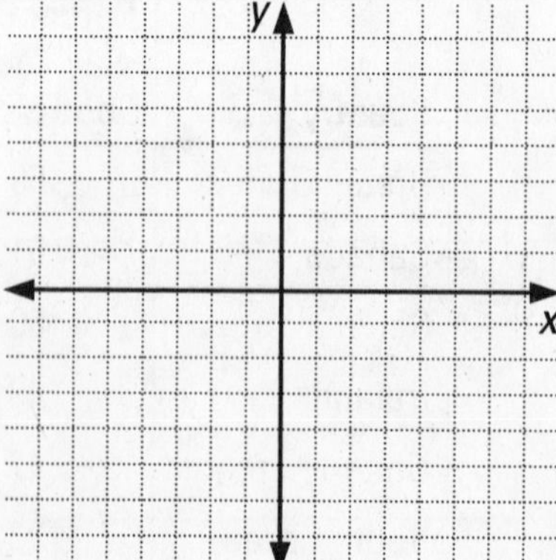

9. Give an equation for the line parallel to $y = 3x - 2$ that contains (-6, -4). **9.** ______________

10. Give an equation for a line with a slope of zero. **10.** ______________

Name

11. In 1995, the one-way bus fare from Hyde Park to downtown Chicago was $1.50 for adults and $.75 for children aged 7–11. A day-camp group consists of *C* children and *A* adults. Write a linear combination to find the total cost of the one-way bus fare for this group. **11.** ____________

12. Does the formula $a_n = n^2 - 4$ generate an arithmetic sequence? Explain why or why not.

____

____

13. What is an equation for the line graphed at the right? **13.** ____________

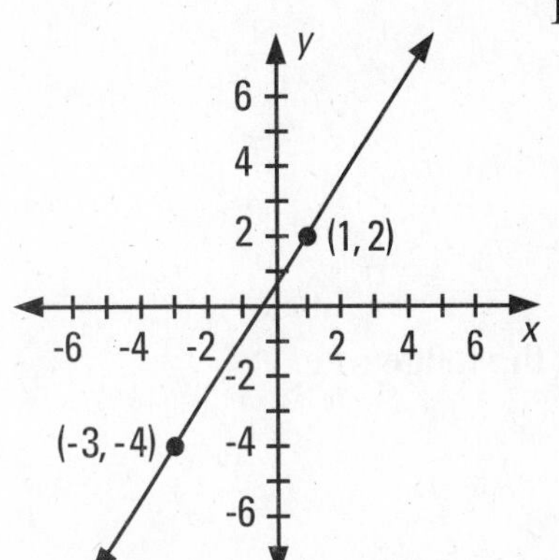

14. *Multiple choice.* There are *p* people waiting in line for a ride at an amusement park. The ride can carry 48 people on each run. Which of the following represents the number of runs needed to carry all the people who are in line? **14.** ____________

(a) $\left\lfloor \frac{p}{48} \right\rfloor$ (b) $\left\lfloor \frac{48}{p} \right\rfloor$ (c) $-\left\lfloor -\frac{p}{48} \right\rfloor$ (d) $\frac{48}{p}$

In 15–17, refer to the lines graphed below. Match each equation with the line that could be its graph.

(a)

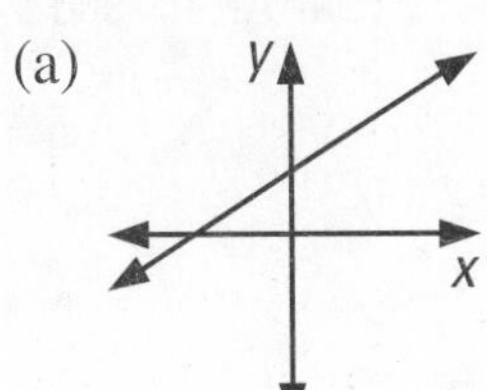

(b)

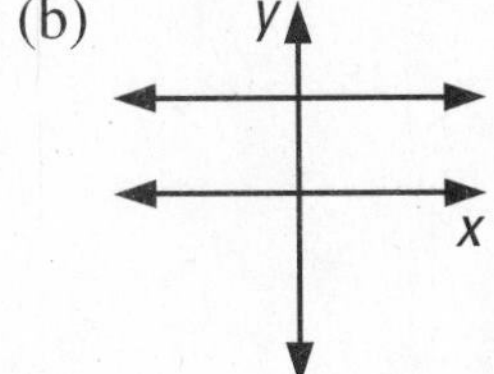

(c)

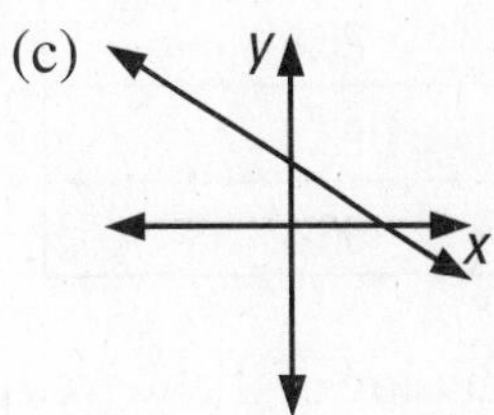

15. $y = \frac{2}{3}x + 4$ **15.** ____________

16. $y = -\frac{2}{3}x + 4$ **16.** ____________

17. $y = 4$ **17.** ____________

Name

18. At the bakery, Kaneesha bought 12 pastries for \$5.40 and Richard bought 30 pastries of the same type for \$13.50. Assuming a linear relationship between the total cost of these pastries and the number bought, what would be the cost of 27 pastries of this type?

18. 

19. a. Graph the function g defined by $g(x) = \lfloor x \rfloor - 3$ on the coordinate axes at the right.

19. a.

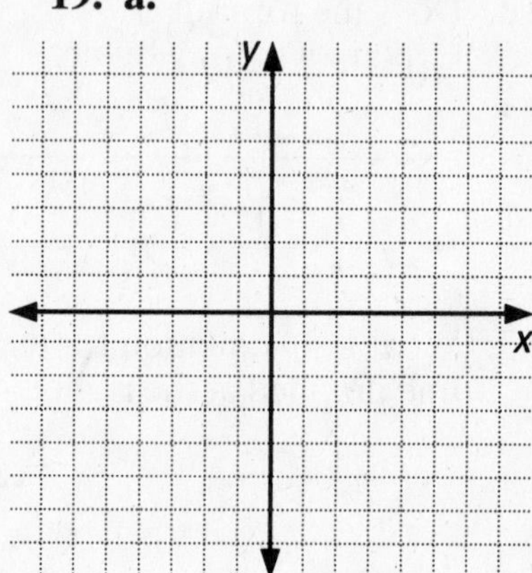

b. Find the domain and the range of g.

b. ____________

____

20. a. The table below gives the number of households in the United States for selected years from 1970 to 1993. Make a scatterplot of the data on the coordinate axes at the right.

Year	Number of Households (Millions)
1970	63.4
1975	71.1
1980	80.8
1985	86.8
1990	93.3
1993	96.4

20. a.

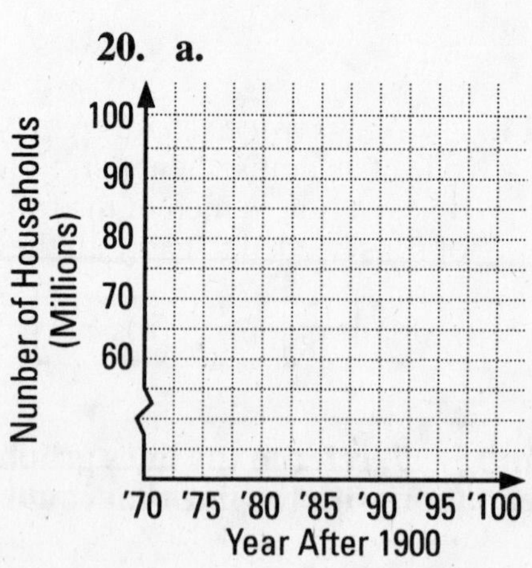

b. Find an equation of the regression line.

b. ____________

c. Find the correlation coefficient.

c. ____________

d. Use your equation for the regression line to predict the number of households in the United States in the year 2000.

d. ____________

Check all your work carefully.

Name

CHAPTER 3 TEST, Form C

1. State as many facts as you can about the line graphed at the right and about the function it represents. (*Hint:* Think of the equation of the line and of properties such as its slope and intercepts.)

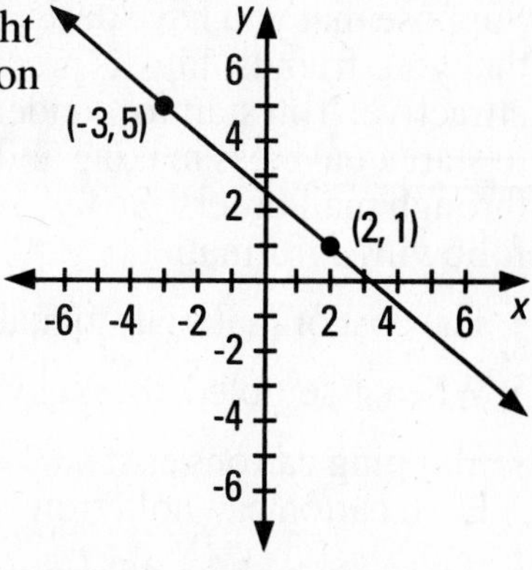

2. Make up two different arithmetic sequences in which the constant difference between terms is -3. Give an explicit formula and a recursive formula for each sequence. How are the formulas for your two sequences alike? How are they different?

3. A relative of yours saw the unfamiliar symbol $\lfloor \quad \rfloor$ in your math book and wondered what it meant. How would you explain it? Write a brief description of what you would say. Include an example of a real-world situation that you can model algebraically with the use of this symbol.

4. The following is a popular children's problem.

   There are a total of 20 chickens and cows in a barnyard. The animals have 52 legs in all. How many of each animal are there?

   Explain how to solve this problem.

5. Jenna entered data about the average basic monthly rate for cable TV service from the years 1970 through 1993 into her calculator. She obtained this display.

   $y = ax + b$
   $a = .655010553$
   $b = -43.15682144$
   $r = .9113235732$

   Explain the meaning of the numbers in the display. How can Jenna use them to predict the rate in the year 2000?

Name

CHAPTER 3 TEST, Form D

Suppose that you have designed a style of tote bag that your friends think is practical and unusually attractive. You start to wonder if you might be able to start a business making and selling the tote bags through mail orders. So far, you have gathered the following information.

Mercury Express Package Deliveries			
Weight Not to Exceed...	Regular Delivery	Two-Day Delivery	Next-Day Delivery
1 lb	$3.43	$10.25	$20.50
2	3.55	11.50	22.00
3	3.67	12.75	23.50
4	3.79	14.00	25.00
5	3.91	15.25	26.50
6	4.03	16.50	28.00
7	4.15	17.75	29.50
8	4.27	19.00	31.00
9	4.39	20.25	32.50
10	4.51	21.50	34.00

- The cost of materials to make one bag is $5.71.
- When assembled, the bag weighs 1.25 pounds.
- Shipping cartons cost $.89 and weigh 12 ounces. Each carton can hold from one to six bags.
- It takes you about 45 minutes to make one bag.
- Advertising brochures cost $25 for any number up to 100. For each brochure over 100, there is an additional $.15 cost.
- The monthly rental fee for a post office box is $35.
- Your parents will let you work out of a spare room in your house, but they ask that you contribute $50 per month for the use of the room and for your business's share of the utilities (heating, electricity, and so on).
- A package delivery service will ship your packages at the rates listed in the chart at the right.

a. Write an equation or set of equations to model each of the following.
  i. the total weight in pounds W of a carton that contains n tote bags
  ii. the cost of regular delivery R for a package whose weight does not exceed p pounds
  iii. the number of full cartons C needed to ship an order of n tote bags
  iv. the advertising cost A for printing b brochures
  v. the cost of materials M to make n tote bags

b. Choose two of the situations listed in part **a** and represent each graphically.

c. Assume that you have 150 brochures printed each month. Then the *fixed expenses* for your business each month are the cost of brochures, the rental of the post office box, and the $50 paid to your parents. The sum of your fixed expenses and the cost of materials is considered to be your *total expenses.* Write an equation that represents your total expenses E in a month when you make n tote bags. Graph your equation.

d. Decide on a price for each tote bag. Then write an equation that represents the total amount of income I that you will receive from the sale of n tote bags. Graph your equation on the same set of axes that you used in part **c**. What information can you read from this graph?

e. Suppose that you are going to apply to a bank for a loan to start your business. Prepare a report that you can submit to the bank along with your application for the loan. In your report, include information about costs, the amount you plan to charge your customers, the amount of profit that you expect to make, and the amount of the loan you are requesting. Your report should include at least one graph.

Name

CHAPTER 3 TEST, Cumulative Form

In 1 and 2, use the equation $.04x + .06(10{,}000 - x) = 480$.

1. Solve the equation. Show your work. **1.** ______

2. Make up a real-world problem that could be solved using the equation.

______

______

3. Find an explicit formula for the nth term of the sequence defined below. **3.** ______

$$\begin{cases} a_1 = -3 \\ a_n = a_{n-1} + 2, \text{ for integers } n \geq 2 \end{cases}$$

4. a. A river that was already 5 feet above flood stage began rising at the rate of 2 inches per hour. Write an equation that relates the number of inches h above flood stage to the number of hours t that the river has been rising. **4. a.** ______

b. How many inches above flood stage will the river be after it has been rising for 24 hours? **b.** ______

5. Find the domain and range of the function graphed at the right. **5.** ______

______

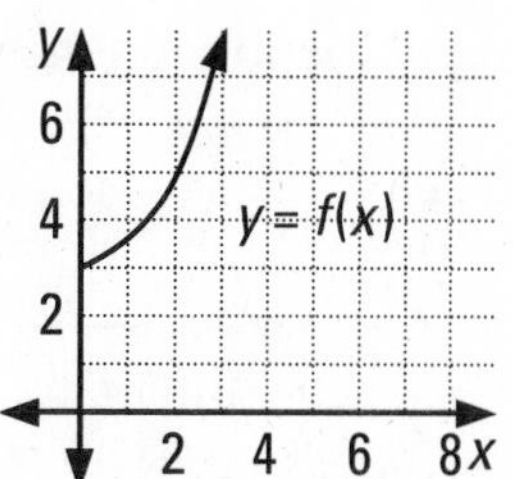

6. Given the function g defined by $g(t) = 9t^2 + 4t - 3$, find $g(-11)$. **6.** ______

7. Give an equation for the line through (-9, -1) and (-5, 4). **7.** ______

8. The time t it takes to travel from Milwaukee to Tampa by car varies inversely with the average speed s of the car. Suppose it takes 23 hours to travel this distance at an average speed of 60 miles per hour. How long would it take to travel this distance at an average speed of 50 miles per hour? **8.** ______

Name

9. The table below gives the cost of parking a car in a city garage for amounts of time up to 24 hours. Graph the cost C as a function of the time t on the coordinate axes at the right.

t = time (hours)	C = cost (dollars)
$0 < t \leq \frac{1}{2}$	.75
$\frac{1}{2} < t \leq 1$	1.25
$1 < t \leq 2$	2.50
$2 < t \leq 3$	3.75
$3 < t \leq 4$	5.00
$4 < t \leq 24$	6.50

9.

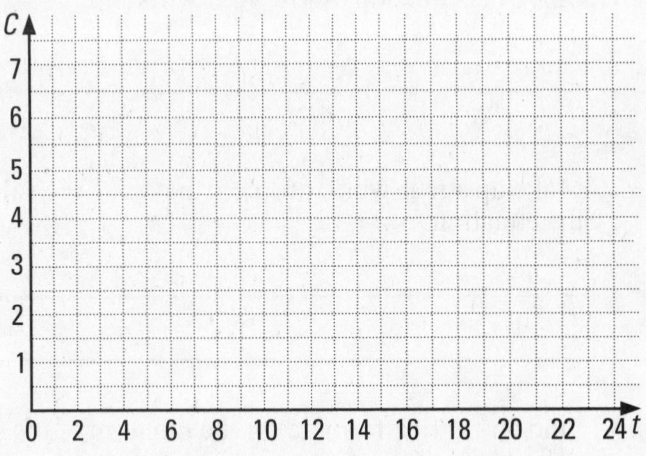

10. a. Consider the equation $y = x^2$. Find the rate of change from (3, 9) to (4, 16).

10. a. ____________

b. Find the rate of change from (4, 16) to (5, 25).

b. ____________

c. *True or false.* This equation can model a constant-increase situation.

c. ____________

11. a. Is 5, 10, 20, 40, . . . an arithmetic sequence? Why or why not?

____

____

b. Write a recursive formula for this sequence.

b. ____________

12. Suppose y varies directly as w^2. How does the value of y change if w is multiplied by 4?

12. ____________

13. Consider the following function. {(4, 2), (9, 3), (1, 1), (16, 4)}

a. Identify the domain of the function.

13. a. ____________

b. Identify the range.

b. ____________

Name

In 14–16, consider the line with equation $y = \frac{2}{3}x - 4$.

14. What is the slope of the line? **14.** ____________

15. What are the x- and y-intercepts of the line? **15.** ____________

16. Graph the line on the coordinate axes at the right. **16.**

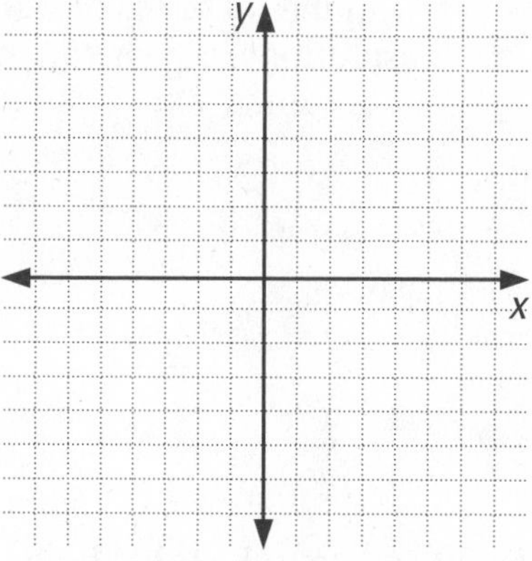

17. *Multiple choice.* Select the equation whose graph is most like that shown at the right. **17.** ____________

(a) $y = kx,\ k > 0$

(b) $y = \frac{k}{x},\ k > 0$

(c) $y = \frac{k}{x^2},\ k > 0$

(d) $y = \frac{k}{x},\ k < 0$

(e) $y = \frac{k}{x^2},\ k < 0$

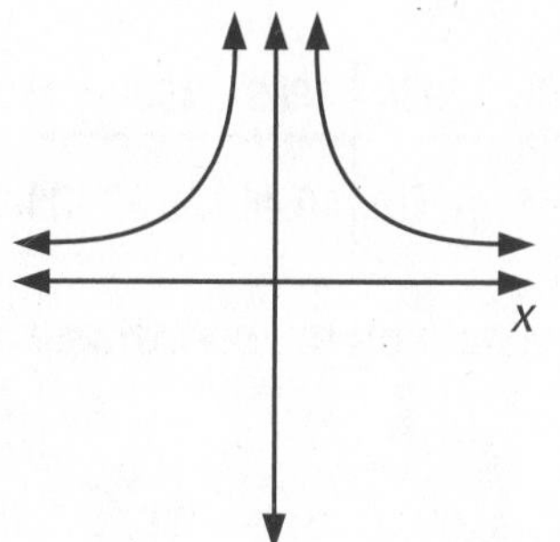

18. a. On the coordinate axes at the right, graph a line that has a slope of zero. **18. a.**

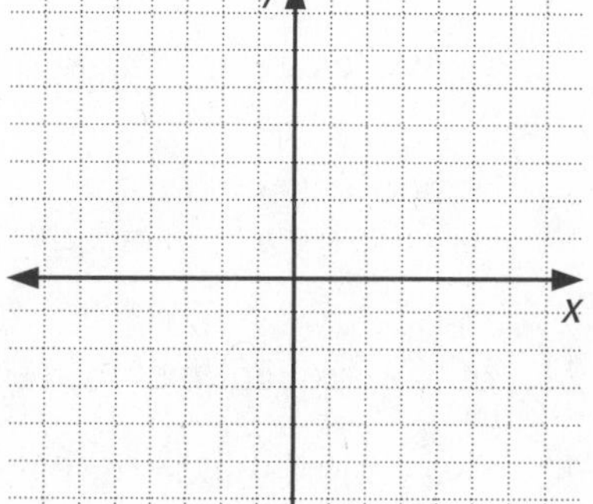

b. Give an equation for the line that you graphed in part **a.** **b.** ____________

Name

19. a. Lynne charges \$12 an hour to tutor an individual and \$20 an hour to tutor a group of 2–4 people. Last week, Lynne earned a total of \$120 tutoring individuals for I hours and tutoring groups for G hours. Write an equation that relates I, G, and the \$120 that she earned.

19. a. ______________

b. Assume that Lynne earns money only for a whole number of hours of tutoring. Graph all the solutions to your equation in part **a** on the coordinate axes at the right.

b.

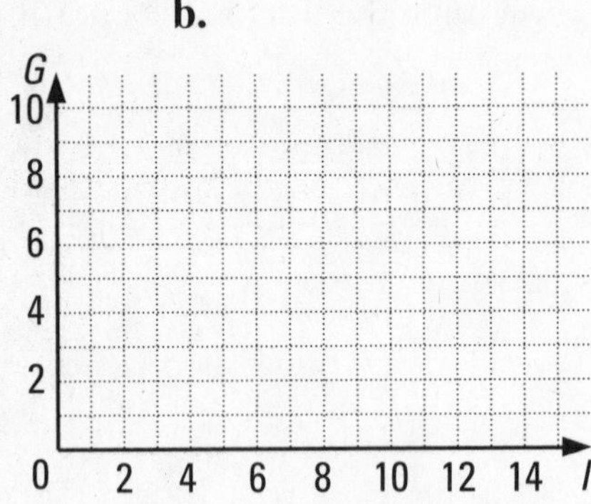

In 20–22, use the table below, which gives the average hourly earnings of production workers in manufacturing industries for selected years from 1980 to 1993.

Year	1980	1985	1988	1989	1990	1991	1992	1993
Average Hourly Earnings (Dollars)	7.27	9.54	10.19	10.48	10.83	11.18	11.46	11.76

20. Make a scatterplot of the data on the coordinate axes at the right.

20.

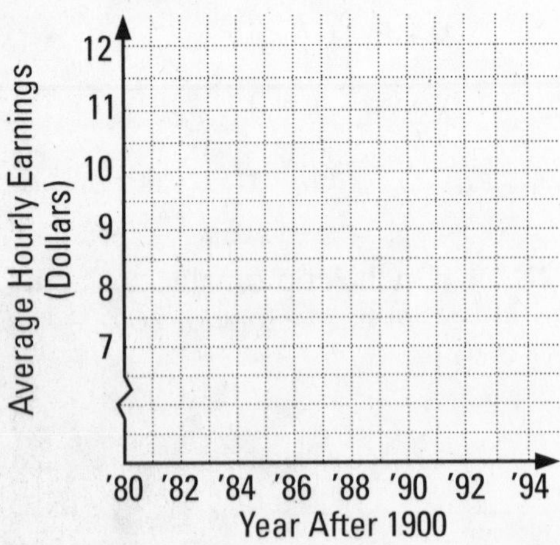

21. Find an equation of the regression line.

21. ______________

22. Use your equation for the regression line to predict the average hourly earnings in the year 2000.

22. ______________

23. Suppose that y varies directly as the cube of x. If $y = 343$, then $x = 3.5$. Find y when $x = 9.5$.

23. ______________

Check all your work carefully.

Name ____

COMPREHENSIVE TEST, Chapters 1–3

Multiple choice. **Give the letter of the correct answer.**

1. What are the first three terms of the following sequence? **1.** ________

$$\begin{cases} t_1 = 5 \\ t_n = 3t_{n-1} + 4, \text{ for integers } n \geq 2 \end{cases}$$

(a) 5, 15, 45 (b) 5, 9, 13

(c) 5, 19, 61 (d) 5, 19, 23

2. If $k < 0$, which could be an equation for the graph at the right? **2.** ________

(a) $y = kx$ (b) $y = \frac{k}{x}$

(c) $y = \frac{k}{x^2}$ (d) $y = kx^2$

3. What is the slope of the line with equation $4x + 9y = 13$? **3.** 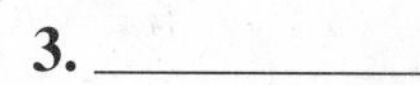

(a) $-\frac{4}{9}$ (b) $\frac{4}{9}$ (c) $-\frac{9}{4}$ (d) $\frac{13}{9}$

4. A river crested at 30 feet above flood stage. Then the water began to recede at the rate of $\frac{1}{2}$ foot per hour. Which equation relates the number of feet h above flood stage to the number of hours t that the water has been receding? **4.** ________

(a) $h = 30 + \frac{1}{2}t$ (b) $h = 30 - \frac{1}{2}t$

(c) $h = \frac{1}{2}t - 30$ (d) $t = 30 - \frac{1}{2}h$

5. Mr. Redbird started a new job at an annual salary of \$22,500. He will receive an increase of 3% at the end of each year. The function S defined by $S(n) = 22{,}500\,(1.03)^{n-1}$ gives his salary during his nth year on this job. What will be his salary during his third year with this company? **5.** 

(a) \$23,175.00 (b) \$23,869.25

(c) \$23,870.25 (d) \$24,586.36

6. The power P in an electric circuit varies jointly with the resistance R and the square of the current I. Which equation represents this situation? **6.** 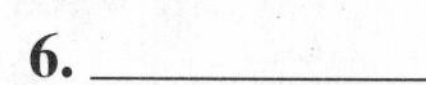

(a) $P = \frac{kR}{I^2}$ (b) $P = \frac{kI^2}{R}$ (c) $P = kIR$ (d) $P = kI^2R$

Name

7. Which graph does *not* represent a function? **7.** ________

(a)
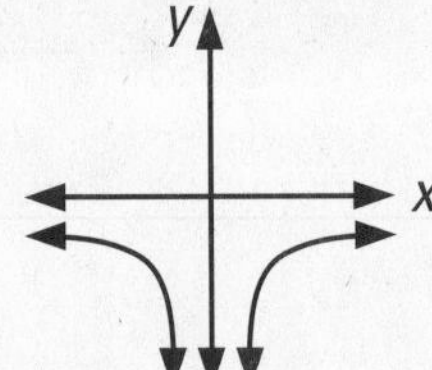

(b)
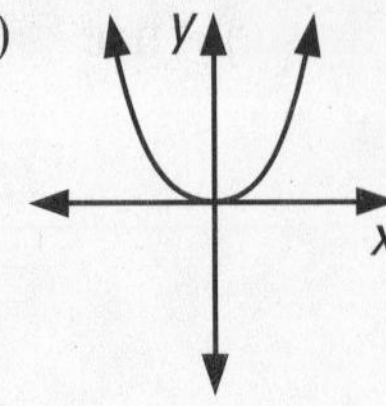

(c)
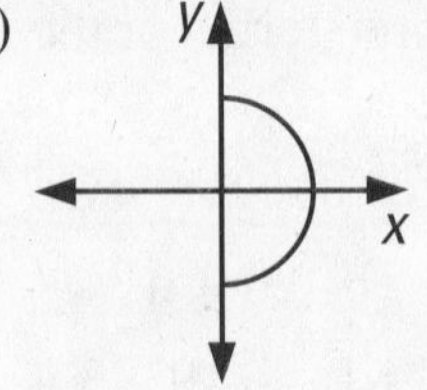

(d)
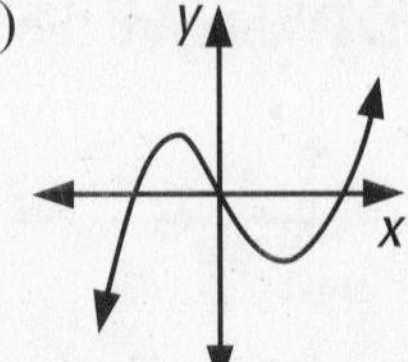

8. Which equation could be an equation of the line graphed at the right ? **8.** ________

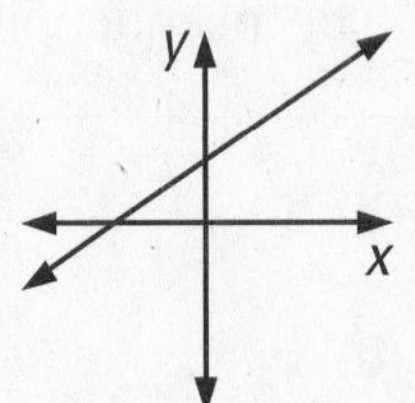

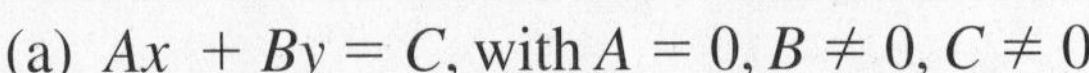
(a) $Ax + By = C$, with $A = 0, B \neq 0, C \neq 0$

(b) $Ax + By = C$, with $A \neq 0, B = 0, C \neq 0$

(c) $Ax + By = C$, with $A \neq 0, B \neq 0, C = 0$

(d) $Ax + By = C$, with $A \neq 0, B \neq 0, C \neq 0$

9. Which is an equation for the line parallel to $y = 5x + 3$ that contains (7, -2)? **9.** ________

(a) $y + 2 = 5(x - 7)$ (b) $y - 2 = 5(x - 7)$

(c) $y - 7 = 5(x + 2)$ (d) $y + 2 = 3(x - 7)$

10. Which is an arithmetic sequence? **10.** ________

(a) $9, \frac{9}{2}, \frac{9}{4}, \frac{9}{8}, \frac{9}{16}, \ldots$ (b) $9, 9\frac{1}{2}, 10, 10\frac{1}{2}, \ldots$

(c) 3, 5, 7, 11, 13, . . . (d) -1, 1, -1, 1, -1, . . .

11. Given the function g defined by $g(r) = 5r^4 - 7$, $g(-6) =$ __?__. **11.** ________

(a) -127 (b) -6487 (c) 6473 (d) 809,993

12. The pitch of an organ pipe varies inversely as the length of the pipe. Suppose you triple the length of the pipe. How is the pitch affected? **12.** ________

(a) There is no effect on the pitch.

(b) The pitch is multiplied by 3.

(c) The pitch is divided by 3.

(d) The pitch is divided by 9.

13. What is the solution to $9x - (2 - 3x) = 19$? **13.** ________

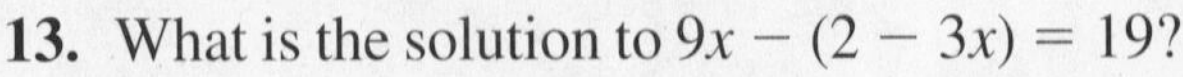
(a) $\frac{17}{6}$ (b) $\frac{21}{6}$ (c) $\frac{17}{12}$ (d) $\frac{7}{4}$

Name

14. Consider the graph of the equation $y = \frac{k}{x^2}$. Which are the equations of the asymptotes to the graph? **14.** ________

I. $x = 0$ II. $y = 0$ III. $y = x$ IV. $y = -x$

(a) I and II only (b) I and III only

(c) II and III only (d) III and IV only

15. Solve for n in the formula $a_n = 4n + 5$. **15.** ________

(a) $4n = a_n + 5$ (b) $n = \frac{a_n}{4} - 5$

(c) $n = \frac{a_n - 5}{4}$ (d) $n = \frac{4}{a_n - 5}$

16. Which is the range of the function graphed at the right? **16.** 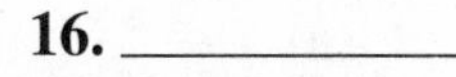

(a) the set of all real numbers

(b) $\{y: y \geq 0\}$

(c) $\{y: y \geq 3\}$

(d) $\{x: x \geq 0\}$

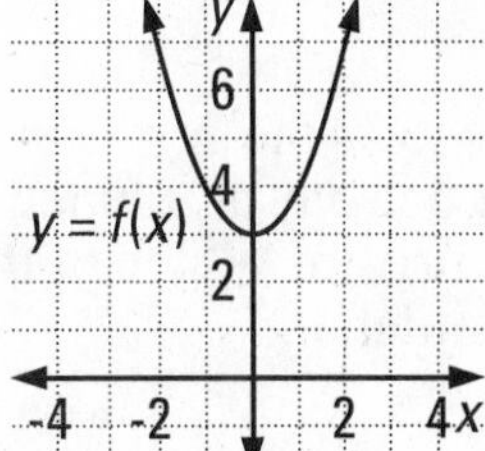

17. Ms. Ramirez earns a monthly base salary of \$1500 and a \$700 commission for each \$10,000 in sales. Which represents her earnings in a month in which the total amount of her sales is m dollars? **17.** ________

(a) $1500 + 700m$ (b) $1500 + 700\lfloor 10{,}000m \rfloor$

(c) $1500 + \left\lfloor \frac{m}{10{,}000} \right\rfloor$ (d) $1500 + 700\left\lfloor \frac{m}{10{,}000} \right\rfloor$

18. Find the equation whose graph looks most like the graph at the right. **18.** ________

(a) $7x - 4y = 28$

(b) $7x + 4y = 28$

(c) $7x + 4y = -28$

(d) $7x - 4y = -28$

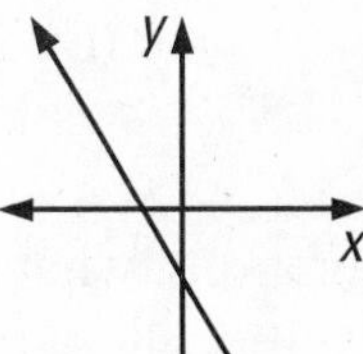

19. Which is an explicit formula for the sequence defined as follows? **19.** ________

$$\begin{cases} a_1 = -4 \\ a_n = a_{n-1} + 6, \text{ for integers } n \geq 2 \end{cases}$$

(a) $a_n = 6n + 2$ (b) $a_n = 6n - 10$

(c) $a_n = -4n$ (d) $a_n = 10 - 6n$

Name

20. Consider the graphs below. The points on the left graph lie on a line through the origin. The points on the right graph lie on or near a parabola. Which equation best approximates the relationship between *y*, *x*, and *z*? **20.** ________

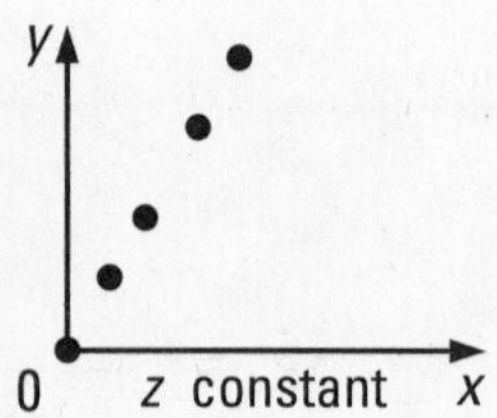

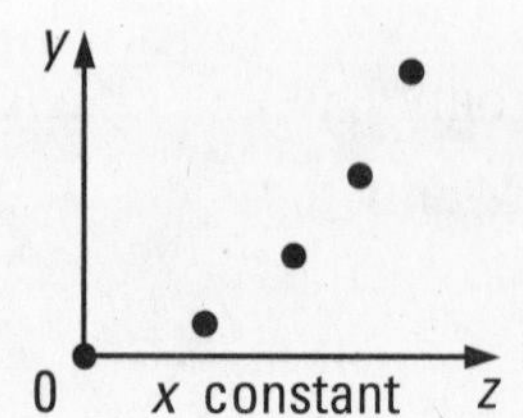

(a) $y = \frac{kx}{z}$ (b) $y = \frac{kz}{x}$ (c) $y = kx^2z$ (d) $y = kxz^2$

21. Which is an equation of a line with an undefined slope? **21.** ________

(a) $y = 5x$ (b) $x = 5y$ (c) $y = 5$ (d) $x = 5$

22. The graph at the right shows the cost *C* in dollars to rent a car for one day as a function of the number *m* of miles driven. Which of the following models the situation? **22.** ________

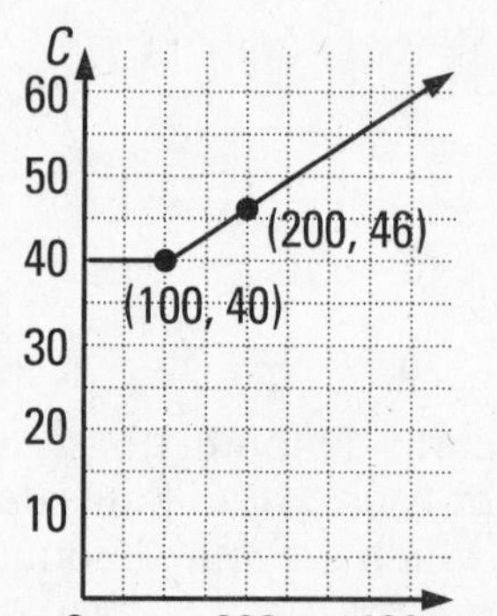

(a) $C = 40m$

(b) $\begin{cases} C = 40, & \text{for } 0 \le m \le 100 \\ C = 40 + .06m, & \text{for } m > 100 \end{cases}$

(c) $\begin{cases} C = 40, & \text{for } 0 \le m \le 100 \\ C = .06m + 34, & \text{for } m > 100 \end{cases}$

(d) $C = 40 + .06m$

23. Given the equation $y = \frac{18}{x}$, what is the rate of change from $x = 2$ to $x = 3$? **23.** 

(a) 1 (b) 3 (c) 18 (d) -3

24. Consider the expression $24 \div 6 + 2 \cdot 5 - 3 + 4$. According to the rules for the order of operations, what is the first step that you should complete when evaluating this expression? **24.** 

(a) $24 \div 6$ (b) $2 \cdot 5$ (c) $5 - 3$ (d) $3 + 4$

25. The volume of a gas at a given temperature varies inversely as the pressure exerted on it. When the volume of a certain gas is 20 ft^3, the pressure is 32 pounds per square inch (psi). What is the volume of this gas if it is held at the same temperature and the pressure is 25 psi? **25.** ________

(a) 25.6 ft^3 (b) 40 ft^3 (c) 819.2 ft^3 (d) 15.625 ft^3

Check all your work carefully.

Name

QUIZ

Lessons 4-1 Through 4-3

1. Pentagon $MNOPQ$ has vertices $M = (-5, -3)$, $N = (-1, -7)$, $O = (6, -2)$, $P = (4, 5)$, and $Q = (-2, 3)$. Write pentagon $MNOPQ$ as a matrix. — 1. ________

2. Calculate $3\begin{bmatrix} -1 & 4 \\ 0 & 7 \end{bmatrix} - 4\begin{bmatrix} 8 & -1 \\ 3 & -5 \end{bmatrix}$. — 2. ________

3. Suppose $\begin{bmatrix} 6 & -3 \\ 4x & -4 \end{bmatrix} = \begin{bmatrix} 2y & -3 \\ 24 & -4 \end{bmatrix}$.

   a. $x =$ __?__ — 3. a. ________

   b. $y =$ __?__ — b. ________

4. Calculate $\begin{bmatrix} 5 & -3 \\ 6 & 1 \end{bmatrix} \times \begin{bmatrix} 0 & -5 \\ -2 & 7 \end{bmatrix}$. — 4. ________

5. *True or false.* If matrix A has dimensions $m \times n$ and matrix B has dimensions $m \times p$, then AB has dimensions $n \times p$. — 5. ________

6. Graph the polygon described by the matrix $\begin{bmatrix} 6 & -4 & 0 \\ 3 & 6 & -6 \end{bmatrix}$ on the coordinate axes at the right. — 6.

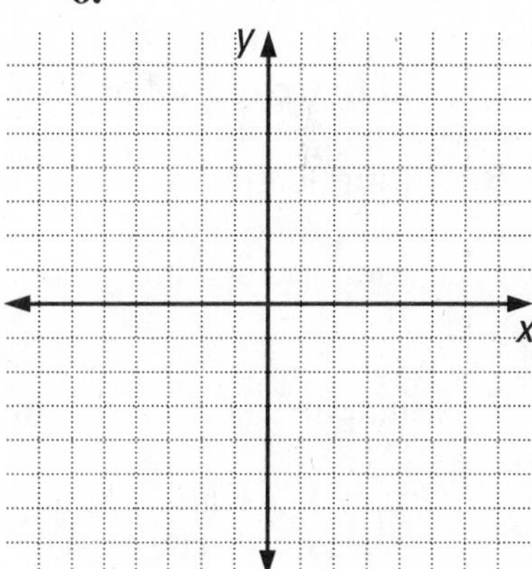

7. A small business that sells storm windows has two outlets. The matrix below summarizes sales during a recent summer. — 7. ________

	Wooden	Aluminum	Double-glazed
Outlet 1	10	130	250
Outlet 2	15	165	300

The selling prices of the wooden, aluminum, and double-glazed storm windows are \$75, \$115, and \$375, respectively. Use matrix multiplication to find the total amount of sales for each outlet during this summer.

Name ______________________________

QUIZ

Lessons 4-4 Through 4-7

1. Explain why the matrix $\begin{bmatrix} 1 & 0 \\ 0 & 1 \end{bmatrix}$ is called the identity for multiplication of 2×2 matrices.

____

2. A polygon is represented by the matrix $\begin{bmatrix} -1 & 6 & 0 \\ -3 & 7 & 10 \end{bmatrix}$. Its image under a certain transformation is represented by the matrix $\begin{bmatrix} -3 & 18 & 0 \\ -12 & 28 & 40 \end{bmatrix}$.

a. Identify the transformation. **2. a.** ____________

b. Write the matrix for the transformation. **b.** ____________

In 3 and 4, write the 2 × 2 matrix for each transformation.

3. r_y **3.** ____________

4. S_5 **4.** ____________

In 5 and 6, write *true* or *false*.

5. Multiplication of 2×2 matrices is commutative. **5.** ____________

6. Under a scale change, a figure and its image are similar. **6.** ____________

7. Triangle *TRY* is represented by $\begin{bmatrix} 5 & -3 & -6 \\ 0 & 1 & -3 \end{bmatrix}$. Graph ΔTRY and its image under $r_{y=x}$ on the coordinate axes at the right. **7.**

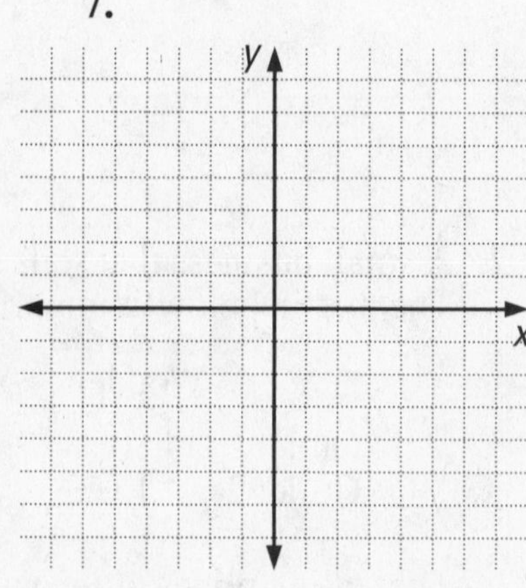

8. Find the matrix for $r_{y=x} \circ r_x$. **8.** ____________

Name

CHAPTER 4 TEST, Form A

1. a. Refer to the graph at the right. Write pentagon *LAUGH* as a matrix. **1. a.** ____________

b. What are the dimensions of your matrix in part **a**? **b.** ____________

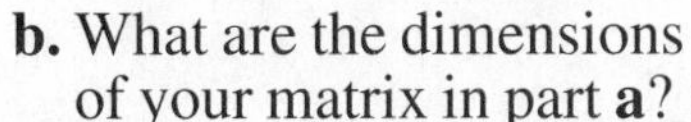

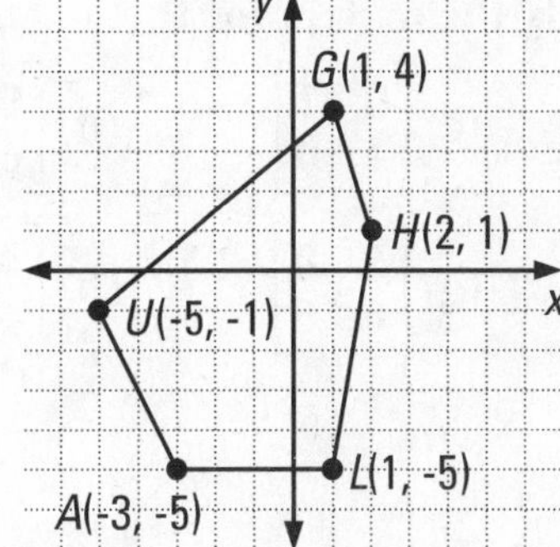

2. The matrix below gives monthly normal temperatures in degrees Fahrenheit for five U. S. cities.

	January	April	July	October
Chicago	21	49	73	54
Denver	30	47	73	52
Miami	67	75	83	78
New York	32	53	77	58
San Francisco	49	55	62	61

a. What is the average temperature in Denver in July? **2. a.** ____________

b. What does the entry in row 4, column 2 represent? **b.** ____________

3. Let $A = \begin{bmatrix} -3 & 3 & 3 \\ -3 & -3 & 3 \end{bmatrix}$ and $B = \begin{bmatrix} 1 & 3 & -2 \\ 1 & -7 & -4 \\ 0 & 8 & 2 \end{bmatrix}$.

a. Which product, *AB* or *BA*, does not exist? Explain why the product does not exist.

____

____

b. Calculate the product that *does* exist. **b.** ____________

4. Solve for *a*. $\begin{bmatrix} 3 & 6 \\ -2 & 5 \end{bmatrix} \bullet \begin{bmatrix} 4 \\ a \end{bmatrix} = \begin{bmatrix} 24 \\ 2 \end{bmatrix}$ **4.** ____________

5. Find two different 2×2 matrices *A* and *B* such that $AB = BA$. **5.** ____________

6. Calculate $-3\begin{bmatrix} 1 & 4 & 2 & 6 \\ -2 & 0 & -3 & 1 \end{bmatrix} + \begin{bmatrix} 5 & -2 & 6 & 1 \\ 3 & -1 & 0 & 2 \end{bmatrix}$. **6.** ____________

Name

In 7–12, *multiple choice.* Identify the matrix for the given transformation.

(a) $\begin{bmatrix} 0 & -1 \\ 1 & 0 \end{bmatrix}$ (b) $\begin{bmatrix} 4 & 0 \\ 0 & 4 \end{bmatrix}$ (c) $\begin{bmatrix} 0 & 1 \\ 1 & 0 \end{bmatrix}$ (d) $\begin{bmatrix} 0 & 5 \\ 6 & 0 \end{bmatrix}$

(e) $\begin{bmatrix} 1 & 0 \\ 0 & -1 \end{bmatrix}$ (f) $\begin{bmatrix} 0 & 1 \\ -1 & 0 \end{bmatrix}$ (g) $\begin{bmatrix} 5 & 0 \\ 0 & 6 \end{bmatrix}$ (h) $\begin{bmatrix} 4 & 4 \\ 4 & 4 \end{bmatrix}$

7. R_{270} **7.** ____________

8. $r_{y=x}$ **8.** ____________

9. R_{90} **9.** ____________

10. r_x **10.** ____________

11. S_4 **11.** ____________

12. $S_{5,6}$ **12.** ____________

13. Find an equation for the line through (10, 5) that is perpendicular to the line with equation $y = 2x - 5$. **13.** ____________

14. Consider the rectangle defined by the matrix $\begin{bmatrix} -4 & 2 & 2 & -4 \\ 2 & 2 & -1 & -1 \end{bmatrix}$.

a. Find the matrix for a scale change that maps this rectangle onto a square with sides of length 6. **14. a.** ____________

b. Give the matrix for the image of the rectangle under the scale change you described in part **a**. **b.** ____________

15. a. Triangle XYZ is represented by $\begin{bmatrix} -2 & 1 & 3 \\ -4 & -6 & 5 \end{bmatrix}$. **15. a.** ____________

Find the matrix for $R_{180}(\Delta XYZ)$.

b. Graph ΔXYZ and $R_{180}(\Delta XYZ)$ on the coordinate axes at the right. **b.**

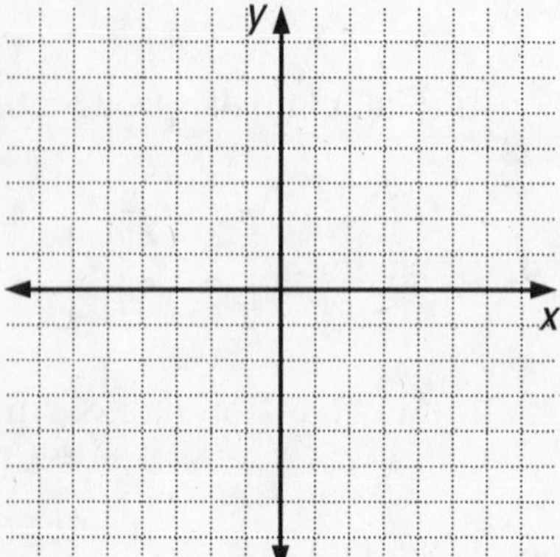

16. Refer to the graph at the right. What translation maps *DEBOR* onto *D'E'B'O'R'*? **16.** ______

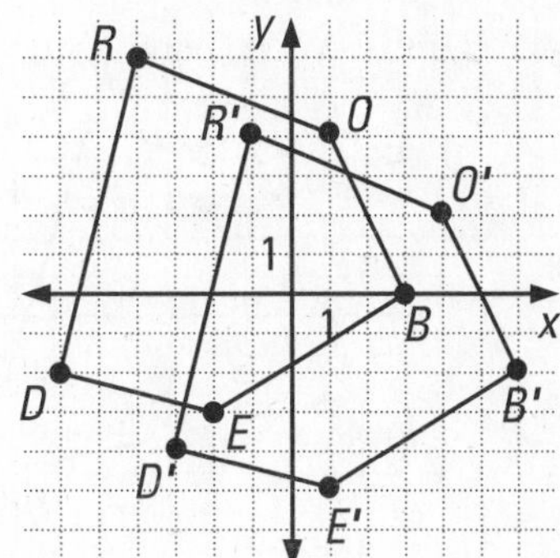

17. a. Find the matrix for $r_x \circ r_y$. **17. a.** ______

b. What single transformation does $r_x \circ r_y$ equal? **b.** ______

18. *True or false.* Under the given transformation, a figure and its image are similar.

a. reflection **18. a.** ______

b. size change **b.** ______

c. scale change that is not a size change **c.** ______

19. There are three local stores. Each sells three different brands of cranberry juice. The matrix below summarizes the bottles of cranberry juice sold at the stores last week. **19.** ______

	Cranbran	Generic	Organic
Opal	800	1200	300
Alfonso's	1200	1000	150
Natural Foods	20	50	900

The selling prices of the Cranbran, Generic, and Organic brands at each store are $1.50, $.85, and $1.75, respectively. Use matrix multiplication to find the total amount of cranberry juice sales at each store last week.

20. The matrix below shows the number of endangered and threatened species of animals and plants as of 1994. **20.** ______

	United States Only	Foreign Only	United States and Foreign
Animals	350	529	75
Plants	453	3	19

Suppose the goal is to reduce these numbers by 50% over the next ten years. Write the matrix that represents this goal.

Check all your work carefully.

Name ______________________________

CHAPTER 4 TEST, Form B

1. **a.** Refer to the graph at the right. Write quadrilateral *JOKE* as a matrix. **1. a.** ____________

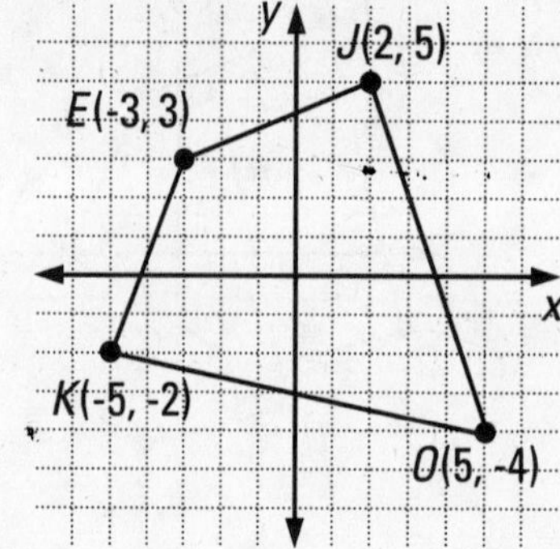

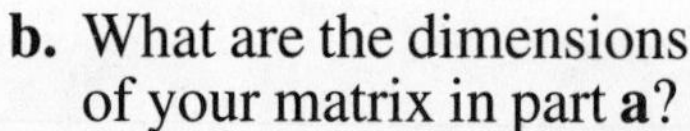

b. What are the dimensions of your matrix in part **a**? **b.** ____________

2. The matrix below gives the six languages, other than English, that were spoken most frequently in American homes in 1990 and in 1980. The entries represent thousands of persons over five years of age.

	Spanish	French	German	Italian	Chinese	Tagalog
1990	17,339	1,703	1,547	1,309	1,249	843
1980	11,549	1,572	1,607	1,633	632	452

a. How many people spoke French in 1980? **2. a.** ____________

b. What does the entry in row 2, column 4 represent? **b.** ____________

3. Let $A = \begin{bmatrix} 5 & 6 & 3 \\ -2 & 7 & 5 \\ -3 & 0 & -1 \end{bmatrix}$ and $B = \begin{bmatrix} 1 & 2 & 7 \\ -3 & -5 & -1 \end{bmatrix}$.

a. Which product, *AB* or *BA,* does not exist? Explain why the product does not exist.

____

____

b. Calculate the product that *does* exist. **b.** ____________

4. Solve for *x*. $[\, 3x \;\; 2x \;\; -x \,] \bullet \begin{bmatrix} 5 \\ -1 \\ 6 \end{bmatrix} = [21]$ **4.** ____________

5. Find two 2×2 matrices *A* and *B* such that $AB \neq BA$. **5.** ____________

6. Calculate $\begin{bmatrix} 5 & 6 \\ -3 & 0 \\ 1 & 7 \end{bmatrix} - 4 \begin{bmatrix} -3 & 2 \\ 0 & -1 \\ 1 & 3 \end{bmatrix}$. **6.** ____________

Name

In 7–12, *multiple choice.* Identify the matrix for the given transformation.

(a) $\begin{bmatrix} 2 & 0 \\ 0 & 5 \end{bmatrix}$ (b) $\begin{bmatrix} -1 & 0 \\ 0 & -1 \end{bmatrix}$ (c) $\begin{bmatrix} 0 & 1 \\ -1 & 0 \end{bmatrix}$ (d) $\begin{bmatrix} 8 & 8 \\ 8 & 8 \end{bmatrix}$

(e) $\begin{bmatrix} 0 & 1 \\ 1 & 0 \end{bmatrix}$ (f) $\begin{bmatrix} 8 & 0 \\ 0 & 8 \end{bmatrix}$ (g) $\begin{bmatrix} -1 & 0 \\ 0 & 1 \end{bmatrix}$ (h) $\begin{bmatrix} 0 & 2 \\ 0 & 5 \end{bmatrix}$

7. R_{180} **7.** ________

8. r_y **8.** ________

9. $S_{2,5}$ **9.** ________

10. $r_{y=x}$ **10.** ________

11. R_{-90} **11.** ________

12. S_8 **12.** ________

13. Given $A = (-6, 8)$ and $B = (4, -2)$, find an equation for the perpendicular bisector of $\overline{AB}$. **13.** ________

14. Consider the square defined by the matrix $\begin{bmatrix} -2 & 1 & 1 & -2 \\ 1 & 1 & -2 & -2 \end{bmatrix}$.

a. Find the matrix for a size change that maps this square onto a square with sides of length 6. **14. a.** ________

b. Give the matrix for the image of the square under the scale change you described in part **a**. **b.** ________

15. a. Triangle *ABC* is represented by $\begin{bmatrix} 1 & 3 & 6 \\ 3 & 6 & 1 \end{bmatrix}$. **15. a.** ________

Find the matrix for $R_{90}(\Delta ABC)$.

b. Graph ΔABC and $R_{90}(\Delta ABC)$ on the coordinate axes at the right. **b.**

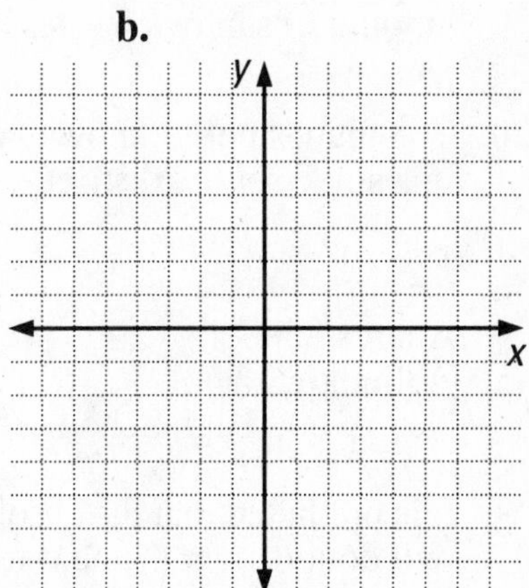

Name

16. Refer to the graph at the right. What translation maps *JANE* onto $J'A'N'E'$?

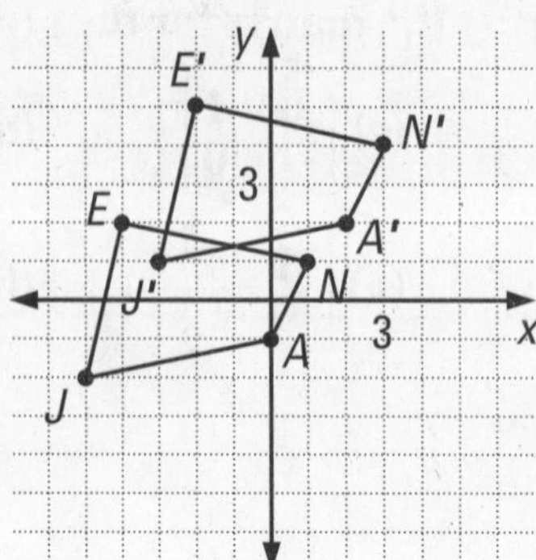

16. ____________

17. a. Find the matrix for $R_{90} \circ r_x$.

b. What single transformation does $R_{90} \circ r_x$ equal?

17. a. ____________

b. ____________

18. *Multiple choice.* A figure and its translation image are

a. parallel.

b. congruent.

c. similar, but not necessarily congruent.

d. not necessarily similar or congruent.

18. ____________

19. Local delicatessens sell four different types of sandwiches. The matrix below summarizes the number of sandwiches of each type sold at the delicatessens last week.

19. ____________

____

	Tuna	Sausage	Veggie	Roast Beef
Eddie's	150	100	125	80
Hilltop	100	75	175	95

The selling prices of the tuna, sausage, veggie, and roast beef sandwiches are \$2.90, \$3.45, \$2.55, and \$4.65, respectively. Use matrix multiplication to find the total amount of sandwich sales at each delicatessen last week.

20. The matrix below shows the number of pupils enrolled in a small school district.

20. ____________

	Boys	Girls
Adams School	423	457
Willettko School	906	823
New Wood High School	602	597

It is predicted that the enrollment of both boys and girls will double over the next ten years. Write the matrix that represents the enrollment ten years from now.

Check all your work carefully.

Name

CHAPTER 4 TEST, Form C

1. Let A be the matrix defined as follows.

$$A = \begin{bmatrix} 5 & -1 \\ -3 & 2 \\ -6 & -4 \end{bmatrix}$$

a. Choose any scalar k other than 0, 1, or -1. Find kA.

b. Create a matrix B in which no element is equal to 0 and for which $A + B$ exists. Find $A + B$.

c. Create a matrix C in which no element is equal to 0 and for which AC exists. Find AC.

2. Ms. Kouros owns a bakery that supplies bread to three markets. These slips of paper show last Monday's deliveries.

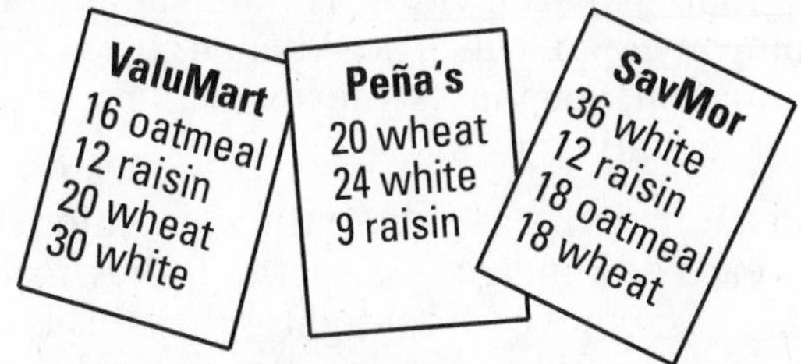

Show how Ms. Kouros could use a matrix to store these data. Then describe at least one way that she might use matrix operations to keep track of her sales.

3. Give equations for two lines that each pass through the point (1, -3) and are perpendicular to each other. How do you know that the lines are perpendicular?

4. While you are studying Chapter 4 together, a friend makes this statement.

For any two distinct transformations A and B, $A \circ B \neq B \circ A$.

Do you think this is true? Explain.

5. Harry drew the graph at the right to illustrate a triangle and its image under the transformation R_{90}. Without performing any calculations, explain how you can tell that the image is incorrect. Now show how to correct the graph. Write a matrix multiplication to represent $R_{90}(\Delta ABC)$.

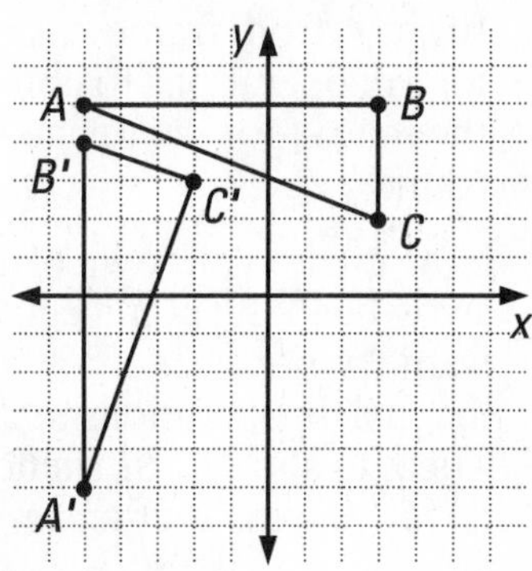

Name

CHAPTER 4 TEST, Form D

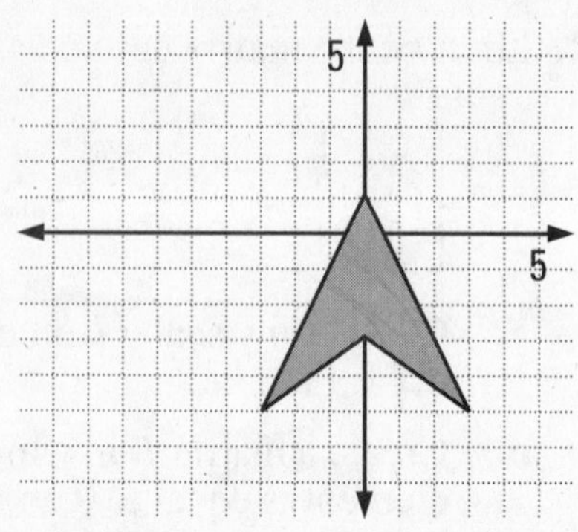

Suppose a family friend is starting a small company that will produce educational videos. The friend has asked you to plan an animation that will serve as the company "signature" at the beginning of each video. The animation must involve the company logo, which is a kite. Once you have planned the animation, you must write instructions for a computer that will actually draw it.

An animation is a series of transformation images of a figure. As each new image of the series is drawn, the preceding image is removed from sight. When this is done with several images in rapid succession, the viewer has the impression that the original figure is in continuous motion. Each image in the series is called a *frame* of the animation.

For instance, the following is a set of instructions for a simple three-frame animation of the arrowhead as positioned on the coordinate axes above.

FRAME 1: original arrowhead
FRAME 2: FRAME 1 under $T_{0,2}$
FRAME 3: FRAME 2 under $T_{-6,0} \circ R_{90}$

a. Write a matrix that represents frame 1 of the animation.

b. Show how to use matrix operations to obtain a matrix for the image in frame 2.

c. Use your matrices from parts **a** and **b** to graph frames 1 and 2 on two different sets of coordinate axes. If you look quickly from frame 1 to frame 2, how does the arrowhead appear to move?

d. Use matrix operations to obtain the image in frame 3. Graph frame 3 on a third set of coordinate axes. If you look quickly from frame 2 to frame 3, how does the kite appear to move?

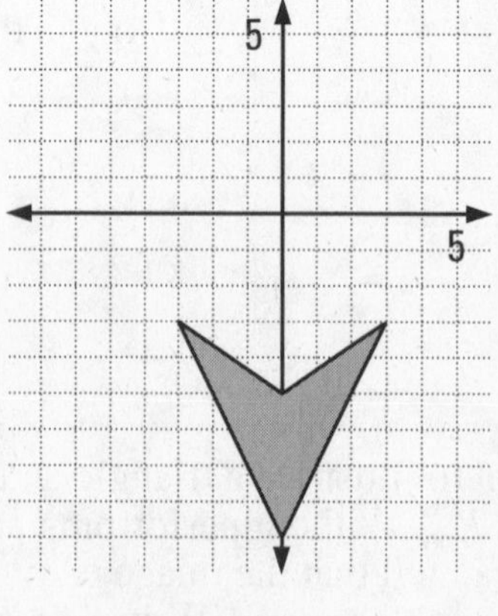

e. Frame 4 is shown at the right. Write an instruction giving the transformation that yields frame 4 from frame 3. Use matrix operations to obtain the matrix for the image in frame 4.

f. Now create your own original animation for the arrowhead. It should contain at least eight frames. For each frame, write a set of instructions like those above and give the matrix operations that correspond to the instructions. Then, to show your friend how the animation will appear, follow the instructions given at the right to create a *flip book.*

How to Make a Flip Book

- Cut a few pieces of graph paper into fourths. This should give you several small pieces, each about 4 in. wide and $5\frac{1}{2}$ in. long.
- Draw a set of coordinate axes at the center of each small piece of graph paper. The origin should be at exactly the same location on each piece.
- Stack the small pieces together. Using staples or tape, join the stack along one of its longer edges to form a "book."
- Working in order from back to front, draw one frame of your animation on each page of the book.

- After all the frames have been drawn, hold the book firmly in your right hand along the edge that is stapled or taped. With your left hand, flip through the pages rapidly from back to front. If you focus your attention on the images, you should be able to see the movement you have created.

Name

CHAPTER 4 TEST, Cumulative Form

In 1–5, $F = (5, 0)$, $A = (3, 4)$, $C = (-1, 6)$, and $T = (-3, -1)$.

1. Give an equation for the line $\overleftrightarrow{FA}$. **1.** ____________

2. a. Write quadrilateral *FACT* as a matrix. **2. a.** ____________

b. What are the dimensions of your matrix in part **a**? **b.** ____________

3. Find the matrix for the image of quadrilateral *FACT* under the transformation $S_{4,2}$. **3.** ____________

4. *True or false.* Under S_3, quadrilateral *FACT* and its image are congruent. **4.** ____________

5. a. Find the matrix for $R_{90}(FACT)$. **5. a.** ____________

b. On the coordinate axes at the right, graph quadrilateral *FACT* and its image under R_{90}. Label the image $F'A'C'T'$. **b.**

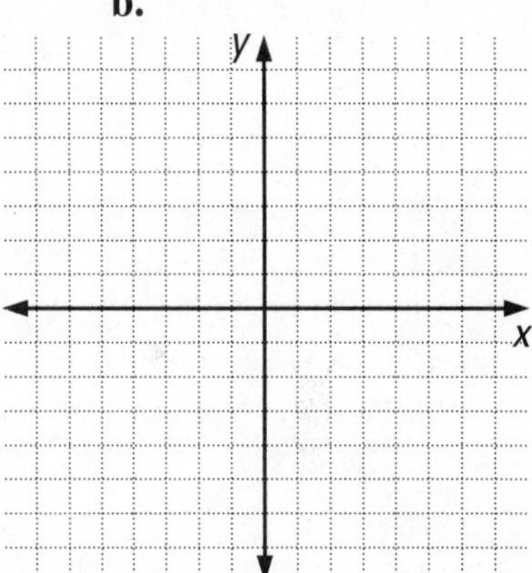

6. Refer to your answer to Question 5b and to the graph at the right. What translation maps quadrilateral $F'A'C'T'$ onto quadrilateral $F''A''C''T''$? **6.** ____________

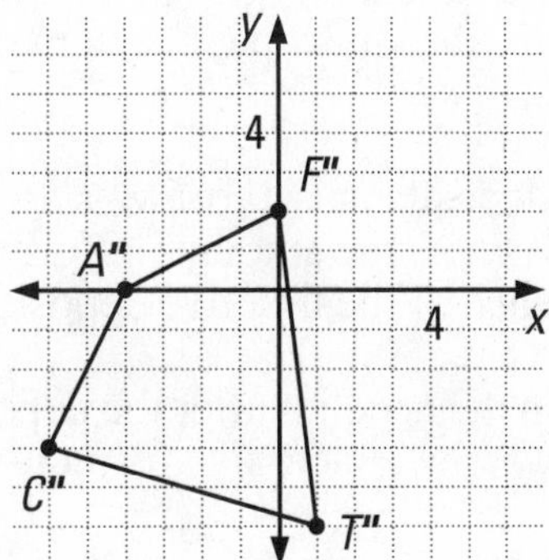

7. a. Find the matrix for $r_y \circ R_{180}$. **7. a.** ____________

b. What single transformation does $r_y \circ R_{180}$ equal? **b.** ____________

Name

In 8 and 9, graph the equation on the coordinate axes at the right.

8. $y = \frac{4}{x^2}$

8.

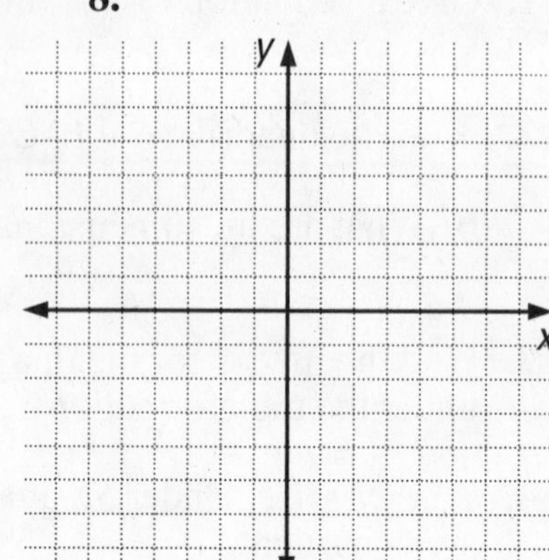

9. $2x - 5y = 10$

9.

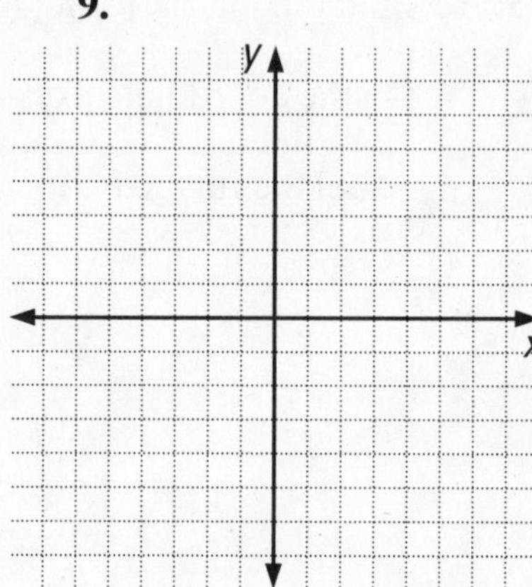

10. Emily started a new job and deposited $100 from her first paycheck into a new savings account. She decided that she would deposit $75 of each subsequent paycheck into this account.

a. Assume that no other deposits or withdrawals are made and interest is ignored. Write the amount in Emily's savings account after each of the first five deposits.

10. a. ____________________

b. Let A_n be the amount in the account after the deposit from Emily's *n*th paycheck. Write a recursive formula for A_n.

b. ____________________

11. Complete the following statement with "directly," "inversely," or "neither directly nor inversely."

When a group of people plans to share a cash prize equally, the amount of the prize that each person receives varies __?__ as the number of people in the group.

11. ____________________

Name

12. Suppose z varies directly as x and inversely as the square of y. If $x = 6$ and $y = 2$, then $z = 54$. Find z when $x = 7$ and $y = 3$.

12. ________________

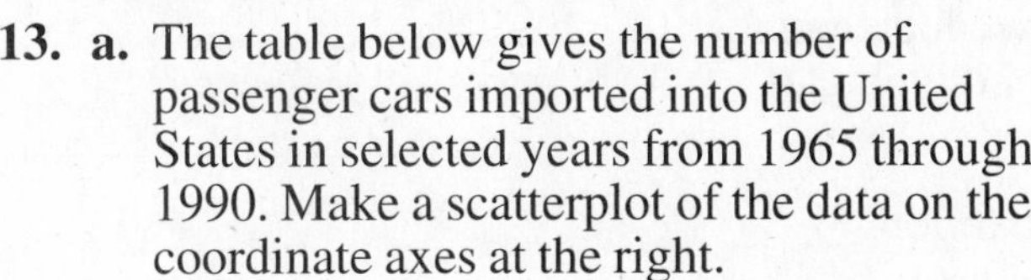

13. a. The table below gives the number of passenger cars imported into the United States in selected years from 1965 through 1990. Make a scatterplot of the data on the coordinate axes at the right.

Year	Number of Cars Imported (Thousands)
1965	563.7
1970	2013.4
1975	2074.7
1980	3116.4
1985	4397.7
1990	3944.6

13. a.

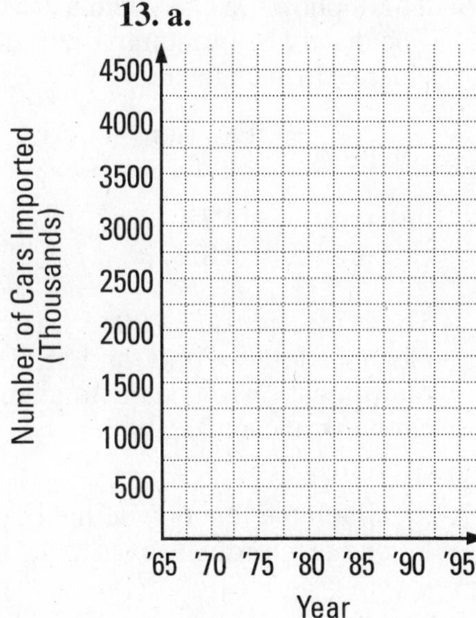

b. Find an equation of the regression line.

b. ________________

c. Find the correlation coefficient.

c. ________________

d. Is a linear equation a reasonable model for these data? Explain why or why not.

____

____

14. The table below shows the population of the northeast and west regions of the United States in selected years from 1970 through 1990. Let $N(x)$ be the population of the northeast region and $W(x)$ be the population of the west region in year x.

	1970	1980	1985	1990
Northeast	49,061,000	48,135,000	49,869,000	50,809,000
West	34,838,000	43,172,000	47,827,000	52,786,000

a. Calculate $N(1985) - W(1985)$.

14. a. ________________

b. What does your answer to part **a** represent?

____

____

Name

▶ **CHAPTER 4 TEST, Cumulative Form** *page 4*

15. Given $A = (-3, 7)$ and $B = (5, 19)$, find an equation for the perpendicular bisector of $\overline{AB}$.

15. ____________

16. The sophomore class held a car wash at two locations. The matrix below summarizes the number of vehicles cleaned at each location.

16. ____________

	Exterior Only	Interior Only	Both Exterior and Interior
Location 1	75	15	120
Location 2	85	5	130

The class charged \$4.00 to wash the exterior only, \$2.00 to clean the interior only, and \$5.00 to do both. Use matrix multiplication to find the total amount they raised from the car wash at each location.

17. a. Graph the function defined by $h(x) = 2\lfloor x \rfloor$ on the coordinate axes at the right.

17. a.

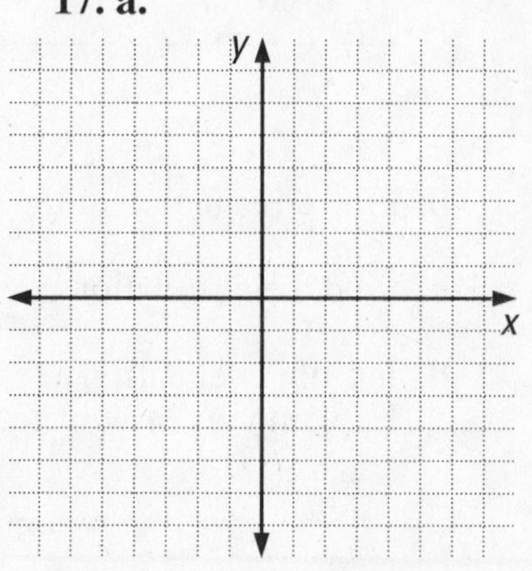

b. Find the domain and range of h.

b. ____________

18. Calculate $5\begin{bmatrix} 1 & 3 \\ -7 & 6 \\ -3 & 1 \\ 4 & 0 \end{bmatrix} - 2\begin{bmatrix} -3 & 1 \\ 6 & 2 \\ -1 & 1 \\ 5 & -1 \end{bmatrix}$.

18. ____________

19. Solve for a and b. $\begin{bmatrix} a & 0 \\ 0 & b \end{bmatrix} \cdot \begin{bmatrix} -3 \\ 2 \end{bmatrix} = \begin{bmatrix} 9 \\ 6 \end{bmatrix}$

19. ____________

20. Solve for v in the formula $f = \dfrac{m(v - v_0)}{t}$.

20. ____________

21. Solve $\frac{3}{4}w + \frac{5}{12} = \frac{1}{3}w$.

21. ____________

Check all your work carefully.

Name

QUIZ

Lessons 5-1 Through 5-4

1. A candidate for admission to the United States Air Force Academy must be at least 17 years old but not yet 22 years old on July 1 of the year of entering the academy.

a. Write the acceptable ages as a compound inequality. **1. a.** ________

b. Graph the solution set on the number line at the right. **b.**

In 2 and 3, solve the system. Show your work.

2. $\begin{cases} 12s - 8t = 56 \\ 5s + 3t = -2 \end{cases}$ **3.** $\begin{cases} 19x + 4y = -7 \\ y = 3x + 6 \end{cases}$

2. ________

3. ________

4. Consider the system graphed at the right.

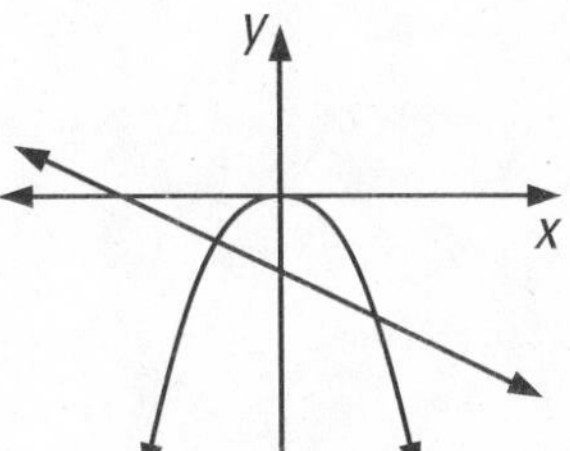

a. Is the system consistent or is it inconsistent? **4. a.** ________

b. How many solutions does the system have? **b.** ________

5. For what value of k does $\begin{cases} kx + 2y = 12 \\ 9x + 2y = 8 \end{cases}$ have no solution?

Justify your answer.

____

____

In 6 and 7, refer to the following situation: At Federal Rent-a-Car, the cost of a one-day rental of a midsize car is $45 plus 27¢ per mile driven. At Ready Rentals, the cost is $27 per day plus 36¢ per mile driven.

6. Let x = the number of miles driven and y = the cost of a one-day rental with x miles driven. Set up a system of two equations to describe this situation. **6.** ________

____

7. a. For what number of miles driven will the cost of a one-day rental be the same at Federal Rent-a-Car and at Ready Rentals? **7. a.** ________

b. What is the cost for this number of miles driven? **b.** ________

Name

QUIZ

Lessons 5-5 Through 5-7

1. Is $\begin{bmatrix} 7 & -5 \\ 11 & 8 \end{bmatrix}$ the inverse of $\begin{bmatrix} 8 & 5 \\ 11 & 7 \end{bmatrix}$? Justify your answer.

____

____

2. **a.** Calculate the determinant of the matrix $\begin{bmatrix} 9 & 4 \\ 5 & 2 \end{bmatrix}$. **2. a.** ____________

   b. Write the inverse of this matrix, if it exists. **b.** ____________

3. Solve $\begin{cases} 9x + 4y - 2z \ = 25 \\ 7x - 2y + 5z \ = 61 \\ -4x + 6y + 11z = 6 \end{cases}$ using matrices. **3.** ____________

   Show your work.

4. **a.** Write an inequality to describe the shaded region at the right. **4. a.** ____________

   b. Identify two points whose coordinates satisfy the inequality. **b.** ____________

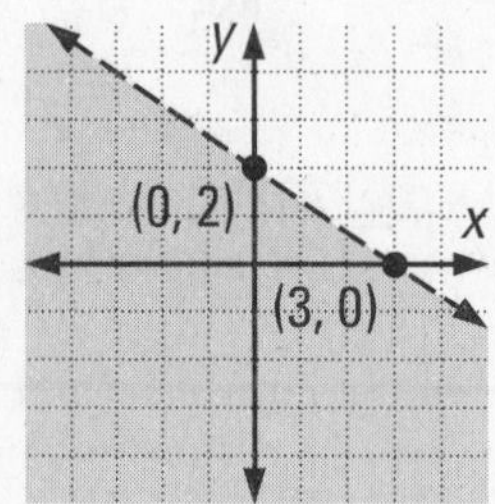

5. Rafael won a \$150 prize, and he hopes to spend some or all of it on videos and compact discs. A local store is having a sale in which all videos cost \$25 each and all compact discs cost \$15 each.

   a. Let x = the number of videos and y = the number of compact discs that Rafael can buy at this sale. Write an inequality relating x, y, and the total amount of his prize. **5. a.** ____________

   b. On the grid at the right, graph all possible combinations of videos and compact discs that Rafael can buy at this sale with his prize money. **b.**

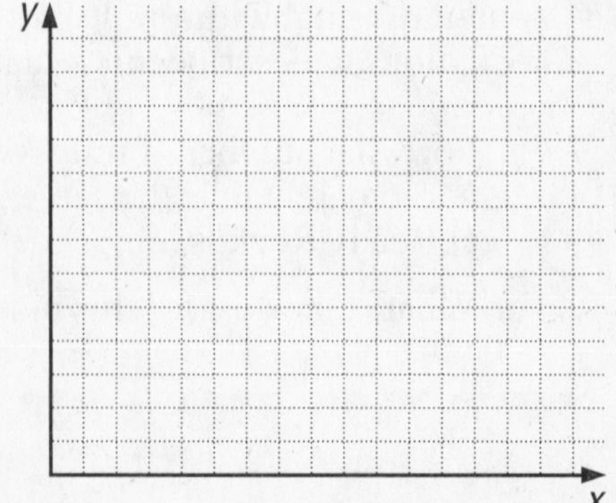

Name

CHAPTER 5 TEST, Form A

1. On the Beaufort scale of wind force, the term "fresh gale" describes wind speeds from 39 mi/h to 46 mi/h.

a. Write a compound inequality to describe "fresh gale" wind speeds. **1. a.** ____________

b. Graph the solution set of the inequality on the number line at the right. **b.**

2. A graph of the system

$$\begin{cases} xy = 6 \\ -2x + y = -2 \end{cases}$$

is shown at the right. From the graph, estimate the solutions. **2.** ____________

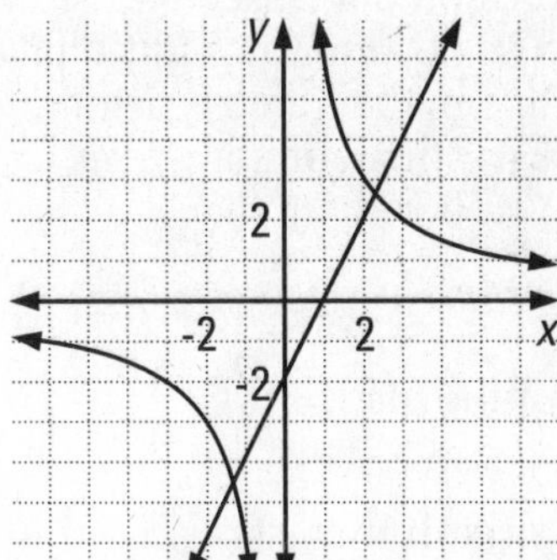

3. *Multiple choice.* Which graph represents an inconsistent system ? **3.** ____________

(a)

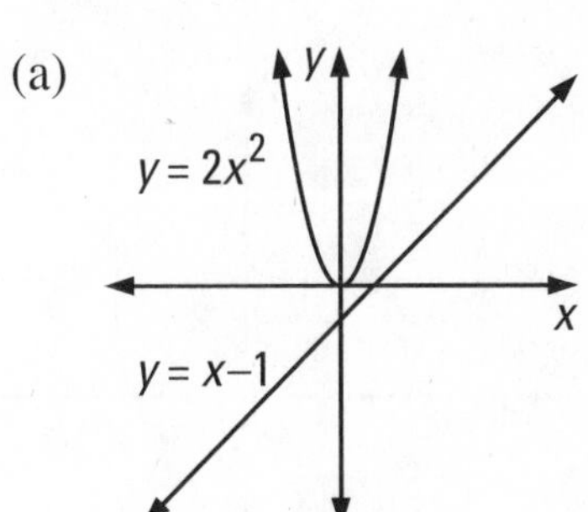

(b)

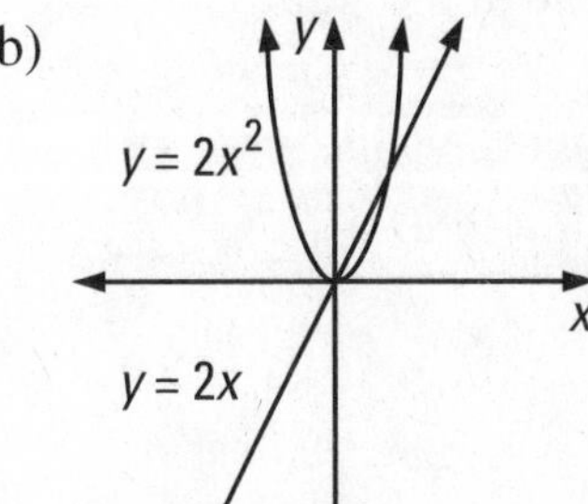

(c)

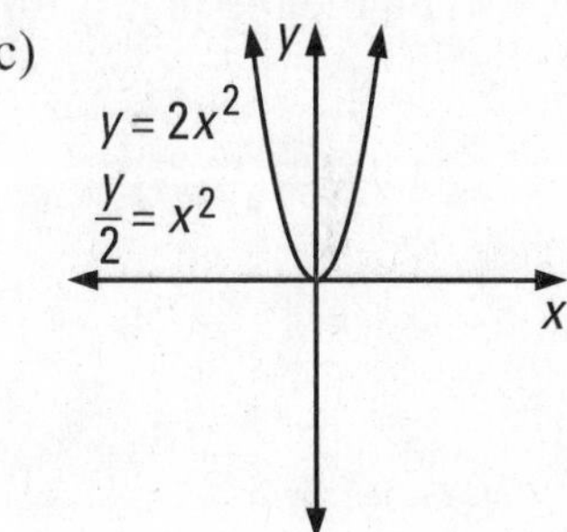

In 4 and 5, solve the system. Show your work.

4. $\begin{cases} 4c + d = -2 \\ 9c - 3d = -36 \end{cases}$

5. $\begin{cases} 5p + 2q - r = 5 \\ p = 2q - 1 \\ r = q + 1 \end{cases}$

4. ____________

5. ____________

Name

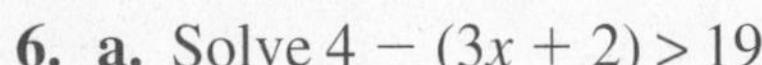

6. a. Solve $4 - (3x + 2) > 19$. **6. a.** ____________

b. Graph the solution set on the number line. **b.**

7. One cellular telephone company has a basic monthly rate of \$22.00, and there is an additional charge of 28¢ per minute for calls in the home territory. For a second company, the monthly rate is \$28.00, and the additional charge is 25¢ per minute for calls in the home territory. For what number of minutes is the first company less expensive? Assume you make calls only in the home territory. **7.** ____________

8. a. Calculate the determinant of the matrix $\begin{bmatrix} 7 & -4 \\ 5 & 3 \end{bmatrix}$. **8. a.** ____________

b. Write the inverse of this matrix, if it exists. **b.** ____________

In 9 and 10, consider the linear inequality $y \geq \frac{4}{3}x - 3$.

9. Graph the inequality on the grid at the right. **9.**

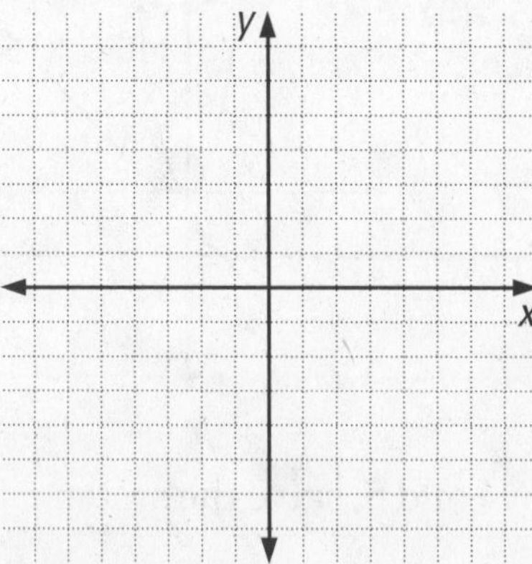

10. Identify two points whose coordinates satisfy the inequality. **10.** ____________

11. For what value of t does $\begin{cases} x + 4y = 4 \\ -3x + ty = -12 \end{cases}$ have infinitely many solutions? **11.** ____________

12. Solve the system $\begin{cases} 3m + 5n = -5 \\ 8m + 2n = 32 \end{cases}$ using matrices. **12.** ____________

Show your work.

Name

In 13 and 14, consider the graph below.

13. Write a system of inequalities that is represented by the feasible region. **13.** ______

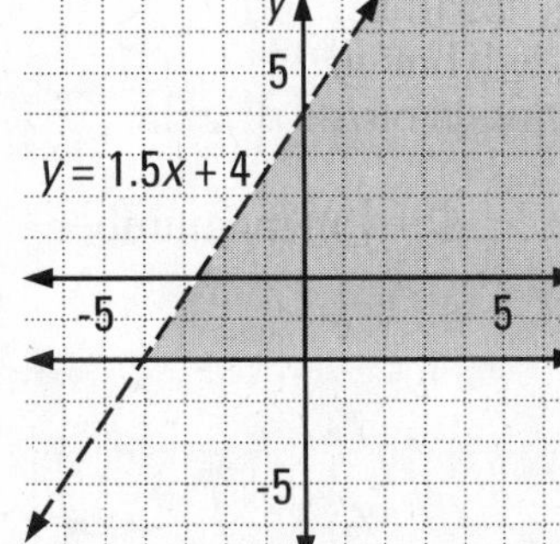

14. Give the coordinates of the vertex of the feasible region. **14.** ______

15. When making a service call, a plumber charges a fixed amount plus an additional fee for each hour of the call. The cost of a one-hour service call is \$52.50 and the cost of a three-hour service call is \$107.50. From this information, determine the cost of a service call of h hours. **15.** ______

16. Jennifer makes machine-stitched quilts. It takes 36 hours and 8 yards of material to make a small quilt and 27 hours and 12 yards to make a large quilt. She has at most 324 hours and 96 yards of material to use in making quilts. She makes a profit of \$100 on each small quilt and \$140 on each large quilt.

a. Let x = the number of small quilts Jennifer makes and y = the number of large quilts. Translate the constraints into a system of inequalities. **16. a.** ______

b. Graph the system on the grid at the right. **b.**

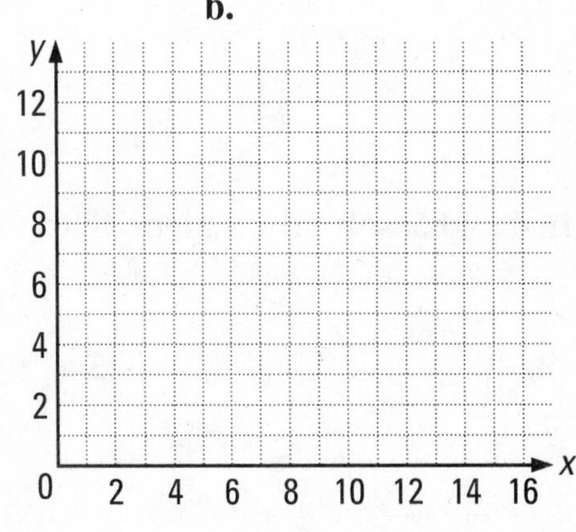

c. Apply the Linear-Programming Theorem to determine the number of each size of quilt Jennifer should make in order to maximize her profit. **c.** ______

Check all your work carefully.

Name

CHAPTER 5 TEST, Form B

1. Meteorologists define "drizzle" as uniform close precipitation of tiny raindrops with diameter less than 0.02 inch.

   a. Write a compound inequality to describe the diameter of a raindrop that is classified as "drizzle." **1. a.** ________

   b. Graph the solution set of the inequality on the number line at the right. **b.**

2. A graph of the system

$$\begin{cases} y = -x^2 + 4 \\ y = .5x \end{cases}$$

is shown at the right. From the graph, estimate the solutions. **2.** ________

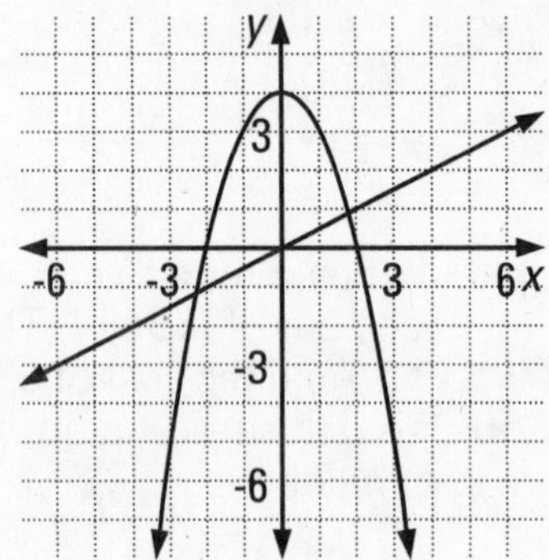

3. *Multiple choice.* Which graph does *not* represent a consistent system? **3.** ________

(a)

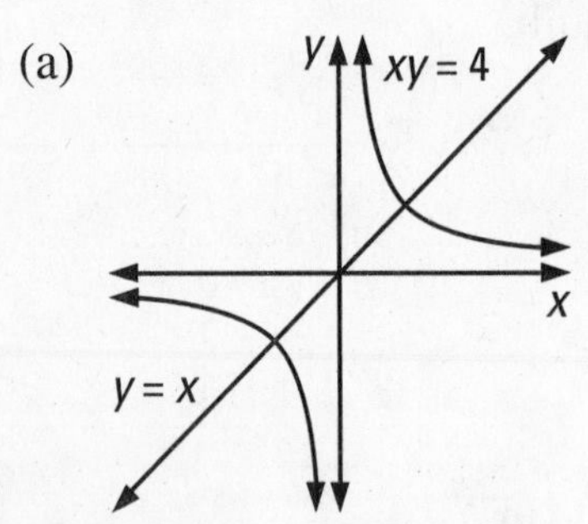

(b)

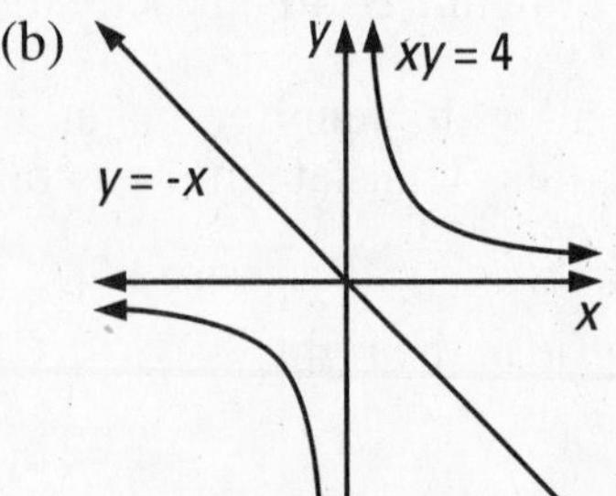

(c)

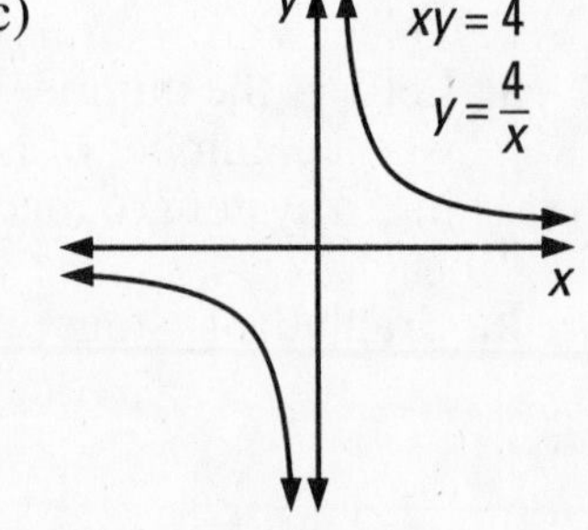

In 4 and 5, solve the system. Show your work.

4. $\begin{cases} 5f - 9g = -17 \\ -4f + 6g = 16 \end{cases}$

5. $\begin{cases} 8a - 2b + 3c = 40 \\ a = 9 + 3b \\ c = 2 - b \end{cases}$

4. ________

5. ________

Name

6. a. Solve $6 - (4x - 3) \geq 12$ **6. a.** ______

b. Graph the solution set of the inequality on the number line at the right. **b.**

7. At one swimming club, the cost of a one-year membership is \$100.00, and there is an additional charge of \$5.00 each time you swim. At a second club, a one-year membership costs \$200.00, and the additional charge is \$3.00 each time you swim. For how many swims in a year is it less expensive to swim at the second club? **7.** ______

8. a. Calculate the determinant of the matrix $\begin{bmatrix} 12 & 8 \\ 4 & 3 \end{bmatrix}$. **8. a.** ______

b. Write the inverse of this matrix, if it exists. **b.** ______

In 9 and 10, consider the linear inequality $y < -\frac{2}{5}x + 2$.

9. Graph the inequality on the grid at the right. **9.**

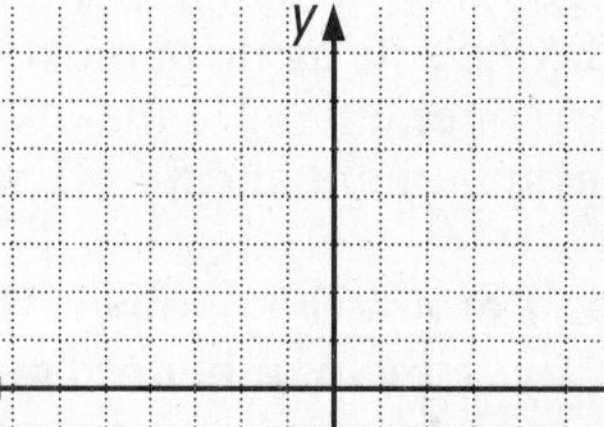

10. Identify two points whose coordinates do *not* satisfy the inequality. **10.** ______

11. For what value of t does $\begin{cases} x - 3y = t \\ -5x + 15y = 75 \end{cases}$ have infinitely many solutions? **11.** ______

12. Solve the system $\begin{cases} -5r + 4s = 38 \\ 3r - 2s = -20 \end{cases}$ using matrices. **12.** ______

Show your work.

▶ CHAPTER 5 TEST, Form B *page 3*

In 13 and 14, consider the graph below.

13. Write a system of inequalities that is represented by the feasible region.

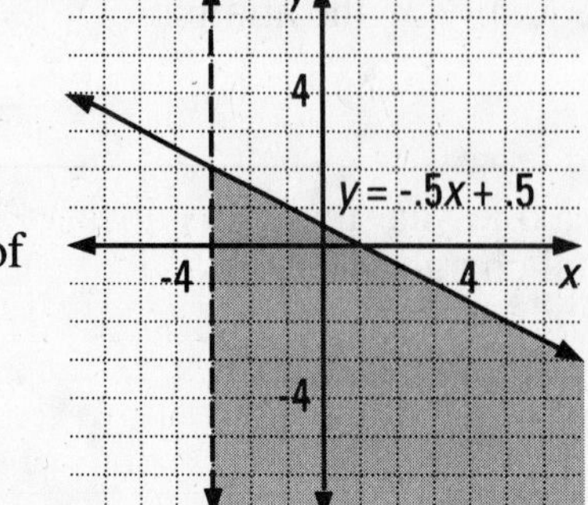

14. Give the coordinates of the vertex of the feasible region.

13. ____________

14. ____________

15. When making a service call, an electrician charges a fixed amount plus an additional fee for each hour of the call. The cost of a one-hour service call is $67.50 and the cost of a four-hour service call is $135. From this information, determine the cost of a service call of *h* hours.

15. ____________

16. Karl sells flowers in an open-air market. To make a holiday arrangement, he uses 3 roses and 6 carnations. To make a "get-well" arrangement, he uses 6 roses and 6 carnations. Each day he sets aside at most 48 roses and 60 carnations to use in arrangements. He makes a profit of $3 on each holiday arrangement and $4.50 on each "get-well" arrangement.

a. Let x = the number of holiday arrangements and y = the number of "get-well" arrangements. Translate the constraints into a system of inequalities.

16. a. ____________

b. Graph the system on the grid at the right.

b.

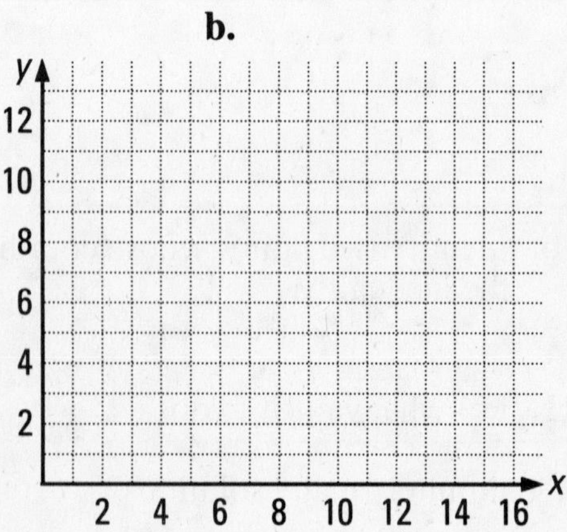

c. Apply the Linear-Programming Theorem to determine the number of each type of arrangement Karl should make in order to maximize his profit on arrangements.

c. ____________

Check all your work carefully.

Name

CHAPTER 5 TEST, Form C

1. a. Arrange -3, -2, 4, and 6 in a 2×2 matrix that does not have an inverse. Explain how you know that the inverse does not exist.

   b. Arrange these same numbers in a 2×2 matrix that *does* have an inverse. Then find the inverse of your matrix.

2. Explain how you know that these two systems are *not* equivalent.

$$\begin{cases} 2p + 5q = 10 \\ -3p - 2q = 7 \end{cases} \quad \begin{cases} p = -5 \\ p + q = 6 \end{cases}$$

Make the systems equivalent by changing just one of the four equations.

3. Siri wrote this matrix multiplication to solve a system of equations. If he wrote the correct matrices, what is the system?

$$\begin{bmatrix} 1 & 4 \\ 0.5 & -2 \end{bmatrix} \begin{bmatrix} a \\ b \end{bmatrix} = \begin{bmatrix} 40 \\ -36 \end{bmatrix}$$

He decided that the system has no solution. Do you agree? Explain. If you disagree, show how to use the matrices to solve the system.

4. How is graphing $x > -2$ on a coordinate plane different from graphing $x > -2$ on a number line? How is it similar?

5. Write a real-world problem that can be solved using the following system.

$$\begin{cases} r + s + t = 78 \\ r = 2s \\ t = s - 6 \end{cases}$$

Show how to use the system to solve your problem.

6. State as many facts as you can about the graph at the right. Explain how you might use this graph in solving a problem.

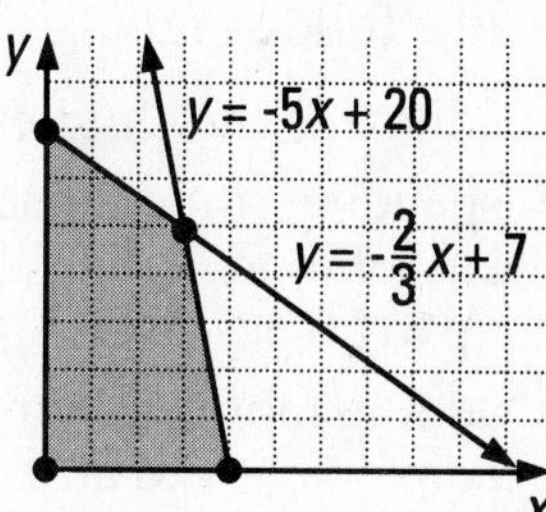

Name

CHAPTER 5 TEST, Form D

Suppose you work for a small regional transit company. You have been asked to analyze the profitability of Route 101, which is one of the company's bus routes. You have been given the following information about the average one-way trip on this route.

- The trip covers 12.5 miles and takes 20 minutes.
- The fare is 95¢ for adults and 45¢ for children under 12.
- There are at least as many children as adult passengers.
- The total number of passengers is from 10 to 20.
- The total operating expenses are $15. (This includes fuel, the driver's salary, depreciation of the equipment, and so on.)

a. Write a sentence in one variable that represents the total number of passengers on each one-way trip. Graph your sentence on a number line.

b. Write a system of open sentences in two variables that represents all the possible combinations of children and adult passengers on each one-way trip. Graph your system on a coordinate grid.

c. How many combinations of children and adult passengers are possible?

d. Suppose you want to calculate the profit that the company makes from each one-way trip. Will your graph from Part a or your graph from Part b be more helpful? Explain.

e. Write an equation that you can use to calculate the company's profit on each one-way trip.

f. Suppose you want to find which combination of children and adult passengers is most profitable for the company. Do you need to check every possible combination in your profit equation? Explain why or why not.

g. Write an analysis of the profitability of Route 101.

h. At the right is information about two other bus routes that the company operates. Analyze the profitability of at least one of these two routes.

i. The owner of the company is considering some ideas that might increase the company's profits. They include the following:

- adjusting the children's fare or the adult fare, or both;
- spending some money on an advertising campaign to attract more adult riders (Each bus can accommodate up to 50 passengers.);
- adding more daily trips to make the bus a more convenient and attractive mode of transportation.

Which idea or ideas would you recommend that the owner pursue? Write a report that summarizes your recommendations. Your report should be as detailed as possible and should include at least one graph.

Route 102
(one-way trip)

- covers 8.3 miles
- takes 14 minutes
- same fares as Route 101
- at least twice as many adult passengers as children
- from 15 to 24 total passengers
- $11.50 total operating expenses

Route 103
(one-way trip)

- covers 15.6 miles
- takes 25 minutes
- same fares as Route 101
- at least twice as many children as adult passengers
- from 24 to 30 total passengers
- $16.75 total operating expenses

Name ______________________________

CHAPTER 5 TEST, Cumulative Form

1. Erika opened a savings account by depositing \$2800 that she received as graduation gifts. Then, when she started her new job, she decided to deposit \$400 of each monthly paycheck into the account.

a. Assume that Erika makes no deposits other than graduation money and the monthly deposits from her paycheck. Write an expression that represents the total she has deposited into the account at the end of t months at her new job.

1. a. ______________

b. After how many months will the amount deposited into this account be at least \$10,000?

b. ______________

2. *Multiple choice.* Which shaded region could be a feasible set in a linear programming situation?

2. ______________

(a)

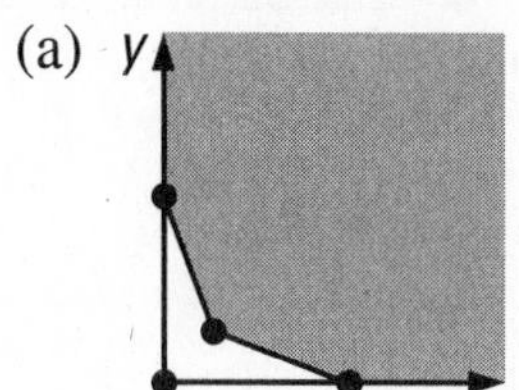

(b)

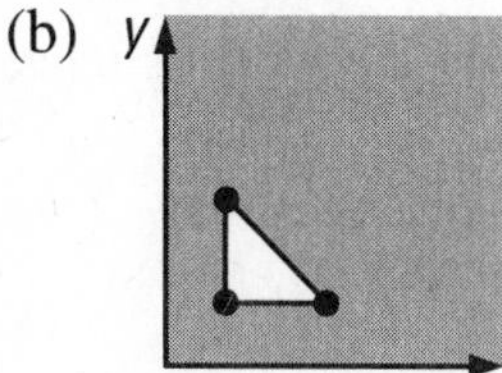

(c)

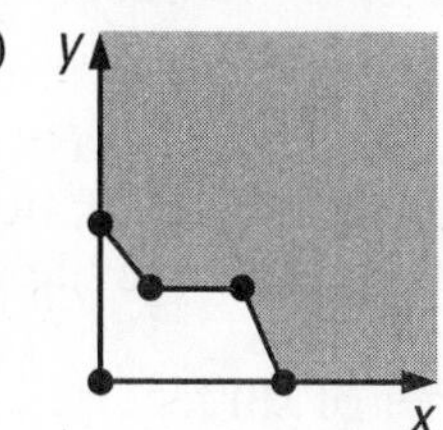

(d)

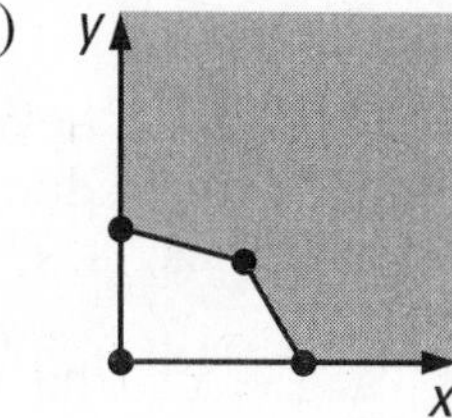

3. Let $A = \begin{bmatrix} 2 & 4 & 9 \\ 3 & 7 & 2 \end{bmatrix}$ and $B = \begin{bmatrix} -1 & 2 & 9 \\ 4 & -1 & 2 \\ 8 & 0 & 3 \end{bmatrix}$

a. Which product exists, AB or BA? Explain your reasoning.

____

____

b. Calculate the product that exists.

b. ______________

4. Find the inverse of $M = \begin{bmatrix} 1 & 2 \\ 3 & 4 \end{bmatrix}$

4. ______________

5. For what values of t is the system $\begin{cases} 2x - 3y = 5 \\ 8x - 12y = t \end{cases}$ inconsistent?

5. ______________

6. Give an equation for the line parallel to $y = 7x - 3$ that contains (-6, 4).

6. ______________

7. The life spans L of the animals of a given species vary inversely as their average heart rates R. Translate this statement into a variation equation.

7. ______________

Name

8. a. On the grid at the right, graph each of the following equations.

$y = 2x^2$, for $x \geq 0$

$y = 3x - 2$, for $x < 0$

8. a.

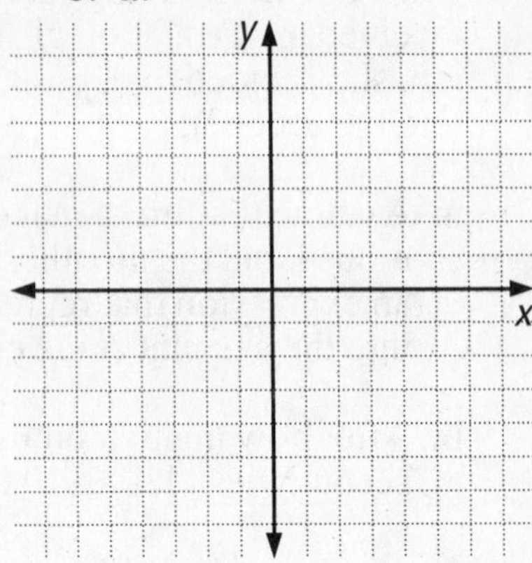

b. *True or false.* The graph represents a function.

b. ______

9. The cost of tickets to the school play was \$5 for students and \$8 for adults. Ten more student tickets were sold than adult tickets. The total ticket revenue was \$570.

a. Let x = the number of student tickets sold and y = the number of adult tickets sold. Set up a system of two equations to describe this situation.

9. a. ______

______

b. How many of each type of ticket were sold?

b. ______

10. a. On the grid at the right, graph the feasible set of

the system $\begin{cases} 2x - 6y < 24 \\ y < 4 - 2x. \\ x > 0 \end{cases}$

10. a.

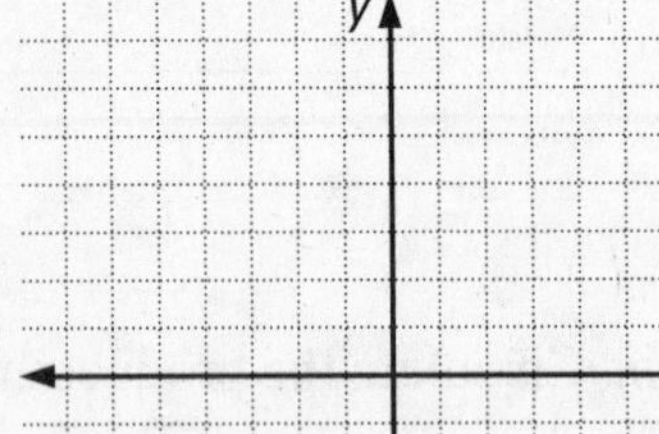

b. Find the coordinates of each vertex of the feasible region.

b. ______

Name ____________________

11. a. Write the first six terms of the sequence defined by $t_n = 3n^2 - 7$.

11. a. ____________________

____

b. Is the sequence arithmetic? Justify your answer.

____

____

12. *Multiple choice.* A manufacturer packages microwave popcorn in boxes that contain three packets. Each day the manufacturer produces p packets of popcorn. Which of the following represents the number of boxes of popcorn produced each day?

12. ____________________

(a) $\lfloor p \rfloor$ (b) $\left\lfloor \frac{p}{3} \right\rfloor$ (c) $\lfloor 3p \rfloor$ (d) $\frac{p}{3}$

In 13 and 14, use the information in the matrices below.

Matrix A: U. S. Deaths
World War I (1917 – 1918)

	Battle	Other
Army	50,510	55,868
Navy	431	6,856
Marines	2,461	390

Matrix B: U. S. Deaths
World War II (1941 – 1945)

	Battle	Other
Army	234,874	83,400
Navy	36,950	25,664
Marines	19,733	4,778

13. a. In Matrix A, what does 6,856 represent?

____

b. In Matrix B, what does the sum of the numbers in the first column represent?

____

14. a. Find $B - A$.

14. a. ____________________

b. Tell what the matrix $B - A$ represents.

____

15. a. Solve $4 - (x + 1) \geq 17$.

15. a. ____________________

b. Graph the solution set on the number line at the right.

b.

Name

16. A graph of the system

$$\begin{cases} y = \frac{5}{x} \\ y = x + 1 \end{cases}$$

is shown at the right. Use the graph to estimate the solutions.

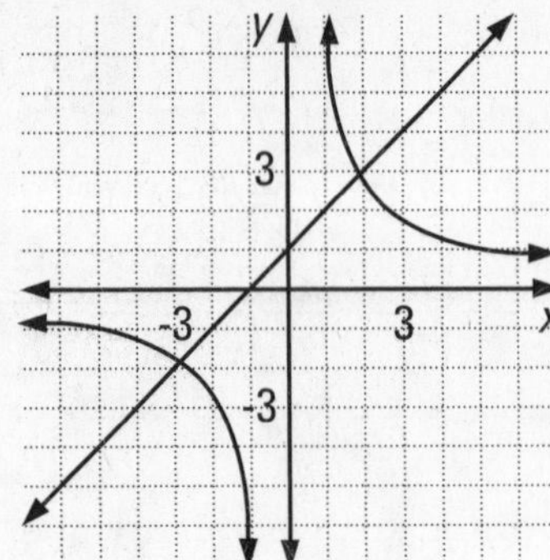

16. ________

In 17 and 18, solve the system. Show your work.

17. $\begin{cases} 6a + 11b = 36 \\ 4a - 2b = -32 \end{cases}$

17. ________

18. $\begin{cases} 3r + 4s - 2t = -11 \\ 8r + s + 5t = 1 \\ 7r + 9s + 3t = -10 \end{cases}$

18. ________

19. When planning a school dance, there is a fixed cost for the room and the band. There is an additional per-person cost for refreshments. If 100 people attend the dance, the total cost will be \$950. If 250 people attend, the total cost will be \$2000. From this information, determine the total cost if *p* people attend.

19. ________

20. Triangle *PQR* is represented by $\begin{bmatrix} 3 & 6 & 6 \\ 7 & 7 & 2 \end{bmatrix}$.

Graph the preimage and image of the triangle under r_x on the grid at the right.

20.

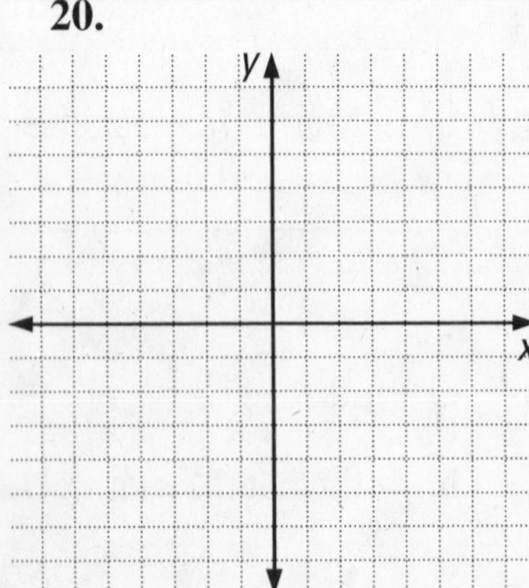

Check all your work carefully.

Name

QUIZ

1. Expand $(3r + 8)^2$. **1.** ______

2. For what real numbers x is it true that $\sqrt{x^2} = -x$? **2.** ______

3. Solve $m^2 + 12 = 48$. Show your work. **3.** ______

4. A rectangular painting 60 cm by 90 cm is to be surrounded by a mat that is w centimeters wide. Find the total area of the painting and the mat. Put your answer in standard form. **4.** ______

5. The parabola at the right is a translation image of $y = -2x^2$.

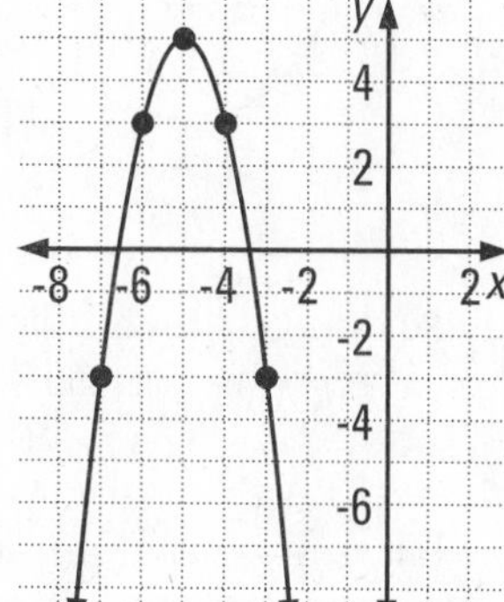

a. What translation maps $y = -2x^2$ onto this image? **5. a.** ______

b. Write an equation for the image in vertex form. **b.** ______

c. Write an equation for the image in standard form. **c.** ______

In 6–8, refer to the following situation. Leslie hit a pop fly from a height of 4 feet above the ground. The initial upward velocity of the ball was 65 feet per second.

6. Write an equation describing the relation between h, the ball's height above the ground, and time t. **6.** ______

7. What is the height of the ball after one second? **7.** ______

8. Estimate how much time it takes the ball to fall to the ground. **8.** ______

Name ______________________________

QUIZ

Lessons 6-5 Through 6-7

1. What number can be added to $q^2 - 30q$ to make a perfect-square trinomial? **1.** ________

2. Consider the parabola with equation $y = 4x^2 - 12x + 7$.

a. Rewrite the equation in vertex form. **2. a.** ________

b. What is the vertex of this parabola? **b.** ________

3. A group of students made the following observations about the maximum number of regions r formed when n chords intersect within a circle.

$n = 1$
$r = 2$

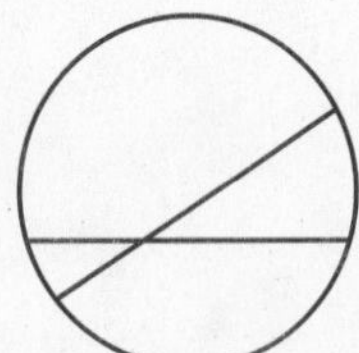

$n = 2$
$r = 4$

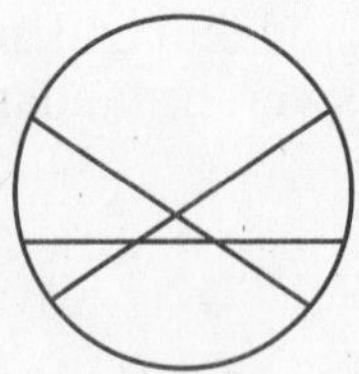

$n = 3$
$r = 7$

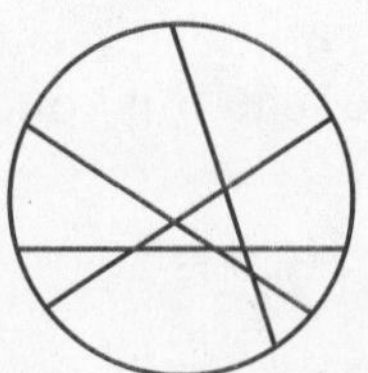

$n = 4$
$r = 11$

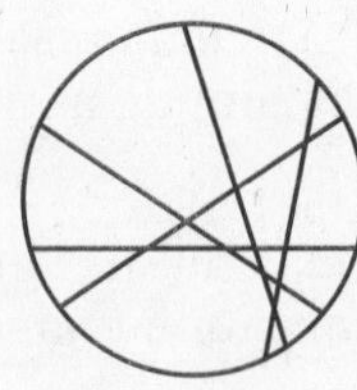

$n = 5$
$r = 16$

a. Fit a quadratic model to these data to find a formula for $r(n)$, the maximum number of regions formed when n chords intersect within a circle. **3. a.** ________

b. According to this model, what is the maximum number of regions formed when 20 chords intersect within a circle? **b.** ________

4. Paul hit a fly ball whose path can be described by the function h, where $h(x) = -.0054x^2 + 2.1x + 3.5$. In this function, x is the distance on the ground (in feet) of the ball from home plate, and $h(x)$ is the height (in feet) of the ball. The ball is traveling toward the outfield fence, which is 8 feet high and 390 feet from home plate. Could the ball go over the fence? Explain your reasoning.

____

____

In 5 and 6, solve the equation. Show your work.

5. $c^2 - 2c - 120 = 0$ **5.** ________

6. $r^2 = 16r + 5$ **6.** ________

Name

CHAPTER 6 TEST, Form A

1. How many real solutions does $7x^2 - 3x + 4 = 0$ have? Explain your answer.

In 2–5, write in $a + bi$ form.

2. $\dfrac{\sqrt{-196}}{\sqrt{-49}}$ **2.** ______

3. $(5 - 2i) - (-3 + 4i)$ **3.** ______

4. $2(3 + 7i) + (5 + i)(-3 + 6i)$ **4.** ______

5. $\dfrac{12 \pm \sqrt{-36}}{6}$ **5.** ______

In 6–8, consider the equation $y = 2x^2 - 8x + 7$.

6. a. Evaluate the discriminant. **6. a.** ______

b. Use the Discriminant Theorem to determine the nature of the roots. **b.** ______

7. Rewrite the equation in vertex form. **7.** ______

8. Write a brief description of the graph of the equation. (You do not have to draw the graph.) Your description should include facts such as the shape of the graph, the number of x-intercepts, the y-intercept, the vertex, and the equation of the axis of symmetry.

Name

In 9 and 10, suppose that the graph of $y = 2x^2$ is translated 4 units to the left and 5 units up.

9. a. Write an equation in vertex form for the image. **9. a.** ____________

b. The point (2, 8) is on the preimage. What point on the image corresponds to this point? **b.** ____________

c. *True or false.* The image is congruent to the preimage. **c.** ____________

10. Write an equation for the image in standard form. **10.** ____________

In 11 and 12, consider the parabola with equation $y + 3 = 3(x + 4)^2$.

11. a. What is its vertex? **11. a.** ____________

b. What are its x-intercepts? **b.** ____________

12. Graph this parabola on the coordinate axes at the right. **12.**

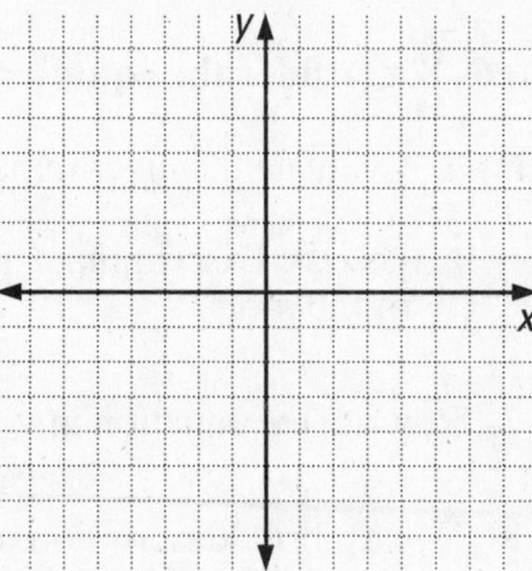

13. For what real numbers does $|x| = -1.5$? **13.** ____________

14. Suppose the height (in meters) of a toy rocket launched from a platform is described by the function h, where $h(t) = -4.9t^2 + 100t + 2$, and t is the time (in seconds) since the rocket was launched.

a. What was height of the rocket at the time of launch? **14. a.** ____________

b. When does the rocket reach its maximum height? **b.** ____________

c. When is the rocket 50 m above the ground? **c.** ____________

Name

15. The figures below show the maximum number of segments s that can be drawn connecting n points.

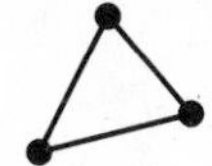
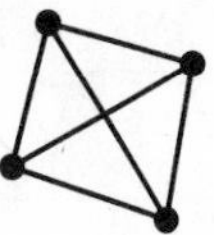
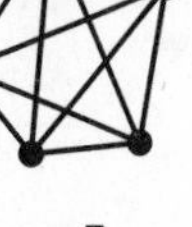
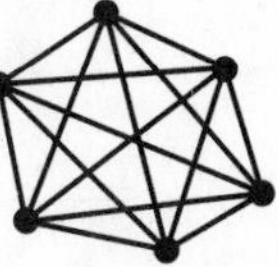

$n = 1$	$n = 2$	$n = 3$	$n = 4$	$n = 5$	$n = 6$
$s = 0$	$s = 1$	$s = 3$	$s = 6$	$s = 10$	$s = 15$

a. Graph the ordered pairs (n, s) on the grid at the right.

15. a.

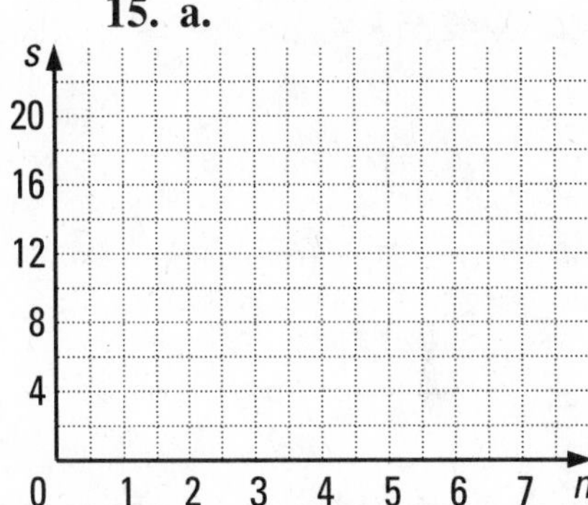

b. Fit a quadratic model to these data to find a formula for $s(n)$, the number of segments formed by connecting n points.

b. ______________

c. According to this formula, how many segments are formed by connecting 70 points?

c. ______________

16. You have a bread recipe that calls for a rectangular baking pan that is 8 inches wide and 14 inches long. Suppose you want to bake the bread in a circular pan. To the nearest inch, what should be the radius of this pan?

16. ______________

17. Expand and simplify $(2c + 5)^2 - (2c - 5)^2$.

17. ______________

18. If $c = 2i - 1$ and $d = 5 - 3i$, what is $c - 2d$?

18. ______________

In 19 and 20, solve the equation. Show your work.

19. $3p^2 - 2p = 4$

20. $(2m - 1)^2 = -16$

19. ______________

20. ______________

Check all your work carefully.

Name ______________________________

CHAPTER 6 TEST, Form B

1. How many real solutions does $5x^2 + 7x + 1 = 0$ have? Explain your answer.

____

____

In 2–5, write in $a + bi$ form.

2. $\sqrt{-225} \cdot \sqrt{-36}$ — **2.** ______________

3. $(-5 + 6i) - (3 - 7i)$ — **3.** ______________

4. $5(6 - i) + (6 - i)(3 - i)$ — **4.** ______________

5. $\dfrac{-8 \pm \sqrt{-64}}{8}$ — **5.** ______________

In 6–8, consider the equation $y = -3x^2 + 6x - 5$.

6. a. Evaluate the discriminant. — **6. a.** ______________

b. Use the Discriminant Theorem to determine the nature of the roots. — **b.** ______________

7. Rewrite the equation in vertex form. — **7.** ______________

8. Write a brief description of the graph of the equation. (You do not have to draw the graph.) Your description should include facts such as the shape of the graph, the number of x-intercepts, the y-intercept, the vertex, and the equation of the axis of symmetry.

____

____

____

____

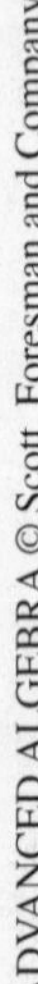

Name

In 9 and 10, suppose that the graph of $y = 5x^2$ is translated 3 units to the right and 6 units down.

9. a. Write an equation in vertex form for the image. **9. a.** __________

b. The point (-5, 125) is on the preimage. What point on the image corresponds to this point? **b.** __________

c. *True or false.* The image is *not* congruent to the preimage. **c.** __________

10. Write an equation for the image in standard form. **10.** __________

In 11 and 12, consider the parabola with equation $y + 2 = 2(x - 5)^2$.

11. a. What is its vertex? **11. a.** __________

b. What are its x-intercepts? **b.** __________

12. Graph this parabola on the coordinate axes at the right. **12.**

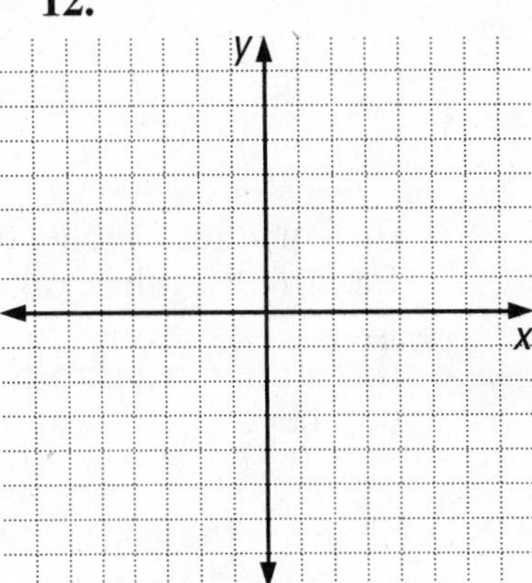

13. Simplify $\sqrt{(-10)^2}$. **13.** __________

14. Suppose you throw a ball straight up from a platform that is 8 feet above the ground, and the initial velocity of the ball is 30 feet per second.

a. Write an equation describing the relation between h, the ball's height above the ground, and time t. **14. a.** __________

b. What is the maximum height of the ball? **b.** __________

c. When does the ball hit the ground? **c.** __________

Name

15. The figures below show the first five *hexagonal numbers.*

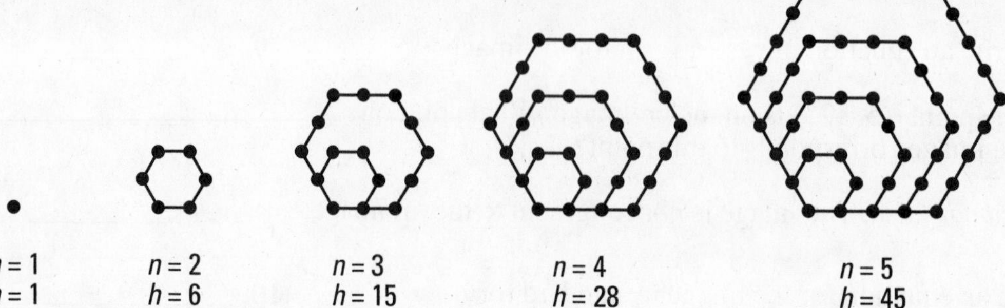

a. Graph the ordered pairs (n, h) on the grid at the right.

15. a.

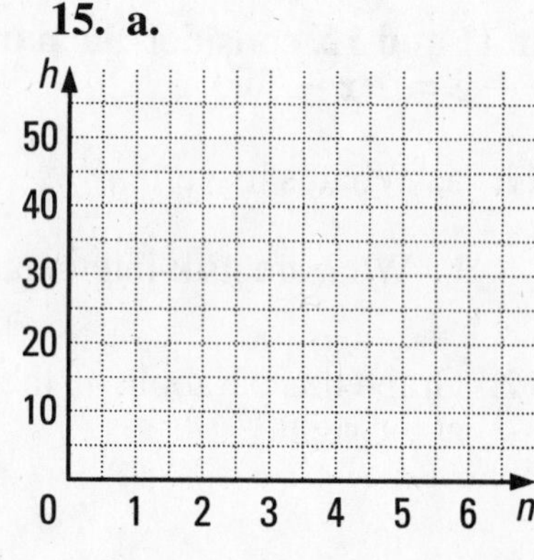

b. Fit a quadratic model to these data to find a formula for $h(n)$, the nth hexagonal number.

b. ______________

c. According to this formula, what is the 60th hexagonal number?

c. ______________

16. A circle has the same area as a right triangle with legs that are 12 cm and 16 cm long. Find the radius of the circle.

16. ______________

17. Expand and simplify $(3m - 7)^2 - (3m + 7)^2$.

17. ______________

18. If $g = 3i - 5$ and $h = -7i + 12$, what is $g + 3h$?

18. ______________

In 19 and 20, solve the equation. Show your work.

19. $5q^2 - 8q = 12$

20. $(4y + 5)^2 = -25$

19. ______________

20. ______________

Check all your work carefully.

Name

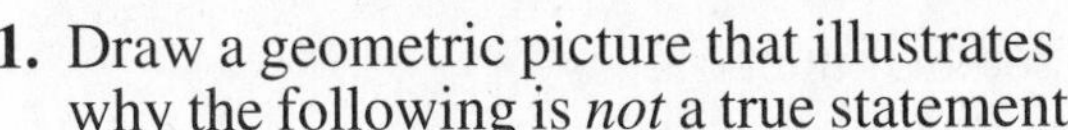

CHAPTER 6 TEST, Form C

1. Draw a geometric picture that illustrates why the following is *not* a true statement.

$$(k + 3)^2 = k^2 + 9$$

Write a brief paragraph that explains your picture.

2. Give an example of a quadratic equation that you can solve by applying the Absolute Value-Square Root Theorem. Explain how to use the theorem to solve your equation.

3. Find two different sets of integers a and b that make the following a true statement.

$$\sqrt{a} \cdot \sqrt{b} = 6i$$

Then find two different sets of integers c and d that make the following a true statement.

$$\sqrt{c} - \sqrt{d} = 6i$$

4. Consider the set of all equations of the form $y = x^2 + 8x + a$, where a is a real number. How are the graphs of these equations related to the graph of $y = x^2$? State as many facts as you can.

5. **a.** Write an equation in vertex form for a parabola with vertex (3, -2) that has no x-intercepts. Change it to standard form and show how to use the discriminant to verify the number of x-intercepts. What are the solutions to your equation?

   b. Repeat Part **a** for a parabola with vertex (3, -2) that has two x-intercepts.

6. Suppose an object is thrown upward. What information do you need to know in order to determine when the object will hit the ground? Describe how you would use this information to find the answer.

Name

CHAPTER 6 TEST, Form D

A new shipment of sale merchandise has arrived at Freddie Function's Discount Warehouse. Freddie wants to arrange the merchandise, which is packaged in cube-shaped boxes, into an attractive display. He has announced a contest among his employees to see who can create the most attractive design for the display. Here are the top two entries so far.

Linda Linear's Design

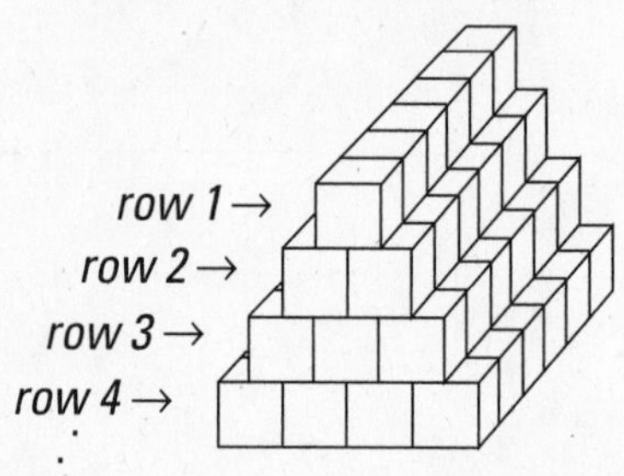

Quentin Quadratic's Design

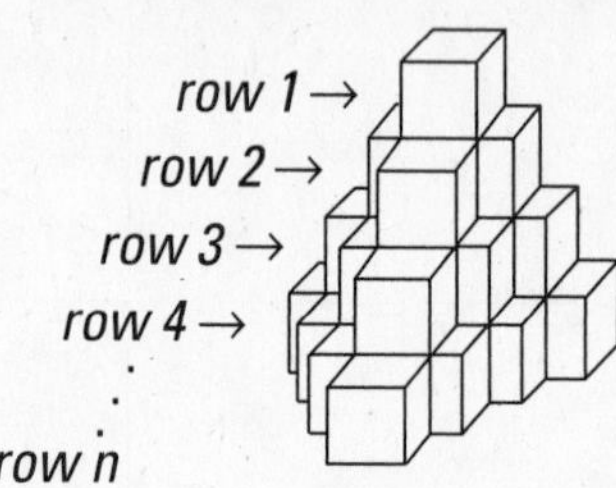

a. Explain how Linda's display is a model of a linear function. (*Hint:* Think of the number of boxes in row n of her display.)

b. Use the same thinking to explain how Quentin's display is a model of a quadratic function. (Note: Quentin's display is designed to be placed against a wall, so the back of the stack is flat.)

c. Freddie seems to favor quadratic functions, so right now Quentin's design is the front-runner. However, Linda argues that a quadratic function is "hidden" in her design. All you have to do, she says, is consider the total number of boxes in the display when there are n rows. Is she correct? Justify your answer.

d. Cassandra Cubic has submitted a last-minute entry. Her proposed display consists of several stacks of merchandise, as shown at the right. Write a function that represents the number of boxes in stack n of her display. Explain why this is *not* a quadratic function.

e. No one thinks Cassandra's design has a chance, because it doesn't appear that a quadratic function is associated with it. But Cassandra, too, says there is a quadratic function hidden in her design. She says you need to count the number of boxes *visible* in each stack. Is she correct? Justify your answer.

f. Create another design for the display that involves a quadratic function. Write a brief report that identifies the quadratic function for your design and explains how you derived it. Also identify any other types of functions "hidden" in your designs.

Cassandra Cubic's Design

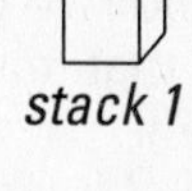

stack 1

stack 2

stack 3

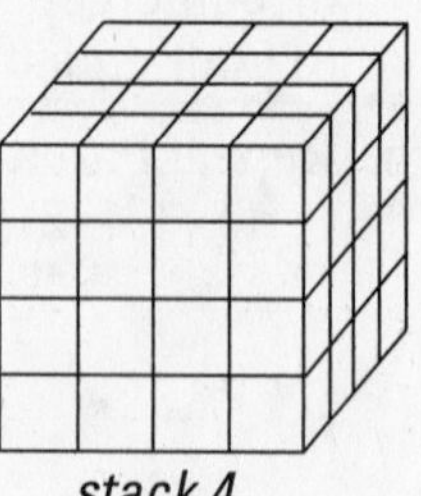

stack 4

⋮

stack n

Name

CHAPTER 6 TEST, Cumulative Form

1. Expand $5(3k - 7)^2$. 1. ______

2. a. Suppose you drop a ball from a height of 26 feet. Write an equation describing the relationship between h, the ball's height (in feet) above the ground, and time t (in seconds). 2. a. ______

   b. When will the ball hit the ground? b. ______

   c. Graph the equation from Part **a** on the coordinate axes at the right. c.

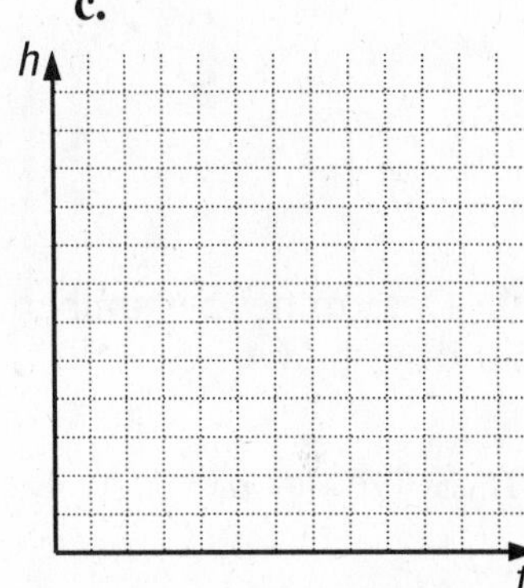

In 3–5, solve. Show your work.

3. $4j^2 + 3j = 3j - 4$

4. $4000(m^2 + 36) = 0$

3. ______

4. ______

5. $\begin{cases} a + b = 7 \\ 2a - b + c = 0 \\ -a + 5b + 3c = -4 \end{cases}$ 5. ______

6. For what value of r does $\begin{cases} 5x - 3y = 12 \\ -15x + ry = -36 \end{cases}$ have infinitely many solutions? 6. ______

In 7 and 8, write in $a + bi$ form.

7. $\sqrt{-216} \cdot \sqrt{6}$ 7. ______

8. $2i(i + 1)^2$ 8. ______

9. Graph the solution set to $y + 2 = -2(x - 1)^2$ on the coordinate axes at the right.

9.

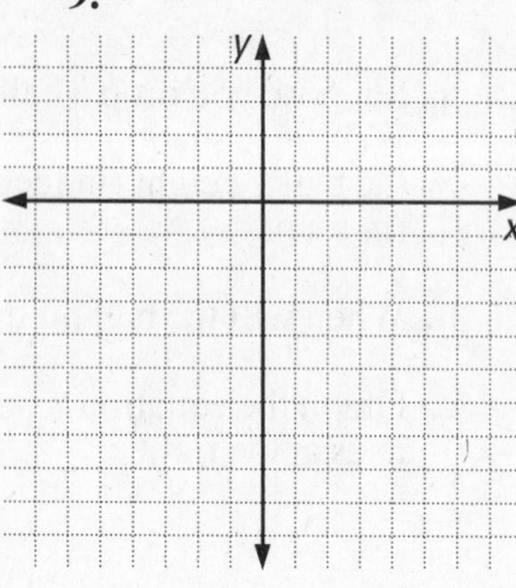

10. Determine the number of x-intercepts of the graph of $y = 2x^2 - 5x - 3$.

10. ________________

11. Solve $y = ax^2 + bx + c$ for a.

11. ________________

12. ABC is a triangle represented by the matrix $\begin{bmatrix} -3 & 3 & 0 \\ -1 & -1 & 7 \end{bmatrix}$. The length of its base is 6 units, and its height is 8 units. Write the matrix for a scale change to map ABC onto a triangle with a base of length 18 units and height 16 units.

12. ________________

13. Graph the system $\begin{cases} x \geq 0 \\ y \geq 0 \\ x + y \leq 4 \end{cases}$ on the coordinate axes at the right.

13.

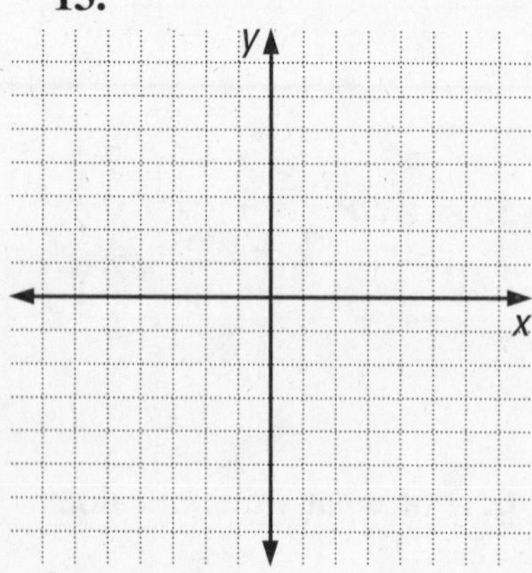

14. Carmelita makes and sells stuffed animals. To make a large animal, it costs her \$1.50 for stuffing and \$6.00 for exterior materials. To make a small animal, it costs her \$.75 for stuffing and \$4.00 for exterior materials. Each month she spends at most \$26.25 for stuffing and at most \$120 for exterior materials. She makes a profit of \$10 on each large animal and \$6 on each small animal. Find the number of each size of animal she should make in order to maximize her profit.

14. 

Name

15. Kweku finds that it costs \$303.50 to make 50 shirts and \$603.50 to make 100 shirts. Assume a linear relationship between the cost and the number of shirts. Let C = the cost of making s shirts. Write a formula relating C to s. **15.** ________

16. Write the first five terms of the sequence defined as follows. **16.** ________

$$\begin{cases} a_1 = -3.7 \\ a_n = a_{n-1} + 6, \text{ for integers } n \geq 2 \end{cases}$$

17. Suppose that m varies inversely as the cube of n. When $n = 4$, $m = .25$. Find m when $n = 2$. **17.** ________

18. A picture ℓ inches by w inches is to be surrounded by a frame that is 2 inches wide. Find the total area of the picture and the frame in expanded form. **18.** ________

19. a. The table below gives the first five partial sums S of the series $2 + 5 + 8 + 11 + \ldots$. Graph the ordered pairs (n, S) on the grid at the right. **19. a.**

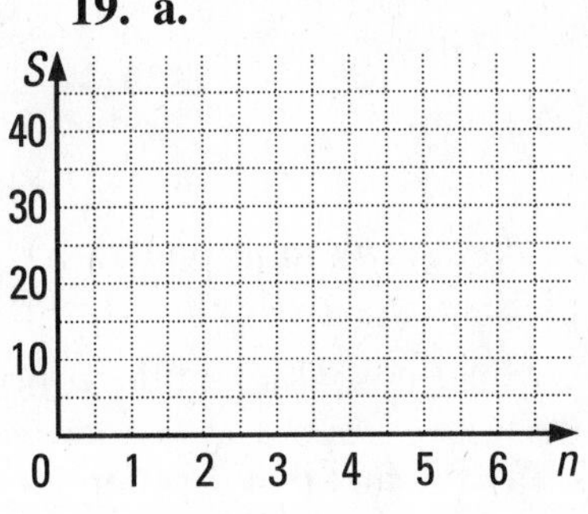

n	S	
1	2 =	2
2	2 + 5 =	7
3	2 + 5 + 8 =	15
4	2 + 5 + 8 + 11 =	26
5	2 + 5 + 8 + 11 + 14 =	40

b. Fit an appropriate model to these data to find a formula for $S(n)$, the sum of the first n terms of this series. **b.** ________

c. Find the sum of the first 100 terms of the series. **c.** ________

20. a. Graph the system $\begin{cases} y = x^2 \\ x + y = 5 \end{cases}$ on the coordinate grid at the right. **20. a.**

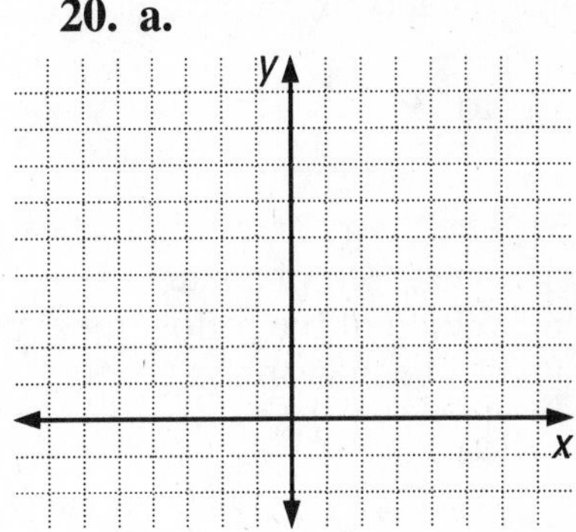

b. Use your graph to estimate the solutions to the system. **b.** ________

Check all your work carefully.

Name

COMPREHENSIVE TEST, CHAPTERS 1-6

Multiple choice. **Give the letter of the correct answer.**

1. Which of the following is *not* true for the graph of the parabola with equation $y + 2 = 3(x - 1)^2$? **1.** ________

(a) The vertex is (1, -2).

(b) The minimum point is (1, -2).

(c) The parabola opens up.

(d) An equation of the axis of symmetry is $y = -2$.

2. Which of the following systems is graphed at the right? **2.** ________

(a) $\begin{cases} x \geq 3 \\ y \leq 2 \end{cases}$ (b) $\begin{cases} x \leq 2 \\ y \geq 3 \end{cases}$

(c) $\begin{cases} x \geq 2 \\ y \leq 3 \end{cases}$ (d) $\begin{cases} x \leq 3 \\ y \geq 2 \end{cases}$

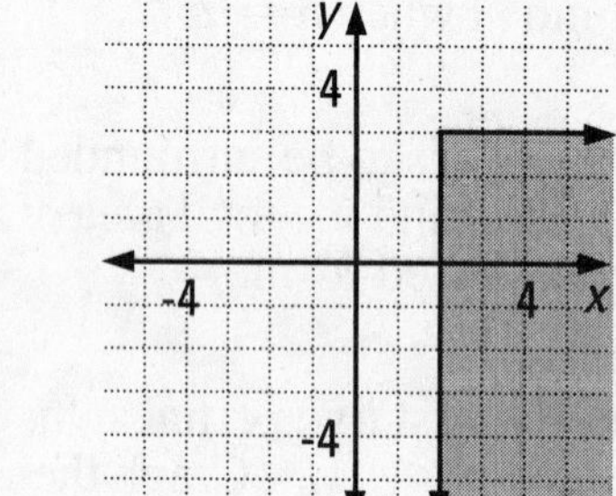

3. The matrix multiplication 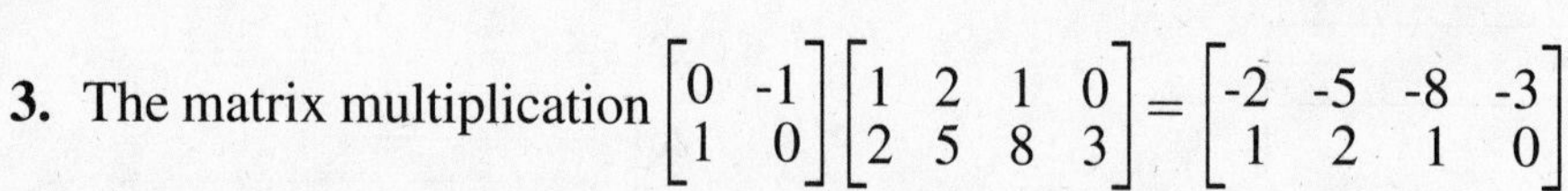 $\begin{bmatrix} 0 & -1 \\ 1 & 0 \end{bmatrix}\begin{bmatrix} 1 & 2 & 1 & 0 \\ 2 & 5 & 8 & 3 \end{bmatrix} = \begin{bmatrix} -2 & -5 & -8 & -3 \\ 1 & 2 & 1 & 0 \end{bmatrix}$ **3.** ________

illustrates which of the following?

(a) the fact that the identity matrix is $\begin{bmatrix} 0 & -1 \\ 1 & 0 \end{bmatrix}$

(b) the reflection of a quadrilateral over the x-axis

(c) the rotation of a quadrilateral 90° about the origin

(d) the fact that matrix multiplication is commutative

4. What is the determinant of the matrix $\begin{bmatrix} 3 & -2 \\ 6 & 5 \end{bmatrix}$? **4.** ________

(a) 3 (b) 27 (c) 0 (d) 12

5. The figure at the right shows the screen of an automatic grapher. Which of the following equations has been graphed? **5.** ________

(a) $y = 2x$

(b) $y = x$

(c) $y = .5x$

(d) $y = .25x$

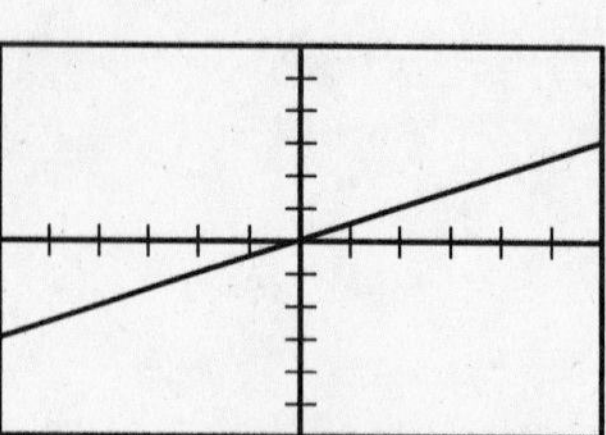

x-scale = 2
y-scale = 1

Name

6. Below are the graphs of three relations. Which could be the graph of a function? 6. ________

I.
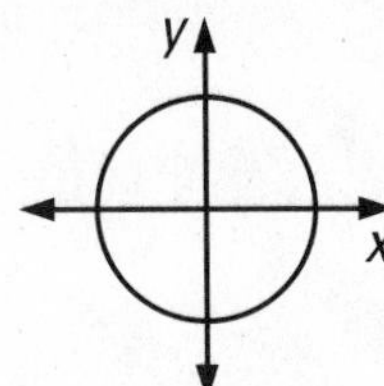

II.
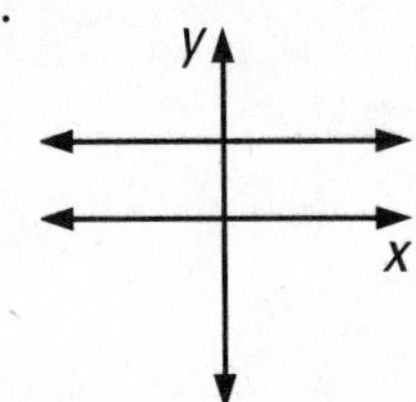

III.
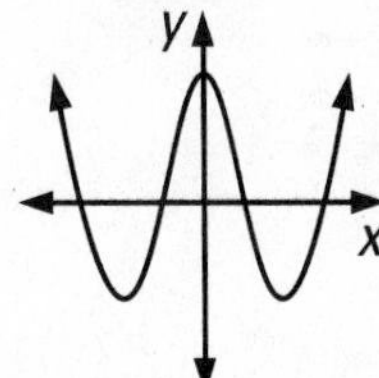

(a) I only (b) II only (c) III only (d) II and III only

7. Consider the line with equation $3x - 5y = 15$. Which of the following statements is true? 7. ________

(a) The slope of the line is $\frac{5}{3}$, and its y-intercept is -3.

(b) The slope of the line is $\frac{3}{5}$, and its y-intercept is 5.

(c) The slope of the line is $\frac{5}{3}$, and its y-intercept is 5.

(d) The slope of the line is $\frac{3}{5}$, and its y-intercept is -3.

8. Which formula defines the sequence -6, -2, 2, 6, 10, 14, . . . ? 8. ________

(a) $a_n = -6 + 4(n - 1)$ (b) $a_n = -6 + 4n$

(c) $\begin{cases} a_1 = -6 \\ a_n = 4a_{n-1}, \\ \quad \text{for integers } n \geq 2 \end{cases}$ (d) $\begin{cases} a_1 = -6 \\ a_n = a_{n-1} - 4, \\ \quad \text{for integers } n \geq 2 \end{cases}$

9. The discriminant of $5x^2 - 2x + 7 = 0$ __?__. 9. ________

(a) 136 (b) -136 (c) $136i$ (d) $\sqrt{-136}$

10. What is the rate of change of $y = \frac{16}{x}$ between $x = 3$ and $x = 4$? 10. ________

(a) $-\frac{4}{3}$ (b) $-\frac{3}{4}$ (c) $\frac{4}{3}$ (d) $\frac{3}{4}$

11. $\sqrt{-25} \cdot \sqrt{-25} =$ __?__. 11. ________

(a) $\sqrt{625}$ (b) -25 (c) $25i$ (d) $-25i$

12. The diameter of a basketball is 10 inches. Use the function defined by $V = \frac{4}{3}\pi r^3$ to find the volume of the basketball to the nearest cubic inch. 12. ________

(a) 524 (b) 105 (c) 21 (d) 1571

Name ____________________

13. Consider the equation $Ax + By = C$, where $A > 0$, $B > 0$, and $C \neq 0$. Which could be the graph of this equation? **13.** ________

(a)
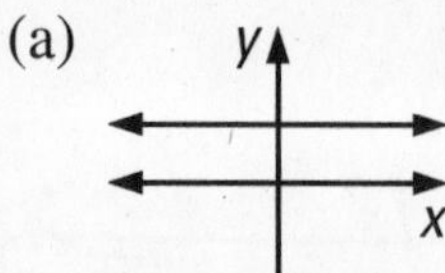

(b)
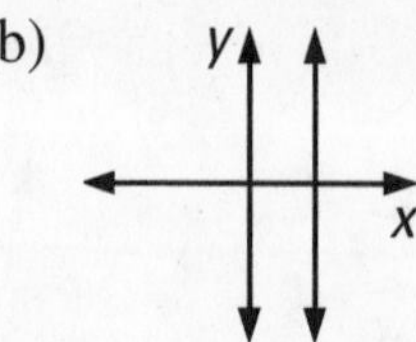

(c)
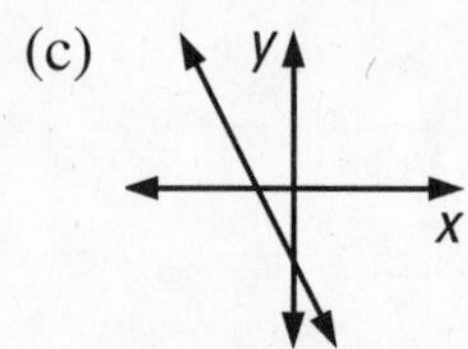

(d)
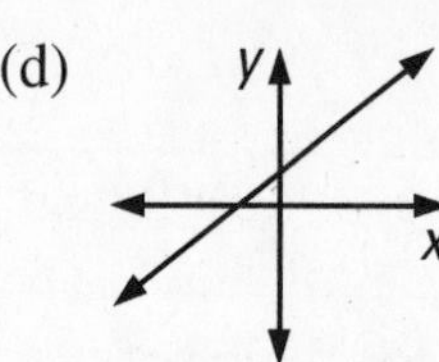

14. The table below describes the function $f: x \rightarrow y$. What is the range of f? **14.** ________

x	0	-1	1	-2	2	-3	-3
y	0	1	1	4	4	9	9

(a) {0, -1, 1, -2, 2, -3, 3}

(b) the set of all real numbers

(c) {0, -1, 1, -2, 2, -3, 3, 4, 9}

(d) {0, 1, 4, 9}

15. Consider the table below. Which statement that follows is true? **15.** ________

x	-4	-3	-2	-1	0	1	2	3	4
y	4	3	2	1	0	1	2	3	4

(a) y is a function of x.

(b) x is a function of y.

(c) $y = \sqrt{x}$

(d) There is no relation.

16. Find the product: $[\,5 \;\; 2 \;\; -1\,]\begin{bmatrix} 6 & 2 \\ 5 & 0 \\ -1 & -7 \end{bmatrix}$. **16.**

(a) $[\,41 \;\; 17\,]$

(b) $\begin{bmatrix} 30 & 10 \\ 10 & 0 \\ 1 & 7 \end{bmatrix}$

(c) $\begin{bmatrix} 41 \\ 17 \end{bmatrix}$

(d) The product does not exist.

17. Philip uses his cellular phone only for local service. One month he paid \$32.50 for 25 minutes of service and another month he paid \$37.00 for 40 minutes of service. Assume a linear relationship exists between the cost and the number of minutes of service, how much will Philip pay for 50 minutes of service? **17.**

(a) \$65.00

(b) \$46.25

(c) \$40.00

(d) \$47.50

Name ______________________________

18. Suppose a person who weighs 80 pounds is put on a diet to gain weight. The goal is to gain three pounds a month. Let w represent the person's weight and m represent the number of months the person has been on the diet. Which equation relates w and m? **18.** ________

(a) $\frac{w}{3} = 80m$ (b) $w = 3(80 + m)$

(c) $w = 3 + 80m$ (d) $w = 80 + 3m$

19. When you ride a roller coaster, your height above the ground varies ___?___ as the number of seconds you have been riding the roller coaster. **19.** ________

(a) directly (b) inversely (c) jointly (d) none of these

20. A system of inequalities is graphed at the right. Which of these ordered pairs does *not* represent a solution to this system? **20.** ________

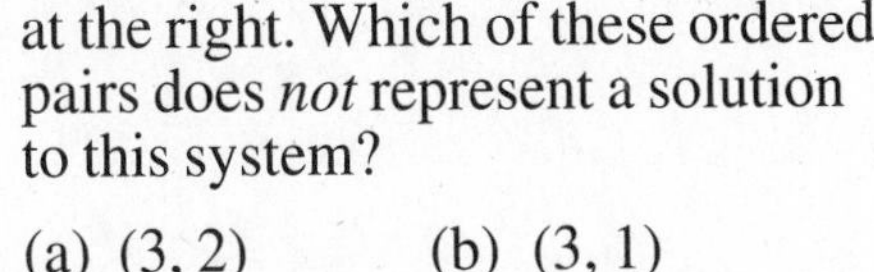

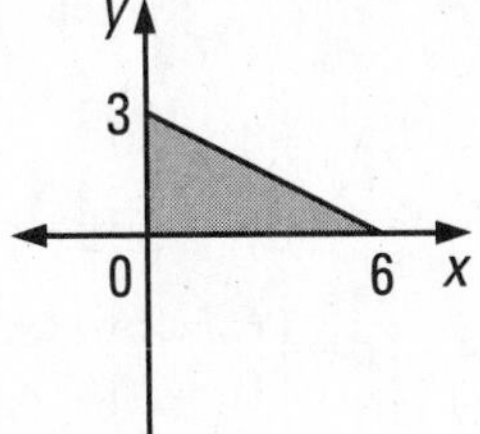

(a) (3, 2) (b) (3, 1)

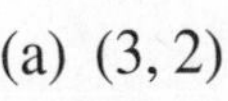

(c) (2, 2) (d) (1, 2)

21. Which inequality is graphed on the number line below? **21.** ________

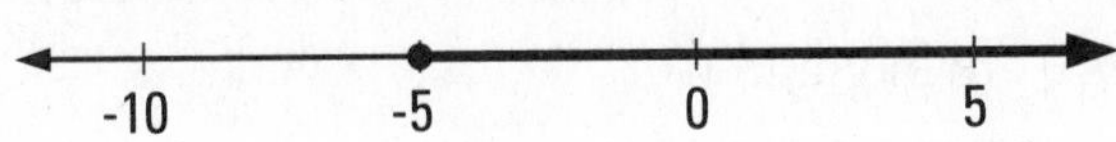

(a) $s \geq -5$ (b) $s > -5$ (c) $s \leq -5$ (d) $s < -5$

22. A triangle is defined by the matrix $\begin{bmatrix} -1 & 6 & 2 \\ -2 & 5 & 7 \end{bmatrix}$. The figure at the right shows the image of this triangle under a transformation. What is the transformation? **22.** ________

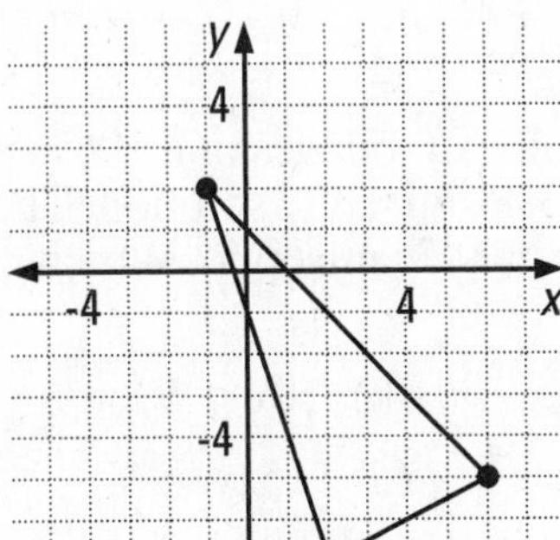

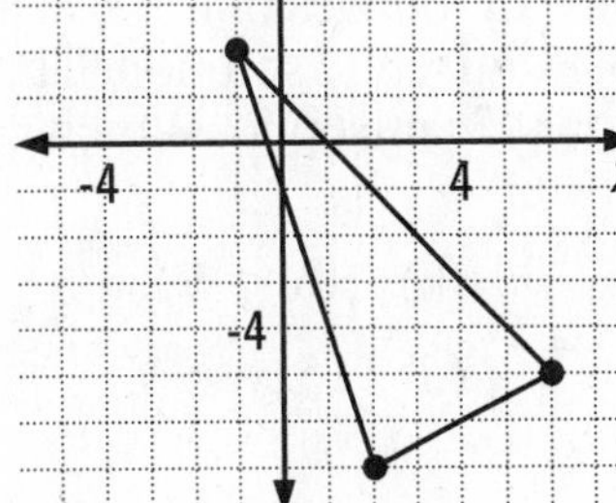

(a) $T_{0,4}$ (b) r_x

(c) r_y (d) R_{90}

23. For what value of x is the inverse variation $y = \frac{k}{x}$ undefined? **23.** ________

(a) 0 (b) k (c) 1 (d) -1

Name

24. A rectangular picture 10 inches by 15 inches is to be surrounded by a frame that is w inches wide. Which of the following gives the total area of the picture and frame, in square inches? **24.** ________

(a) 150 (b) $(10 + 2w)(15 + 2w)$

(c) $150 + 4w^2$ (d) $(10 + w)(15 + w)$

25. Given $A = (1, 3)$ and $B = (-1, -5)$, which is an equation for the perpendicular bisector of $\overline{AB}$? **25.** ________

(a) $y - 3 = 4(x - 1)$ (b) $y + 1 = -\frac{1}{4}x$

(c) $y + 5 = -\frac{1}{4}(x + 1)$ (d) $y - 5 = -\frac{1}{4}(x - 1)$

26. Which is a single matrix for $\begin{bmatrix} 5 & -2 \\ 6 & -3 \end{bmatrix} - \begin{bmatrix} -1 & 1 \\ 6 & -1 \end{bmatrix}$? **26.** ________

(a) $\begin{bmatrix} -17 & 7 \\ -24 & 9 \end{bmatrix}$ (b) $\begin{bmatrix} 17 & -7 \\ 24 & -9 \end{bmatrix}$

(c) $\begin{bmatrix} 4 & -1 \\ 12 & -4 \end{bmatrix}$ (d) $\begin{bmatrix} 6 & -3 \\ 0 & -2 \end{bmatrix}$

27. The students at Woodnew High School are in grades 9, 10, 11, and 12. Of all the students, $\frac{1}{4}$ are in grade 9, $\frac{1}{3}$ are in grade 10, and $\frac{1}{6}$ are in grade 11. If there are 300 students in grade 12, how many students are in grade 11? **27.** ________

(a) 300 (b) 400 (c) 200 (d) 1200

28. A pharmacist combines x ounces of a 10% antiseptic solution with y ounces of a 5% antiseptic solution. The final mixture contains 12 ounces of 8% antiseptic. Which equation represents this situation? **28.** ________

(a) $x + y = 12$ (b) $10x + 5y = 8$

(c) $.1x + .05y = .96$ (d) $.15xy = 12$

29. If $f(x) = x^2 - 2x + 5$, find $\dfrac{f(6) - f(4)}{6 - 4}$. **29.** ________

(a) 29 (b) 13 (c) 16 (d) 8

30. Suppose y varies directly as the square of x. How does the value of y change if x is tripled? **30.** 

(a) y is multiplied by 3. (b) y is multiplied by 9.

(c) y is divided by 3. (d) y is divided by 9.

Check all your work carefully.

Name

QUIZ

In 1–3, write as a whole number or a simple fraction.

1. 7^{-3} **1.** ______

2. $4^5 \cdot 4^6$ **2.** ______

3. $\left(\frac{2}{5}\right)^{-2}$ **3.** ______

In 4 and 5, simplify. There should be only positive exponents in your answer.

4. $(6a^4)^{-2} \cdot (3ab^2)^3$ **4.** ______

5. $\dfrac{(x^5y^7)^4}{x^3y^{-2} \cdot x^6y^{-9}}$ **5.** ______

6. *Multiple choice.* Which could be the graph of the function with equation $y = x^{11}$? **6.** ______

(a)

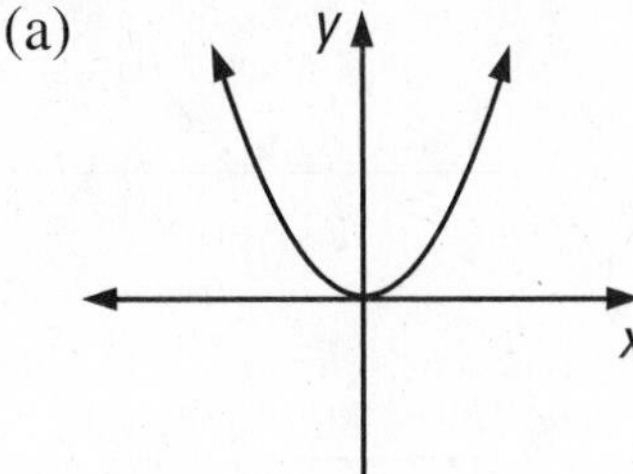

(b)

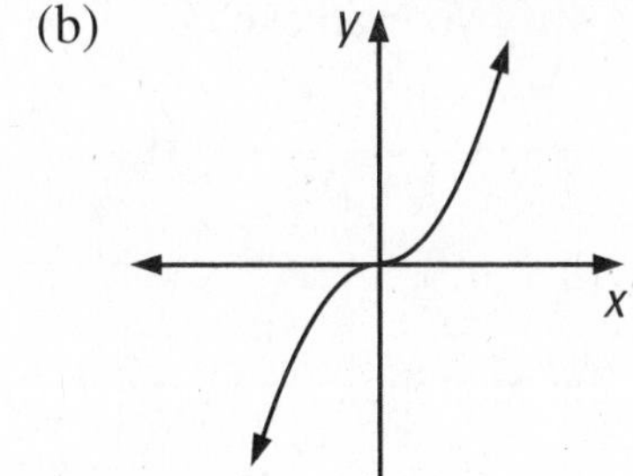

(c)

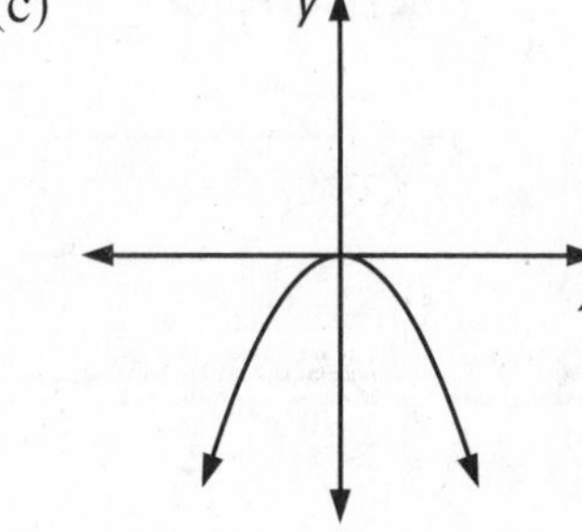

7. Consider the function f defined by $f(x) = x^n$. If n is even, what is the range of f? **7.** ______

8. Describe the symmetry of the graph of $f(x) = x^n$ if n is odd.

______

______

9. In 1990, the population of the United States was approximately 2.49×10^8. In that year, the United States generated about 3.90×10^{11} pounds of trash. Find the average number of pounds of trash per person in 1990. **9.** ______

Name

QUIZ

Lessons 7-4 Through 7-6

In 1 and 2, evaluate.

1. $128^{\frac{1}{7}}$ **1.** ____________

2. $-625^{\frac{1}{4}}$ **2.** ____________

3. Is $-i\sqrt{3}$ a fourth root of 81? Justify your answer.

____

____

In 4–6, consider the sequence defined as follows:

$$\begin{cases} t_1 = 6 \\ t_n = .5t_{n-1}, \text{ for integers } n \geq 2 \end{cases}$$

4. Write the first three terms of the sequence. **4.** ____________

5. Is the sequence geometric? Justify your answer.

____

____

6. Give an explicit formula for the sequence. **6.** ____________

7. A bond paying 5.5% compounded annually has matured after 10 years, giving the owner $5000. How much was invested 10 years ago? **7.** ____________

8. Suppose a person puts $5000 in a savings account that pays 3% interest, compounded monthly. How much money will be in the account after 3 years, assuming no other deposits or withdrawals are made? **8.** ____________

Name

CHAPTER 7 TEST, Form A

In 1–4, write as a whole number or a simple fraction.

1. 4^{-2} **1.** ______

2. $(1{,}000{,}000)^{\frac{2}{3}}$ **2.** ______

3. $\left(\frac{64}{729}\right)^{-\frac{5}{6}}$ **3.** ______

4. $(13^{-1})^0$ **4.** ______

In 5–7, consider the sequence $\frac{3}{2}, \frac{9}{8}, \frac{27}{32}, \frac{81}{128}, \ldots$.

5. Give the constant ratio of the sequence. **5.** ______

6. Find a recursive formula for the sequence. **6.** ______

7. Find an explicit formula for the *n*th term. **7.** ______

8. Consider the function f with equation $f(x) = x^n$, where n is an even positive integer.

a. State the domain and the range of f. **8. a.** ______

______

b. In which quadrants is the graph of f? **b.** ______

9. *Multiple choice.* Which graph could represent the function with equation $y = -x^{14}$? **9.** ______

(a)
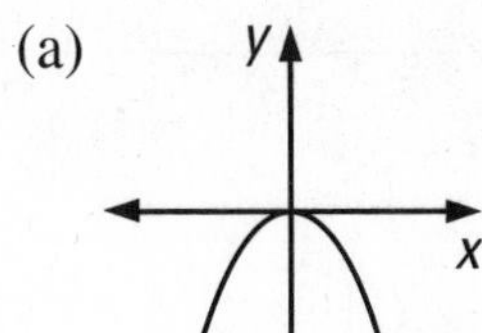

(b)
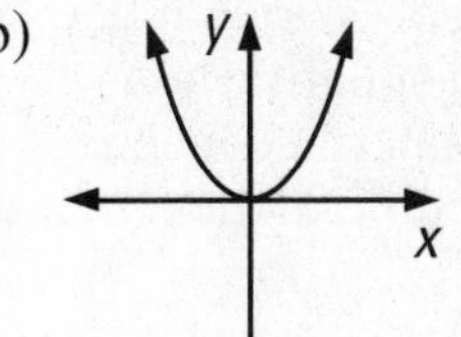

(c)
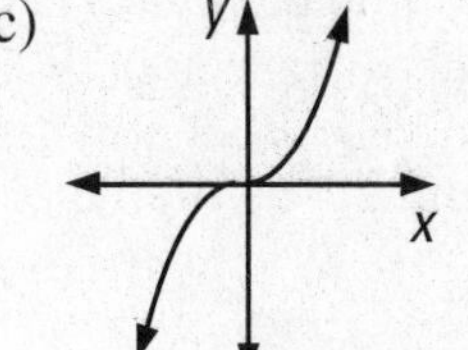

(d)
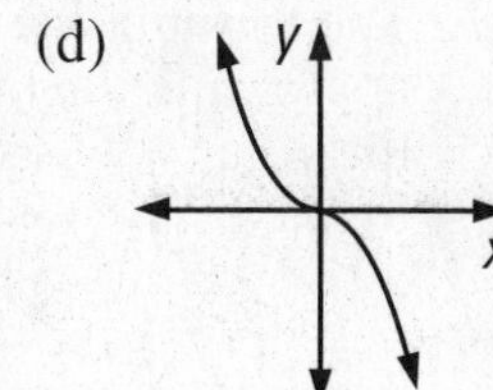

10. Is $3i$ a sixth root of 729? Justify your answer.

____

____

11. Helmer puts $750 in a savings account that pays 3.7% interest, compounded annually. Assuming that he makes no other deposits or withdrawals, how much money will he have in this account after four years? **11.** ________

In 12 and 13, simplify. There should be only positive exponents in your answer.

12. $(3a^5b)^4(5a^6b^7)$ **12.** ________

13. $\dfrac{36m^5n^{-2}}{9m^{-2}n^6}$ **13.** ________

14. Describe how to use a graph to estimate the real 6th roots of 18. How many such roots are there? Justify your answer.

____

____

15. In 1992, the total energy consumption of the United States was about 8.24×10^{16} Btu (British thermal units). The population of the United States in that year was approximately 2.55×10^8. Find the average energy consumption per person in 1992. **15.** ________

16. Estimate $(875)^{\frac{2}{5}}$ to the nearest hundredth. **16.** ________

17. The formula $S.A. = 4.84V^{\frac{2}{3}}$ gives an excellent approximation of the surface area, *S.A.*, of a sphere when the volume V is known. About how much material is needed to make a beach ball with a volume of 805 cubic inches? **17.** ________

Name

18. Suppose a ball is dropped from a height of 4 feet, and it bounces up to 50% of its previous height after each bounce.

a. Let h_n be the greatest height of the ball after the nth bounce. Find an explicit formula for h_n. — **18. a.** ____________

b. Find the greatest height of the ball after the third bounce. — **b.** ____________

In 19 and 20, find all real solutions.

19. $6w^6 - 15 = 369$ — **19.** ____________

20. $m^{-\frac{3}{2}} = 125$ — **20.** ____________

21. Suppose $0 < x < 1$. Arrange from least to greatest. — **21.** ____________

$x^{\frac{3}{2}}, x^{-4}, x^2, x$

In 22 and 23, solve.

22. $3^{\frac{3}{2}} \cdot 3^{-4} = (3p)^2$ — **22.** ____________

23. $4^3 \cdot 7^{-3} = q^3$ — **23.** ____________

24. a. At the right is the graph of an nth power function. Write an equation for this function. — **24. a.** ____________

(-3, 6561)

y

x

b. Give the coordinates of four other points that lie on the graph of this function. — **b.** ____________

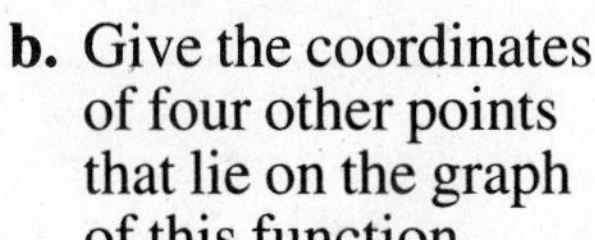

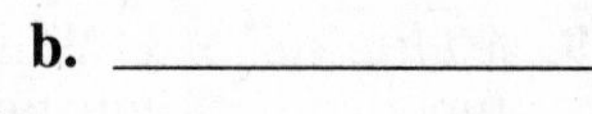

25. Peggy Lou now has \$8000 in a savings account that has been earning interest at a rate of 3.9%, compounded quarterly. How much was in the account five years ago, assuming that she made no deposits or withdrawals in that time period? — **25.** ____________

Check all your work carefully.

Name

CHAPTER 7 TEST, Form B

In 1–4, write as a whole number or a simple fraction.

1. 7^{-2} 1. ____________

2. $(1000)^{\frac{5}{3}}$ 2. ____________

3. $\left(\frac{32}{243}\right)^{-\frac{4}{5}}$ 3. ____________

4. $(2^{-5})^0$ 4. ____________

In 5–7, consider the sequence $\frac{1}{2}, \frac{3}{10}, \frac{9}{50}, \frac{27}{250}, \ldots$.

5. Give the constant ratio of the sequence. 5. ____________

6. Find a recursive formula for the sequence. 6. ____________

7. Find an explicit formula for the *n*th term. 7. ____________

8. Consider the function *f* with equation $f(x) = x^n$, where n is an odd positive integer.

   a. State the domain and the range of *f*. 8. a. ____________

   ____

   b. In which quadrants is the graph of *f*? b. ____________

9. *Multiple choice.* Which graph could represent the function with equation $y = x^{15}$? 9. ____________

(a)
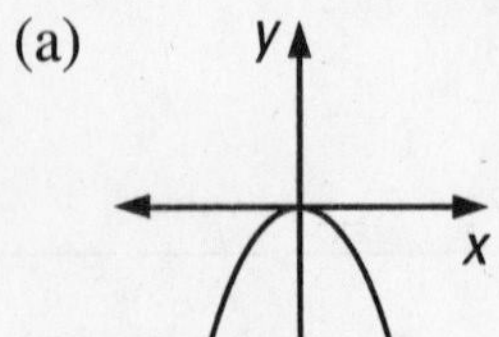

(b)
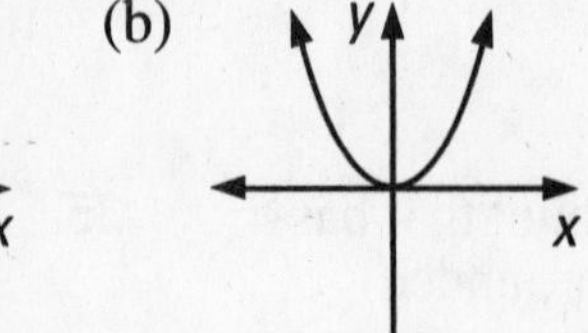

(c)
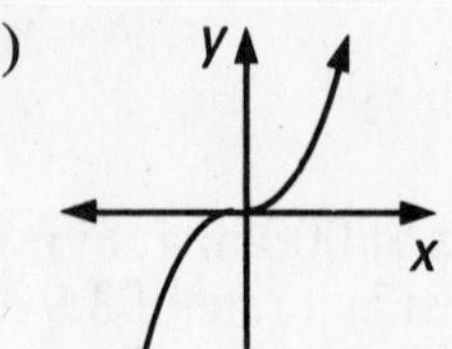

(d)
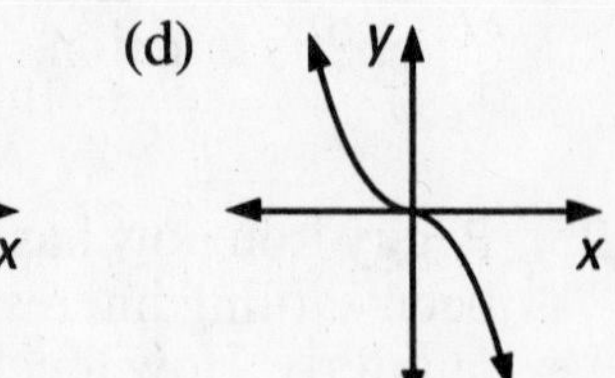

Name

10. Is $5i$ a fourth root of 625? Justify your answer.

____

____

11. Keisha puts \$875 in a savings account that pays 3.6% interest, compounded monthly. Assuming that she makes no other deposits or withdrawals, how much money will she have in this account after 2 years?

11. ______________

In 12 and 13, simplify. There should be only positive exponents in your answer.

12. $(4m^3n)^2(3m^5n^4)$

12. ______________

13. $\dfrac{21a^{-2}b^3}{3a^{-6}b^{-2}}$

13. ______________

14. Describe how to use a graph to estimate the real 5th roots of -15. How many such roots are there? Justify your answer.

____

____

15. In 1992, the population of the United States was approximately 2.55×10^8. In that year, Americans consumed about 1.44×10^{11} pounds of dairy products. Find the average energy consumption per person in 1992.

15. ______________

16. Estimate $(962)^{\frac{3}{4}}$ to the nearest hundredth.

16. ______________

17. The formula $d = 1.82r^{\frac{2}{3}}$ gives an excellent approximation of a planet's average distance d from the sun, in millions of miles, when the number of Earth days r that it takes for the planet to make one revolution around the sun is known. Mars revolves around the sun once every 687 days. What is the average distance of Mars from the sun?

17. ______________

Name

18. Suppose a ball is dropped from a height of 4 m, and it bounces up to 60% of its previous height after each bounce.

a. Let h_n be the greatest height of the ball after the nth bounce. Find an explicit formula for h_n. **18. a.** ______________

b. Find the greatest height of the ball after the fourth bounce. **b.** ______________

In 19 and 20, find all real solutions.

19. $5w^4 + 3 = 408$ **19.** ______________

20. $m^{-\frac{2}{3}} = 25$ **20.** ______________

21. Suppose $x > 1$. Arrange from least to greatest. **21.** ______________

$x^{-2}, x^{\frac{5}{4}}, x^{\frac{1}{2}}, x$

In 22 and 23, solve.

22. $4^5 = (4p)^3$ **22.** ______________

23. $3^3 \cdot 5^{-3} = q^3$ **23.** ______________

24. a. At the right is the graph of an nth power function. Write an equation for this function. **24. a.** ______________

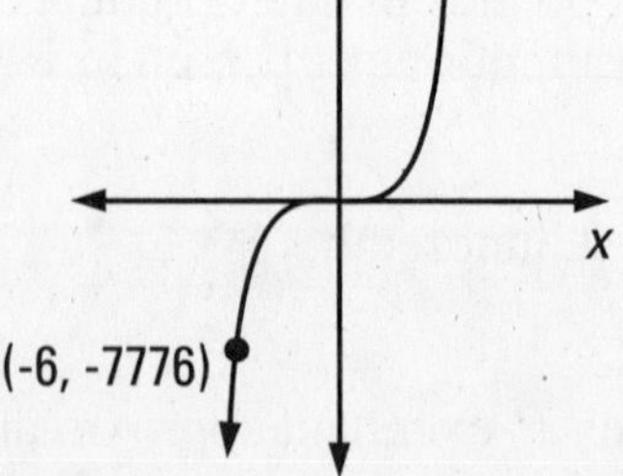

b. Give the coordinates of four other points that lie on the graph of this function. **b.** ______________

25. Hoa now has $4000 in a savings account that has been earning interest at a rate of 3.8%, compounded quarterly. How much was in the account four years ago, assuming that he made no deposits or withdrawals in that time period? **25.** ______________

Check all your work carefully.

Name

CHAPTER 7 TEST, Form C

1. a. Given that x, m, and n are integers greater than 1, and that $m \neq n$, find values of x, m, and n for which the value of $x^{\frac{m}{n}}$ is between 10 and 20. Show how to evaluate the expression for these values of x, m, and n.

   b. Repeat Part **a**, but this time find values of x, m, and n for which the value of $x^{\frac{m}{n}}$ is between 0 and 1.

2. Karl says the statements at the right are all true. So, he says, $x^4 = 1296$ has four real solutions.

   $6^4 = 1296$
   $(-6)^4 = 1296$
   $(6i)^4 = 1296$
   $(-6i)^4 = 1296$

   Do you agree or disagree with Karl? Justify your response.

3. Suppose that the following is a true statement:

$$\frac{2^a \cdot 5^b}{2^c \cdot 5^d} = (2 \cdot 5^{\frac{1}{2}})^4$$

   What can you say about the relationship between a and c? What can you say about the relationship between b and d?

4. Create a geometric sequence whose first term is a positive integer and whose constant ratio is 0.5. Write an explicit formula and a recursive formula for this sequence. Describe a real-world situation that might be modeled by this sequence.

5. Tamara wants to invest \$1000 for a period of six years. She saw a sign at a bank advertising one type of account that pays 4% interest and a second type that pays 4.03% interest. She thinks her \$1000 will definitely earn more interest if she chooses the second type of account, since 4.03% is more than 4%. Is her reasoning correct? Give examples to justify your answer.

6. Consider the function f with $f(x) = x^n$, where n is a positive integer. Compare the graph of f obtained when n is even to the graph of f when n is odd. How are they alike? How are they different? State as many similarities and differences as you can.

Name

CHAPTER 7 TEST, Form D

Your parents want to remodel the kitchen of your house. The house is very old, so the remodeling will be expensive. In fact, the lowest estimate for the cost of the remodeling is $18,000. However, your parents have only $15,000 available. They wonder if they should wait awhile and let the $15,000 earn some interest.

*Friendly Savings Bank Certificates of Deposit**	
Period	*Rate*
6 months	4.750%
1 year	5.000%
2 years	5.500%
3 years	6.000%
5 years	6.650%

*Interest on all CDs is compounded quarterly.

a. Suppose your parents deposit the $15,000 in a savings account that pays 4% interest, compounded monthly. If they make no additional deposits or withdrawals, will they earn enough interest in two years to have a total of $18,000? Justify your answer.

b. A local bank is offering the CDs described in the list at the right. Will your parents have a total of $18,000 if they place the $15,000 in any of these CDs? Justify your answer.

c. Your parents have spoken to a *stock broker* who believes that their money can earn as much as 15% annually if they invest it in the stock market. If your parents invest the $15,000 in stocks under these conditions, about how long would it take to have a total of $18,000? Justify your answer. (*Hint:* Use trial and error and the general compound interest formula.)

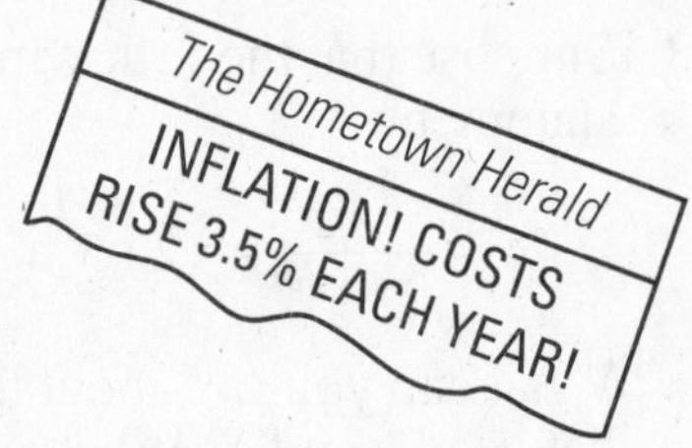

d. Your parents have been thinking about the cost of the remodeling as $18,000. However, one day the headline at the right appeared in your local newspaper. Your parents realized that the $18,000 cost is likely to increase with each year that passes. Assume that 3.5% is an annual rate of inflation that remains steady. Make a table that shows the estimated cost of the remodeling in each of the next ten years.

e. What type of sequence is formed by the costs in your table in Part **d**? Write an explicit formula and a recursive formula for this sequence.

f. Use the information given above. Make a plan for investing the $15,000 so that it earns enough interest and dividends to pay for the remodeling. Be sure to allow for the effect of inflation on the cost of the remodeling. Also, keep in mind that financial advisors suggest that an amount like $15,000 should be invested in two or three types of accounts. They recommend that you consider the following:

- A savings account generally does not pay as much interest as other investments, but your money is always available for an emergency.
- CDs usually offer higher interest rates, but you pay a penalty if you must withdraw the money before the period expires.
- Stocks are a risk. There is no guarantee that you will earn 15%. The percent might be much less, and you might even lose money.

Summarize your plan in a report for your parents. Include a statement of the amount of interest and dividends that you expect the money to earn, the amount of time it will take, and the reasons for your choices.

Name

CHAPTER 7 TEST, Cumulative Form

In 1–4, write as a whole number or a simple fraction.

1. $\left(\frac{256}{625}\right)^{\frac{3}{4}}$ **1.** ____________

2. $81^{-\frac{3}{4}}$ **2.** ____________

3. $(7776)^{\frac{1}{5}}$ **3.** ____________

4. a. A bamboo plant can grow as much as 35.4 inches in one day. What is the height of a new bamboo plant that was growing at this rate for *d* days? **4. a.** ____________

b. On which day of growth would the height of this bamboo plant reach 50 feet? **b.** ____________

5. Explain how to use the Discriminant Theorem to determine the nature of the solutions to $7x^2 + 15x = 25$.

____

____

6. State the domain and range of the function f with equation $f(x) = x^{10}$. **6.** ____________

7. *Multiple choice.* Which matrix represents r_x? **7.** ____________

(a) $\begin{bmatrix} 0 & 1 \\ -1 & 0 \end{bmatrix}$ (b) $\begin{bmatrix} 1 & 0 \\ 0 & -1 \end{bmatrix}$ (c) $\begin{bmatrix} -1 & 0 \\ 0 & 1 \end{bmatrix}$ (d) $\begin{bmatrix} 0 & -1 \\ 1 & 0 \end{bmatrix}$

8. Graph $y = \frac{4}{3}x + 5$ on the coordinate axes at the right. **8.**

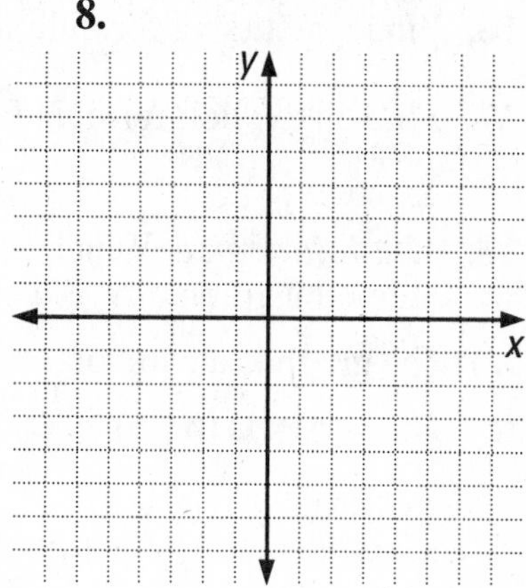

Name

In 9 and 10, find all real solutions.

9. $5w^{\frac{5}{7}} = 160$ **9.** ____________

10. $120t^4 - 50.5 = 17{,}957$ **10.** ____________

11. a. Suppose a ball is thrown from the top of a building that is 50 feet high with an initial upward velocity of 15 feet per second. Write an equation to describe the height h of the ball after t seconds. **11. a.** ____________

b. When will the ball be 20 feet above the ground? **b.** ____________

12. Simplify $(4 + 3i)(2 - 6i)$. **12.** ____________

13. Give an equation for the line that contains (7, -4) and is perpendicular to $9x + 2y = 15$. **13.** ____________

14. *Multiple choice.* Which could be an equation for the graph at the right? **14.** ____________

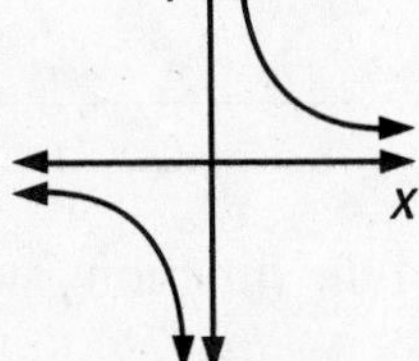

(a) $y = 4x$ (b) $y = 4x^2$

(c) $y = \frac{4}{x}$ (d) $y = \frac{4}{x^2}$

15. In 1993, there were 9.78×10^8 acres of farmland in the United States. There were a total of 2.07×10^6 farms. What was the average number of acres of land per farm? **15.** ____________

In 16 and 17, consider the sequence $3, \frac{9}{4}, \frac{27}{16}, \frac{81}{64}, \ldots$

16. Find a recursive formula for the sequence. **16.** ____________

17. Find an explicit formula for the nth term. **17.** ____________

18. *Multiple choice.* Which of the following is *not* true about the graph of $y + 6 = 3(x - 5)^2$? **18.** ____________

(a) The graph is a parabola. (b) The graph opens up.

(c) The vertex is (5, -6). (d) The x-intercepts are -3.5 and -6.4.

▶ CHAPTER 7 TEST, Cumulative Form *page 3*

19. The top row of a display of soup cans contains one can. Each of the other rows contains two more cans than the row above it. How many cans are in the 15th row of this display? **19.** ____________

20. For what integer values of n and x does $x^{\frac{1}{n}}$ have meaning? **20.** ____________

____

21. Simplify $\frac{45a^{-5}b^{7}}{24a^{-2}b^{12}}$. There should be only positive exponents in your answer. **21.** ____________

22. Solve $4^{5} \cdot 9^{-5} = k^{5}$. **22.** ____________

23. Malinda's plumber charged $115 for a two-hour service call and $201.80 for a four-hour service call. She knows that the plumber charges a fixed amount plus an additional fee for each hour of the call. Determine the fixed amount and the hourly fee. **23.** ____________

24. On the number line at the right, graph the solution set for $t \geq 2$ and $t < 5$. **24.**

25. The formula $r = .54V^{\frac{1}{3}}$ gives an excellent approximation of the radius r of the cylinder that has the least surface area for a given volume. About what is the least amount of material needed to make a can that has a volume of 100 cubic inches? **25.** ____________

26. Graph $y - 2 = 2(x + 1)^2$ on the coordinate axes at the right. **26.**

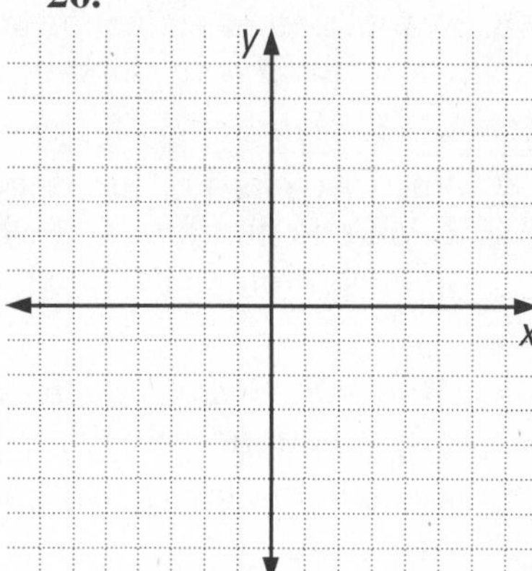

27. Tim puts $1000 in a savings account that pays 3.7% interest, compounded quarterly. Assuming that he makes no other deposits or withdrawals, how much money will he have in this account after four years? **27.** ____________

Check all your work carefully.

Name

QUIZ

Lessons 8-1 Through 8-3

In 1–4, let $f(x) = 4x - 7$, $g(x) = |x - 4|$, and $h(x) = 2x^2 + 4x + 1$.

1. Evaluate $f(g(4))$. **1.** ____________

2. Evaluate $g \circ f(4)$. **2.** ____________

3. Evaluate $f \circ h(-3)$. **3.** ____________

4. Find a formula for $f(f(x))$. **4.** ____________

5. a. Graph the inverse of the function with equation $y = x^3$ on the coordinate axes at the right. **5. a.**

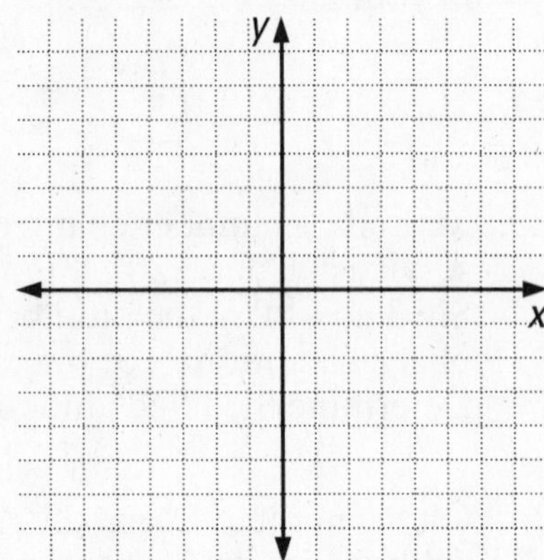

b. Give an equation for the inverse of this function. **b.** ____________

c. Is the inverse a function? Why or why not?

____

____

6. A function has equation $y = 5x - 3$. Give an equation for its inverse in slope-intercept form. **6.** ____________

7. Suppose g is a linear function whose domain is the set of all real numbers and whose range is $\{y: y = -2\}$. What are the domain and range of g^{-1}? **7.** ____________

____

8. *Multiple choice.* Which transformation maps the graph of a function f onto the graph of its inverse f^{-1}? **8.** ____________

(a) R_{90} (b) r_x (c) r_y (d) $r_{y=x}$

9. *True or false.* For any function f that has an inverse f^{-1}, $f \circ f^{-1}(x) = -x$ for all x in the range of f. **9.** ____________

Name

QUIZ

Lessons 8-4 Through 8-6

In 1–3, write as a whole number or simple fraction.

1. $\sqrt[5]{243}$ — 1. ____________

2. $\sqrt[3]{\sqrt{4096}}$ — 2. ____________

3. $\sqrt[4]{\frac{125}{3}} \times \sqrt[4]{\frac{5}{27}}$ — 3. ____________

4. Estimate $\sqrt[4]{29.015}$ to the nearest hundredth. — 4. ____________

In 5 and 6, simplify. Assume $m > 0$ and $n > 0$.

5. $\sqrt[5]{9n^{11}} \cdot \sqrt[5]{27 \cdot n^4}$ — 5. ____________

6. $\sqrt[4]{128m^7}$ — 6. ____________

7. Rationalize the denominator of $\frac{1}{\sqrt{2t}}$, where $t > 0$. — 7. ____________

8. *True or false.* $\sqrt[3]{a} \cdot \sqrt[5]{b} = \sqrt[15]{ab}$ — 8. ____________

9. Rationalize the denominator of $\frac{1}{\sqrt{5} - 2}$ and simplify. — 9. ____________

10. The five planets farthest from the sun are called the *outer planets.* Their equatorial diameters (in thousands of kilometers) are given below. What is the geometric mean of the diameters? — 10. ____________

Jupiter	142.80
Saturn	120.66
Uranus	51.80
Neptune	49.50
Pluto	2.29

Name

CHAPTER 8 TEST, Form A

In 1 and 2, let $f(x) = 4x + 3$ and $g(x) = x^2 - 1$.

1. Evaluate $g(f(7))$. **1.** __________

2. Find a formula for $f \circ g(x)$. **2.** __________

3. Suppose $p(x) = x - 1$ and $q(x) = x + 1$. Are p and q inverses of each other? Justify your answer.

____

____

4. Evaluate $\sqrt[5]{-32}$. **4.** __________

5. Evaluate $\sqrt[4]{625}$. **5.** __________

6. Suppose $x \geq 0$ and $\sqrt[4]{\sqrt{x^{13}}} = x^y$. Give the value of y. **6.** __________

7. Estimate $\sqrt[6]{764}$ to the nearest hundredth. **7.** __________

In 8 and 9, consider the function with equation $y = x^2$.

8. Give an equation for the inverse of this function. **8.** __________

9. Is the inverse a function? Why or why not?

____

____

10. Suppose $m > 0$. Rationalize the denominator of $\frac{6}{\sqrt{2m}}$ and simplify. **10.** __________

Name

11. a. The end of a glacier is moving at an average speed of 25 cm per week. Write an equation for $d(w)$, the number of centimeters the glacier travels in w weeks.

11. a. 

b. Find $d^{-1}(1500)$ and tell what it represents.

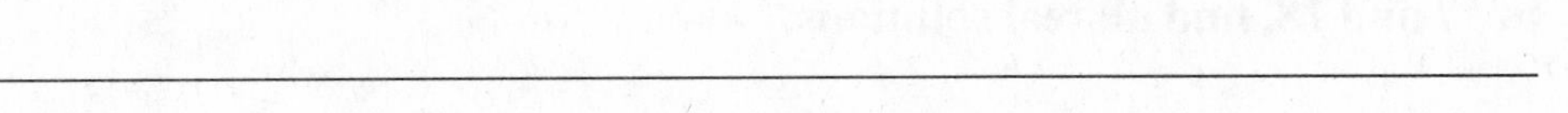

12. *Multiple choice.* Which of the following graphs pictures a function whose inverse is *not* a function?

12. 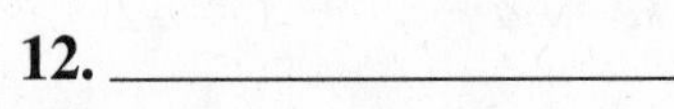

(a)

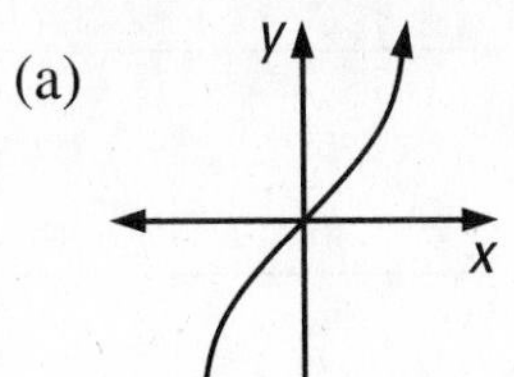

(b)

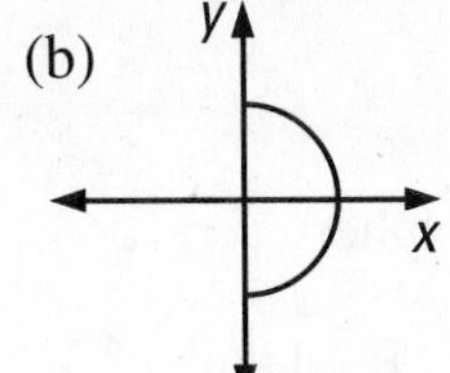

(c)

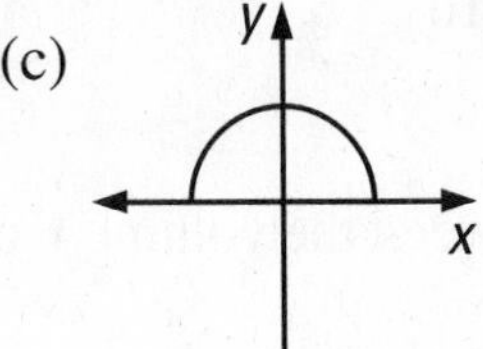

(d)

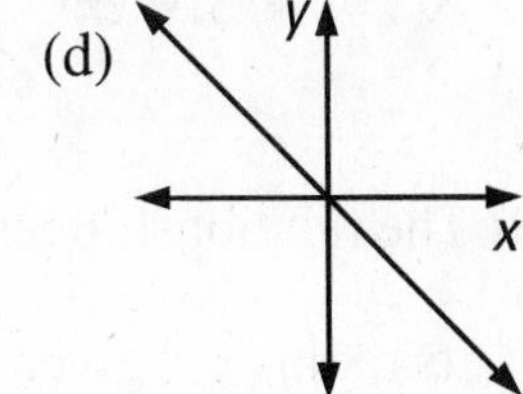

In 13–15, let $r(x) = \sqrt[6]{x}$.

13. Graph $r(x)$ and $r^{-1}(x)$ on the coordinate axes at the right.

13.

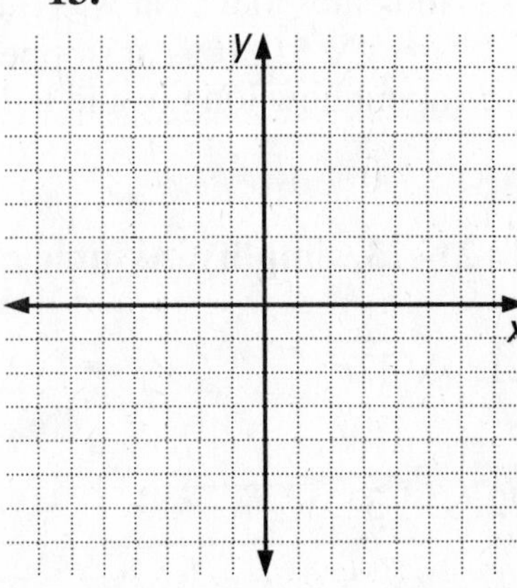

14. State the domain and the range of r.

14. ____________

____

15. State the domain and the range of r^{-1}.

15. ____________

____

Name

16. Give a counterexample to the statement. For all real numbers k, $\sqrt[4]{k^4} = k$.

In 17 and 18, find all real solutions.

17. $\sqrt[3]{a-1} + 1 = -2$ **17.** ________

18. $\sqrt[4]{2m} + 3\sqrt[4]{2m} = 16$ **18.** ________

19. The relationship between the volume V of a sphere and its radius r is given by the formula $r = \sqrt[3]{\frac{3V}{4\pi}}$. Find the radius of a sphere whose volume is 800 cm^3. **19.** ________

20. Recall that on some roads, a skid mark of length L feet indicates that a car was traveling at least s mph, where $s \approx 2\sqrt{5L}$. If a car stopped quickly from a speed of 55 mph, about how long would the skid marks be? **20.** ________

In 21–23, simplify. Assume $r > 0$, $s > 0$, and $t > 0$.

21. $\sqrt[4]{32r^8}$ **21.** ________

22. $\sqrt[3]{-343s^4}$ **22.** ________

23. $\sqrt[3]{\sqrt{4096t^7}}$ **23.** ________

24. *True or false.* If the graph of a function h passes the Horizontal-line Test, then the inverse of h is a function. **24.** ________

Check all your work carefully.

Name ________________________________

CHAPTER 8 TEST, Form B

In 1 and 2, let $r(x) = 7x^2 + 1$ and $t(x) = 3x - 6$.

1. Evaluate $t(r(3))$. **1.** ____________

2. Find a formula for $r \circ t(x)$. **2.** ____________

3. Suppose $f(x) = x + 3$ and $g(x) = 3 - x$. Are f and g inverses of each other? Justify your answer.

____

____

4. Evaluate $\sqrt[3]{-512}$. **4.** ____________

5. Evaluate $\sqrt[6]{729}$. **5.** ____________

6. Suppose $t \geq 0$ and $\sqrt{\sqrt[3]{t^{11}}} = t^x$. Give the value of x. **6.** ____________

7. Estimate $\sqrt[5]{965}$ to the nearest hundredth. **7.** ____________

In 8 and 9, consider the function with equation $y = x^5$.

8. Give an equation for the inverse of this function. **8.** ____________

9. Is the inverse a function? Why or why not?

____

____

10. Suppose $y > 0$. Rationalize the denominator of $\frac{2}{\sqrt{6y}}$ and simplify. **10.** ____________

Name

11. a. The current in the Mississippi River flows at an average speed of about two miles per hour. Write an equation for $d(h)$, the number of miles traveled by a stick caught in the current for h hours.

11. a. 

b. Find $d^{-1}(18)$ and tell what it represents.

12. *Multiple choice.* Which of the following graphs represents a function whose inverse is *not* a function?

12. 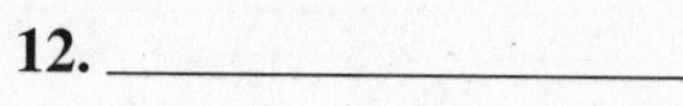

(a) 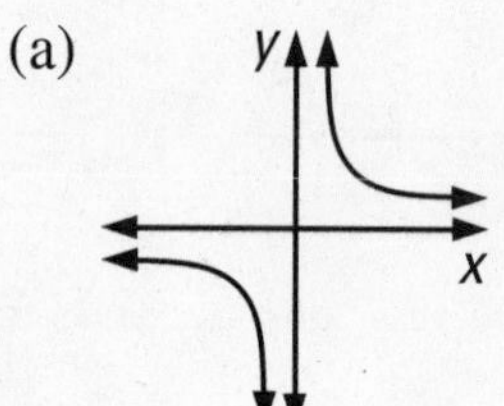

(b) 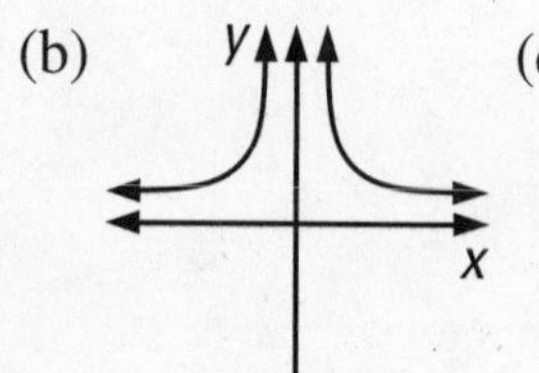

(c) 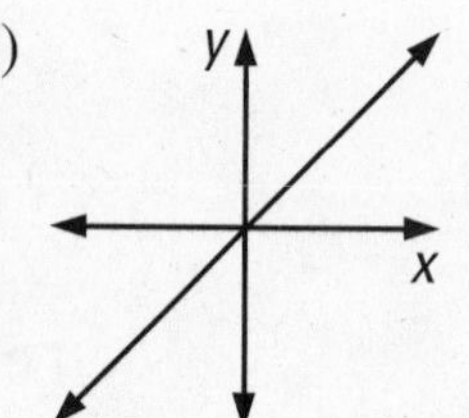

(d) 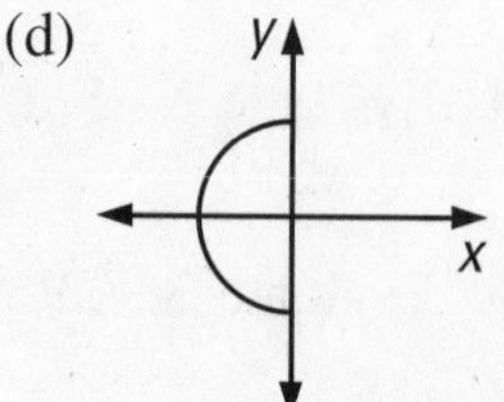

In 13–15, let $p(x) = \sqrt[5]{x}$.

13. Graph $p(x)$ and $p^{-1}(x)$ on the coordinate axes at the right.

13.

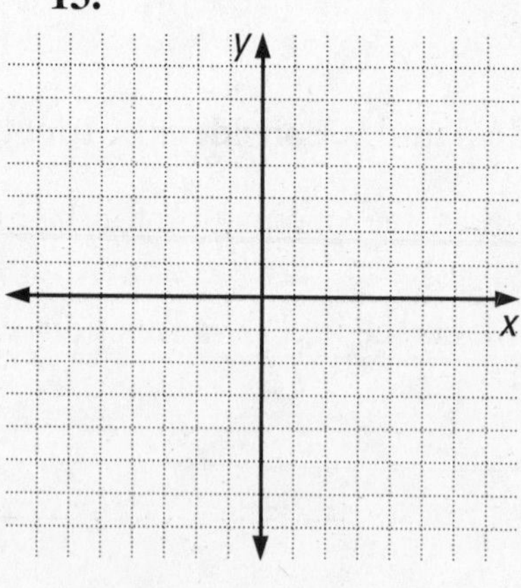

14. State the domain and the range of p.

14. ______________

____

15. State the domain and the range of p^{-1}.

15. ______________

____

Name

16. Give a counterexample to the statement. For all real numbers h, $\sqrt[8]{h^8} = h$.

____

____

In 17 and 18, find all real solutions.

17. $\sqrt[4]{b + 1} - 1 = -4$ **17.** ______________

18. $\sqrt[3]{4n} + 2\sqrt[3]{4n} = 12$ **18.** ______________

19. The relationship between the volume V of a hemisphere and its radius r is given by the formula $r = \sqrt[3]{\frac{3V}{2\pi}}$. Find the radius of a hemisphere whose volume is 325 cm^3. **19.** ______________

20. Recall that a skid mark of length L feet indicates that a car was traveling at least s mph, where $s \approx 2\sqrt{5L}$. If a car stopped quickly from a speed of 65 mph, about how long would the skid marks be? **20.** ______________

In 21–23, simplify. Assume $b > 0$, $c > 0$, and $d > 0$.

21. $\sqrt[5]{64b^{10}}$ **21.** ______________

22. $\sqrt[3]{-125c^4}$ **22.** ______________

23. $\sqrt{\sqrt{1296d^5}}$ **23.** ______________

24. *True or false.* Suppose a function T has an inverse T^{-1}. Then the transformation R_{90} maps the graph of T onto the graph of T^{-1}. **24.** ______________

Check all your work carefully.

Name

CHAPTER 8 TEST, Form C

1. Let $f(x) = 3x - 2$. Find a function g such that $g(f(4)) = 5$. Then use your function g to find $f(g(4))$.

2. When $x \geq 0$, $f(x) = x^2$ and $g(x) = \sqrt{x}$ are inverse functions. So Peter reasons that, when $x \geq 0$, $h(x) = (5x)^2$ and $k(x) = \sqrt{5x}$ also are inverse functions. Do you agree or disagree? Justify your answer.

3. How is solving $\sqrt[3]{m + 1} + 8 = 6$ similar to solving $\sqrt[4]{m + 1} + 8 = 6$? How is it different? Solve each equation.

4. Demonstrate the fact that $\frac{1}{2 - \sqrt{3}}$ is equal to $2 + \sqrt{3}$ by rationalizing the denominator. Then explain how you can use a calculator to verify the result.

5. Rewrite the expression below, replacing each box with an integer greater than 1 to make a true statement.

$$\sqrt[3]{\blacksquare a^{\blacksquare} b^{\blacksquare}} \cdot \sqrt[3]{\blacksquare a^{\blacksquare} b^{\blacksquare}} = 4ab^2 \sqrt[3]{a^2}$$

Is your statement true for all real numbers a and b, or must you restrict the values of a and b? Explain your answer.

6. On the coordinate axes below, graph a function other than $f(x) = x$ that is its own inverse. Justify your answer.

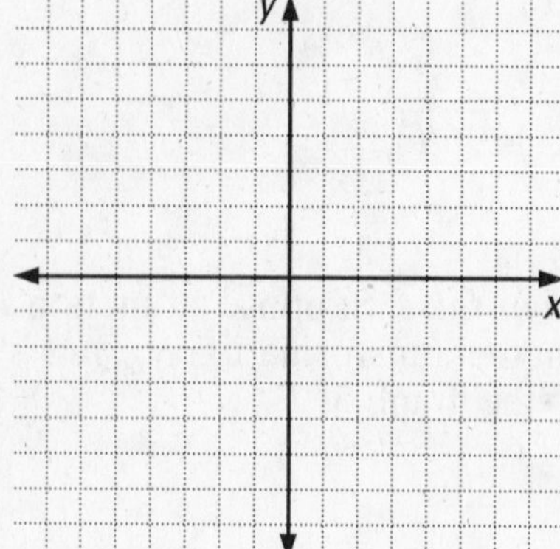

Name

CHAPTER 8 TEST, Form D

Suppose you work for a state Parks Department. You have been asked to plan an observation tower for Silver Lake State Park. The hope is that a visitor will be able to see all of the park from the tower. You also are to consider whether it is possible for the tower to serve as a location from which a park ranger can monitor the adjacent Greenwood State Forest.

a. In a reference book, you learn that the function $d(h) = \sqrt{7920h}$ gives an approximation of the maximum distance in miles that you can see from a height of h miles. Use this formula to approximate the maximum distance you could see if you were in an airplane at a height of two miles.

b. There are 5280 feet in one mile, so you can use the function $c(h) = \frac{h}{5280}$ to change a height h in feet to a height $c(h)$ in miles. Using the function d that was defined in Part **a**, write a formula for $d(c(h))$. Use your new formula to find the distance you can see from a height of 100 feet.

c. Write a formula for the inverse of your function from Part **b**. Use your new formula to find the height at which you must be in order to see a distance of 5 miles.

d. The map below shows Silver Lake State Park. One proposal is to place a twenty-foot-tall observation tower just inside the main entrance. Could a visitor see all of the park from this tower? Justify your answer.

e. Using the map and the guidelines below, make two plans for the tower.

- In one plan, identify a height and a location for the tower so that an observer at the top can see all of Silver Lake State Park.
- In the second plan, identify a height and a location for the tower so that an observer at the top can see all of Silver Lake State Park *and* all of Greenwood State Forest.

In each plan, try to minimize construction costs by making the tower as short as possible You may assume that all of the park and the forest are of the same altitude. Present your plans in a report that includes a detailed account of the calculations you used to arrive at your conclusions.

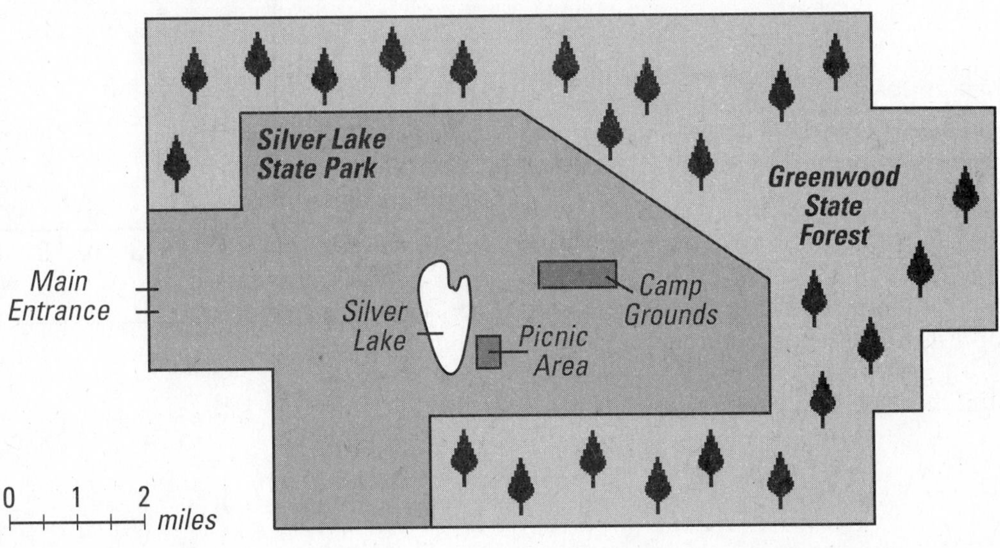

Name ____________________

CHAPTER 8 TEST, Cumulative Form

1. For what values of x is $\sqrt[4]{x^4} = x$? **1.** ________

2. Consider the sequence defined by $g_n = -3 \cdot (-2)^{n-1}$, for integers $n \geq 1$.

   a. Write the first six terms of the sequence. **2. a.** ________

   b. Find a recursive formula for the sequence. **b.** ________

3. Suppose you deposit \$100 in an account that pays 5% interest compounded annually. You make no additional deposits or withdrawals. Will the amount of money in the account double within ten years? Justify your answer.

   ____

   ____

4. The figures below show the first five of what might be called "house numbers."

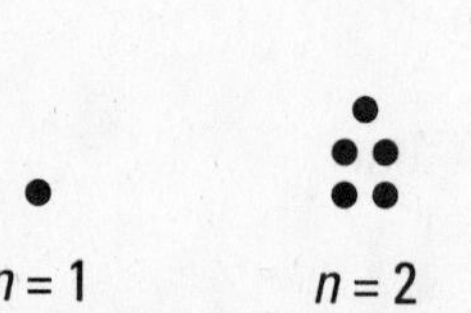
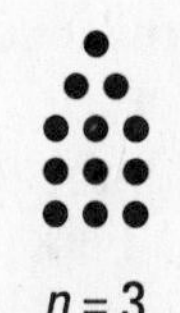
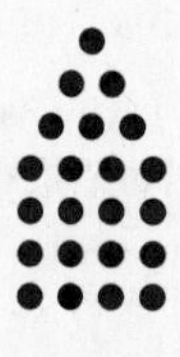
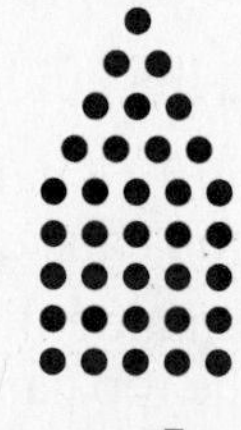

$n = 1$, $h = 1$ | $n = 2$, $h = 5$ | $n = 3$, $h = 12$ | $n = 4$, $h = 22$ | $n = 5$, $h = 35$

   a. Graph the ordered pairs (n, h) on the grid at the right. **4. a.**

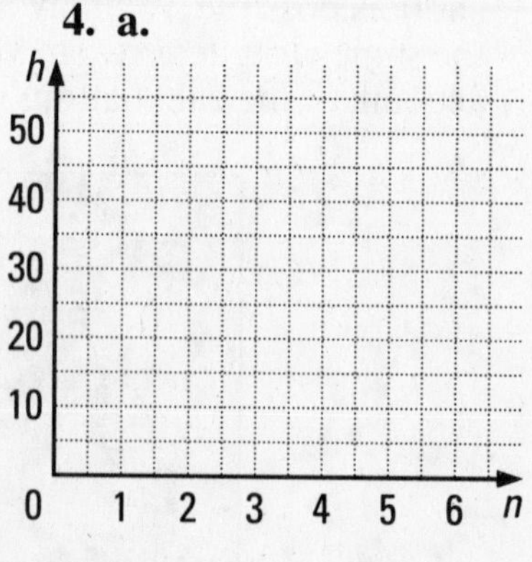

   b. Fit a quadratic model to these data to find a formula for $h(n)$, the nth house number. **b.** ________

   c. Find the 50th house number. **c.** ________

Name

5. You can use the formula $d = 3.57\sqrt{h}$ to approximate the maximum distance d you can see (in kilometers) from the top of a building of height h (in meters). From the top of the north tower of the World Trade Center in New York City, the maximum distance you can see is about 72.9 km. What is the height of this tower, to the nearest meter?

5. 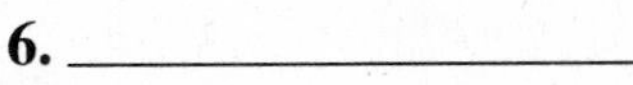

6. *Multiple choice.* Which of the following graphs pictures a function whose inverse also is a function?

6. ____________

(a) 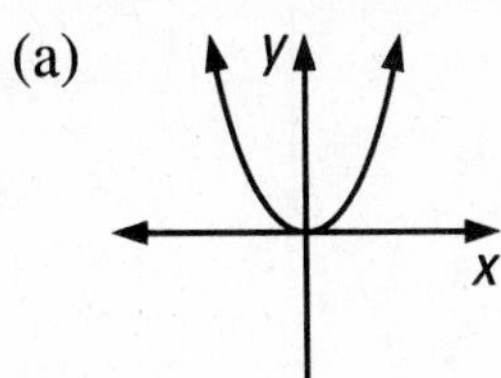

(b) 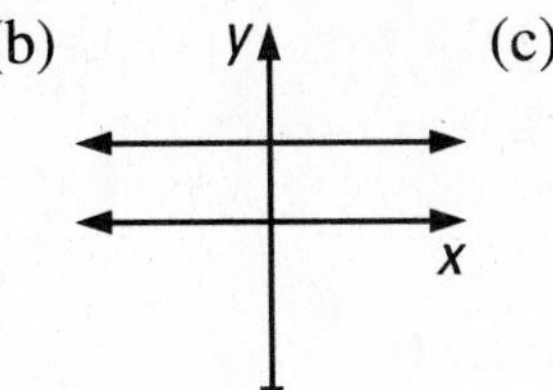

(c) 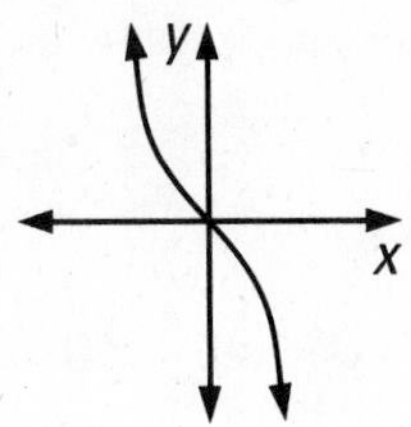

(d) 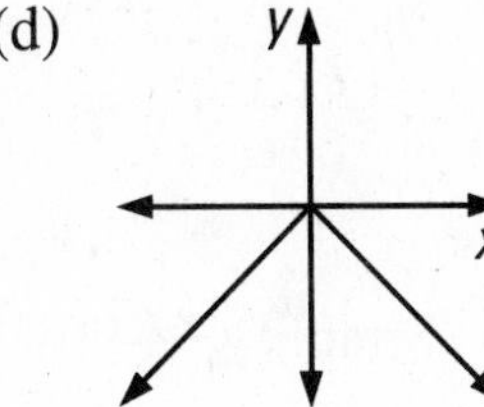

7. Let $f(x) = x^3 + 1$ and $g(x) = 4x^2 + 3$.

a. Evaluate $f(g(1))$. **7. a.** ____________

b. Evaluate $g(f(1))$. **b.** ____________

8. *Multiple choice.* For $n > 0$, $\left(\frac{1}{n}\right)^{-\frac{5}{9}} =$ __?__. **8.** ____________

(a) $-n^{\frac{9}{5}}$ (b) $-n^{\frac{5}{9}}$ (c) $\left(\sqrt[9]{n}\right)^5$ (d) $\left(\sqrt[5]{n}\right)^9$

In 9 and 10, find all real solutions.

9. $m^{-\frac{4}{5}} = 16$ **9.** ____________

10. $50\sqrt[3]{d - 4} = 250$ **10.** ____________

11. Explain how you can use a graph to show that the equation $x^4 = -16$ has no real solutions.

____

____

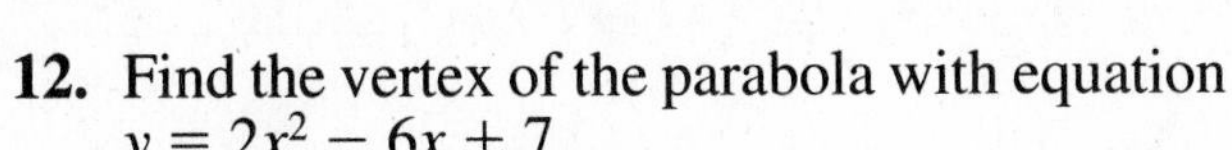

12. Find the vertex of the parabola with equation $y = 2x^2 - 6x + 7$.

12. 

Name

13. Graph $3x - 6y \leq 15$ on the coordinate axes at the right. 13.

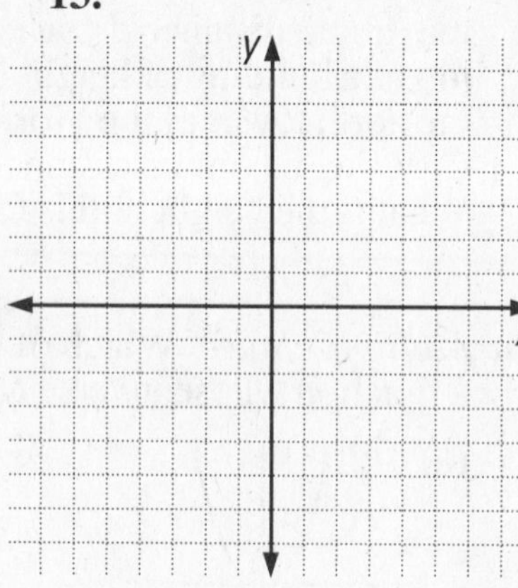

14. Simplify $\sqrt[5]{-96x^{11}y^{20}}$. Assume $x > 0$ and $y > 0$. 14. ____________

15. The slope of a line is -8. What is the slope of its image under R_{90}? 15. ____________

16. The Pan-tastic Company makes frying pans. It costs \$1500 to make 300 pans, and it costs \$2550 to make 600 pans. Assuming a linear relationship between the cost and the number made, what is the cost of making *p* pans? 16. ____________

In 17–19, write as an integer or a simple fraction.

17. $\sqrt[5]{-7776}$ 17. ____________

18. $\sqrt[6]{\frac{64}{729}}$ 18. ____________

19. 7^{-3} 19. ____________

20. In the graph of $y = \frac{k}{x}$ shown at the right, what are the possible values of *k*? 20. ____________

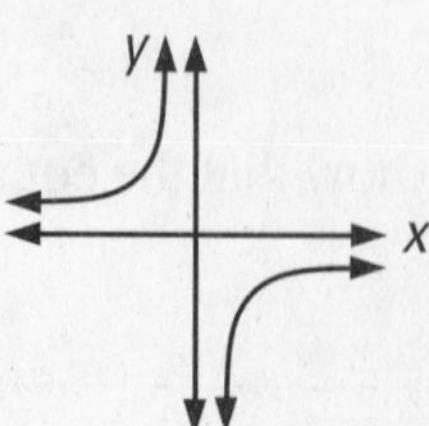

21. *True or false.* $-5 = \sqrt[4]{(-25)^2}$ 21. ____________

Check all your work carefully.

Name

QUIZ

Lessons 9-1 Through 9-3

1. *True or false.* The number e is rational. 1. ____________

2. Suppose \$350 is invested at an annual interest rate of 4% compounded continuously. What is the amount in the account after $3\frac{1}{2}$ years? 2. ____________

3. *Multiple choice.* Which could be the graph of $y = ab^x$, where $a > 0$ and $b > 1$? 3. ____________

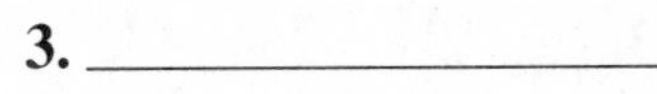

(a)

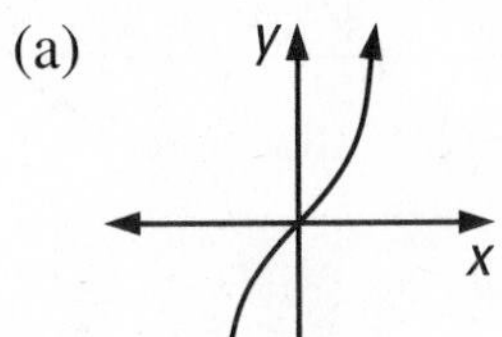

(b)

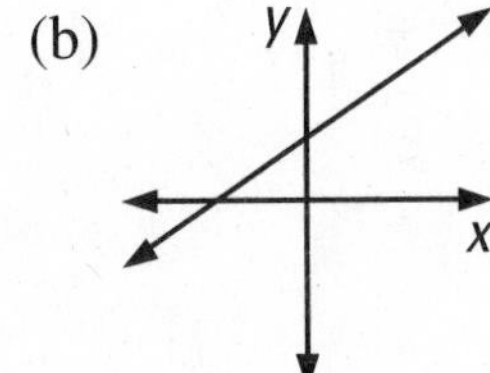

(c)

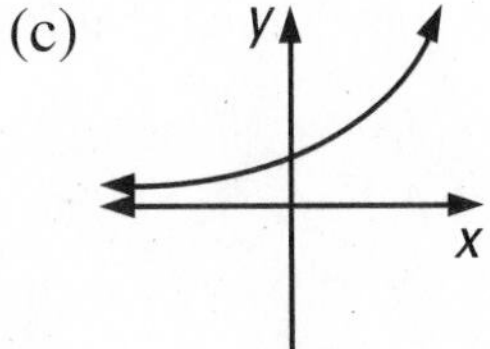

(d)

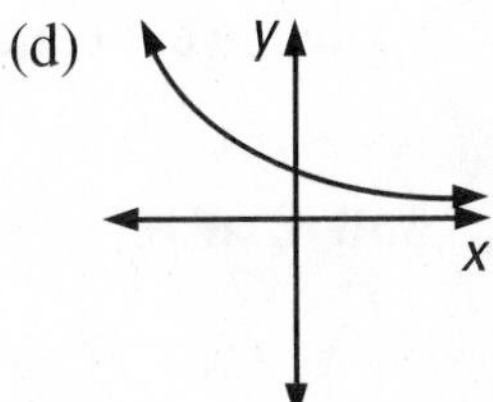

4. a. Graph $f(x) = 5 \cdot \left(\frac{1}{2}\right)^x$ on the coordinate axes at the right. 4. a.

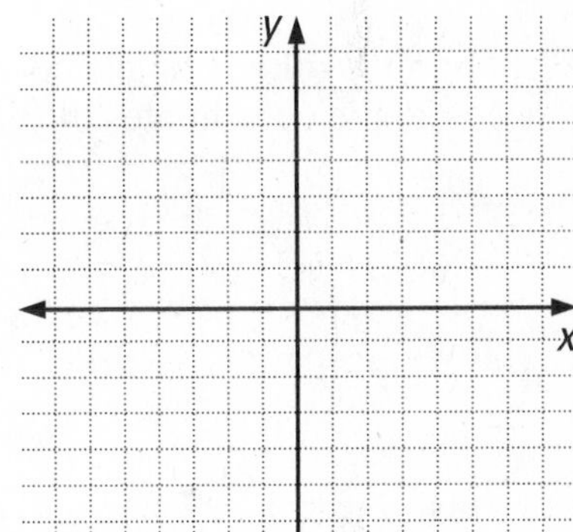

b. What is the growth factor of the function f? b. ____________

c. Is f an exponential growth function or an exponential decay function? c. ____________

5. A farmer projected the value of this year's harvest to be \$120,000. However, severe flooding has delayed getting the harvest to market. For each day of delay, it is estimated that the total value V of the harvest decreases 10%. Then an equation that models this situation is $V = 120{,}000(.9)^t$, where t is the number of days of delay. Find the estimated value of the harvest after a one-week delay. 5. ____________

6. In 1990, the population of Albuquerque, New Mexico, was 384,619. During the early 1990s, the population of Albuquerque was growing at a rate of about 1.8% annually. Suppose this growth rate continues. What would be the population of Albuquerque in the year 2010? 6. ____________

Name

QUIZ

Lessons 9-4 Through 9-7

In 1–3, write each number as a decimal.

1. $\log(.01)$ **1.** ____________

2. $\log_2 32$ **2.** ____________

3. $\log 10^{\frac{7}{4}}$ **3.** ____________

4. Write the equivalent logarithmic form for $25^{-\frac{3}{2}} = \frac{1}{125}$. **4.** ____________

In 5 and 6, solve.

5. $\log x = 5$ **5.** ____________

6. $\log_x 6 = \frac{1}{3}$ **6.** ____________

7. Graph $y = \log x$ on the coordinate axes at the right. Label the coordinates of three points on the graph. **7.**

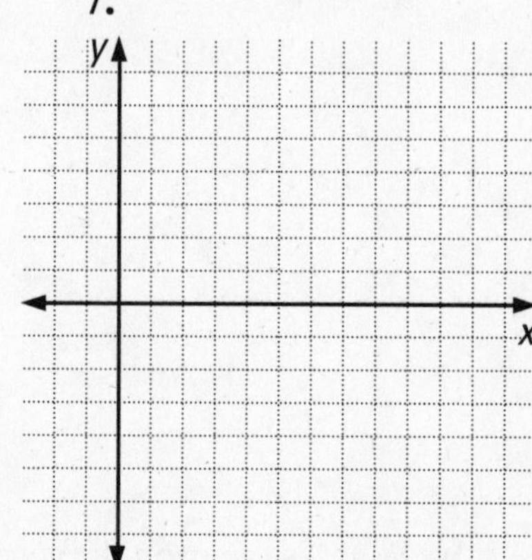

8. *True or false.* On a logarithmic scale, the units are spaced so that the difference between successive units is the same. **8.** ____________

9. How many times more acidic is a solution with pH = 1.6 than a solution with pH = 3.6? **9.** ____________

10. The table below gives the population of New Jersey from 1985 to 1993.

Year After 1985 t	0	1	2	3	4	5	6	7	8
Population (millions) P	7.566	7.622	7.671	7.712	7.726	7.730	7.773	7.820	7.879

a. Find an exponential equation of the form $P = ab^t$ to fit these data. **10. a.** ____________

b. Use your model to predict the population of New Jersey in 1996 to the nearest thousand. **b.** ____________

Name ______________________________

CHAPTER 9 TEST, Form A

1. *Multiple choice.* Which equation defines an exponential-growth function? **1.** __________

(a) $y = x^{\pi}$ (b) $y = \pi^{-x}$ (c) $y = \left(\frac{1}{\pi}\right)^{-x}$ (d) $y = \pi x$

In 2 and 3, rewrite as the logarithm of a single number.

2. $5 \ln 4$ **2.** __________

3. $\log 36 + \log 5$ **3.** __________

In 4 and 5, evaluate each expression exactly without using a calculator.

4. $\log_7 \sqrt{7}$ **4.** __________

5. $\log_3 81$ **5.** __________

In 6–10, consider the function with equation $y = \log_2 x$.

6. Graph the function on the coordinate axes at the right. **6.**

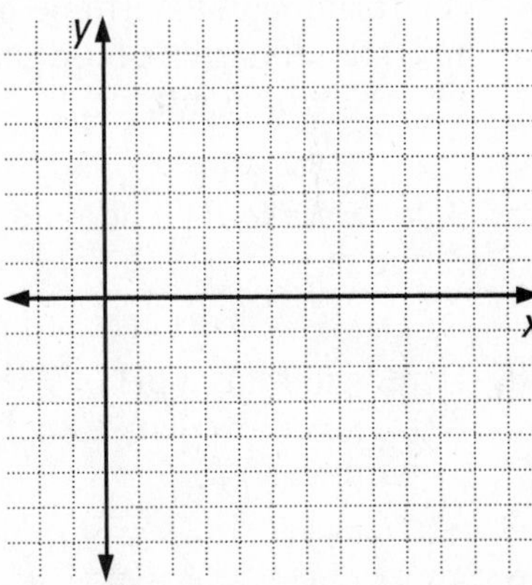

7. Identify the domain of the function. **7.** __________

8. Write an equation for the inverse of the function. **8.** __________

9. Is the inverse a function? Justify your answer.

____

____

10. Identify the domain of the inverse. **10.** __________

Name

11. Suppose the thickness of a lampshade reduces the intensity I of the light that passes through it by 5% for each 2 mm of thickness. An equation that models this situation is $I = (.95)^{\frac{d}{2}}$, where I is the fraction of light that passes through and d is the thickness of the lampshade in millimeters. At what thickness would only 80% of the light pass through the lampshade?

11. ________________

In 12–15, solve. If necessary, round to the nearest hundredth.

12. $2 \cdot 3^s = \frac{2}{9}$

12. ________________

13. $\log_2 t^3 - 1 = -3$

13. ________________

14. $\ln p = 9.3$

14. ________________

15. $8^{q+5} = 123$

15. ________________

16. Project managers in the U.S. space program have determined that an individual's reaction time R can be calculated by the formula $R = 0.17 + 0.44 \log N$, where N is the number of choices presented to the individual. Use the formula to determine how many choices would result in a reaction time of .42 second. Round your answer to the nearest whole number.

16. ________________

17. *True or false.* The domain of $y = \log x$ is equal to the range of $y = 10^x$.

17. ________________

18. Pure water has a pH of 7.0. Many soft drinks have a pH of 3.0. These soft drinks are how many times as acidic as pure water?

18. ________________

19. a. At the right are the graphs of $y = 2.5^x$ and $y = 3^x$. Which equation corresponds to the graph of f?

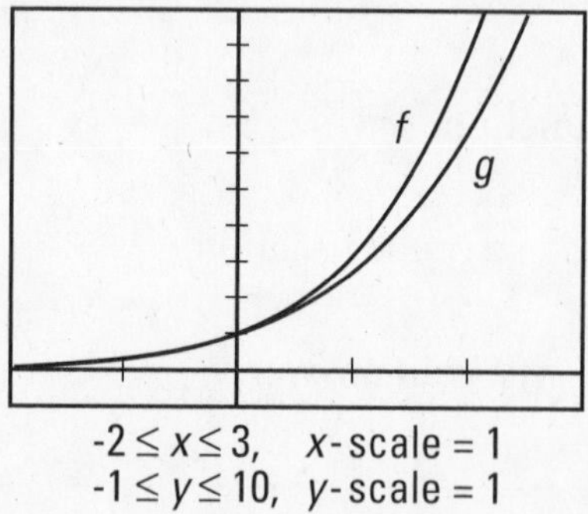

$-2 \leq x \leq 3$, x-scale = 1
$-1 \leq y \leq 10$, y-scale = 1

19. a. ________________

b. Describe how the graph of $y = e^x$ is related to the graphs of f and g.

____

____

Name

▶ CHAPTER 9 TEST, Form A *page 3*

20. The table below gives the population of California in ten-year intervals from 1900 to 1990.

Year After 1900 t	0	10	20	30	40	50	60	70	80	90
Population (millions) P	1.5	2.4	3.4	5.7	6.9	10.6	15.7	20.0	23.7	29.8

a. Make a scatterplot of the data on the coordinate axes at the right.

20. a.

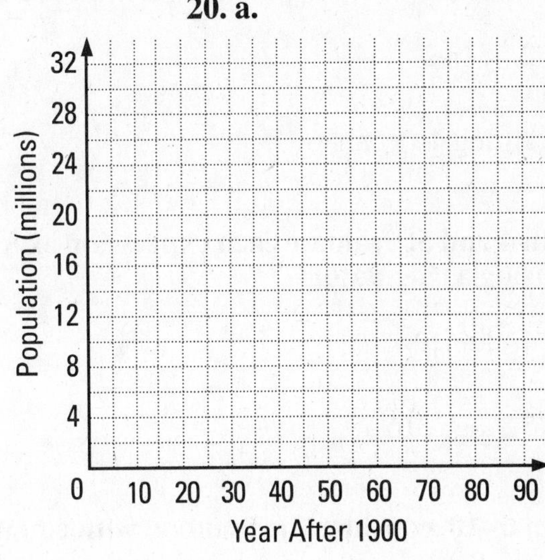

b. Fit an exponential model to these data. **b.** ____________

c. Use your model to predict the population of California in the year 2000. **c.** ____________

21. *True or false.* $\ln\left(\frac{x^3}{y^4}\right) = \frac{3 \ln x}{4 \ln y}$ **21.** ____________

In 22 and 23, refer to the following situation. Suppose $4000 is invested at an annual interest rate of 6.1% compounded continuously. Assume that there are no other deposits or withdrawals in this account.

22. What is the amount in the account after three years? **22.** ____________

23. How long would it take for the amount in the account to quadruple? **23.** ____________

Check all your work carefully.

Name

CHAPTER 9 TEST, Form B

1. *Multiple choice.* Which equation defines an exponential-decay function? 1. ________

(a) $y = x^{\pi}$ (b) $y = \pi^{-x}$ (c) $y = \left(\frac{1}{\pi}\right)^{-x}$ (d) $y = \pi x$

In 2 and 3, rewrite as the logarithm of a single number.

2. $8 \ln 2$ 2. ________

3. $\log 42 - \log 6$ 3. ________

In 4 and 5, evaluate each expression exactly without using a calculator.

4. $\log_{12} \sqrt[5]{12}$ 4. ________

5. $\log_6 216$ 5. ________

In 6–10, consider the function with equation $y = \log_3 x$.

6. Graph the function on the coordinate axes at the right. 6.

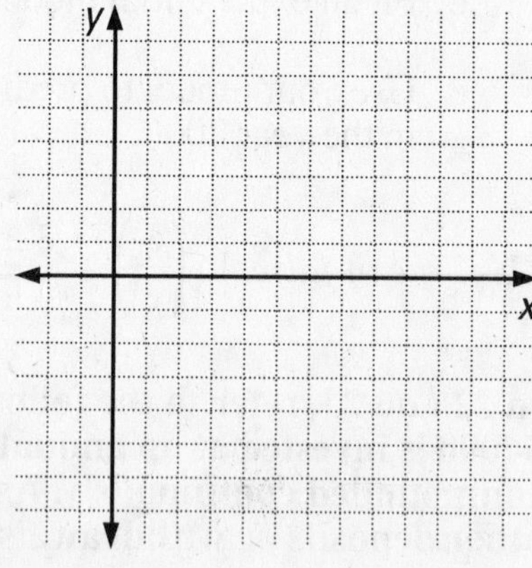

7. Identify the domain of the function. 7. ________

8. Write an equation for the inverse of the function. 8. ________

9. Is the inverse a function? Justify your answer.

____

____

10. Identify the domain of the inverse. 10. ________

Name

11. Suppose a lake is clouded with sediment so that the intensity I of the light that passes through the water is reduced by 10% for each 15 cm of depth. An equation that models this situation is $I = (.9)^{\frac{d}{15}}$, where I is the fraction of light that can pass through and d is the depth in centimeters. At what depth would only 3% of the light pass through the water? **11.** ________

In 12–15, solve. If necessary, round to the nearest hundredth.

12. $3 \cdot 5^t = \frac{3}{25}$ **12.** ________

13. $\log_4 s^3 = 8$ **13.** ________

14. $\ln x = -1.1$ **14.** ________

15. $7^{r-3} = 200$ **15.** ________

16. Project managers in the U.S. space program have determined that an individual's reaction time R can be calculated by the formula $R = 0.17 + 0.44 \log N$, where N is the number of choices presented to the individual. Use the formula to determine how many choices would result in a reaction time of .56 second. Round your answer to the nearest whole number. **16.** ________

17. *True or false.* The domain of $y = \ln x$ is equal to the range of $y = e^x$. **17.** ________

18. Pure water has a pH of 7.0. Some acid rain has a pH of 4.5. Acid rain is how many times as acidic as pure water? **18.** ________

19. a. At the right are the graphs of $y = 3^x$ and $y = 4^x$. Which equation corresponds to the graph of f? **19. a.** ________

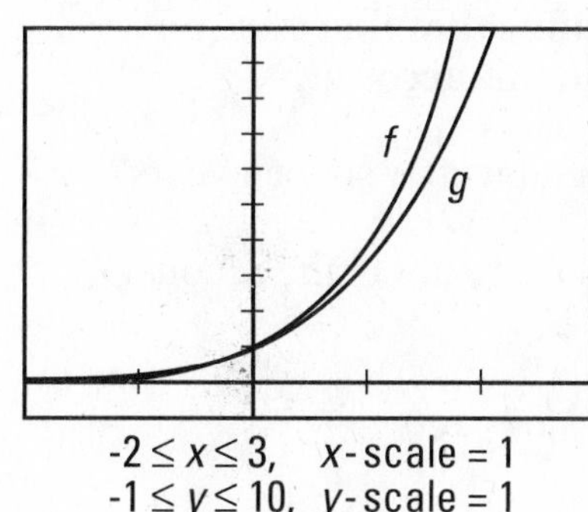

$-2 \le x \le 3$, x-scale = 1
$-1 \le y \le 10$, y-scale = 1

b. Describe how the graph of $y = e^x$ is related to the graphs of f and g.

____

____

Name

20. A population of bacteria was counted every hour for a period of eight hours with the following results.

Time (hours) h	1	2	3	4	5	6	7	8
Population (ten-thousands) P	1.9	3.6	6.9	13	25	47	85	140

a. Make a scatterplot of the data on the coordinate axes at the right.

20. a.

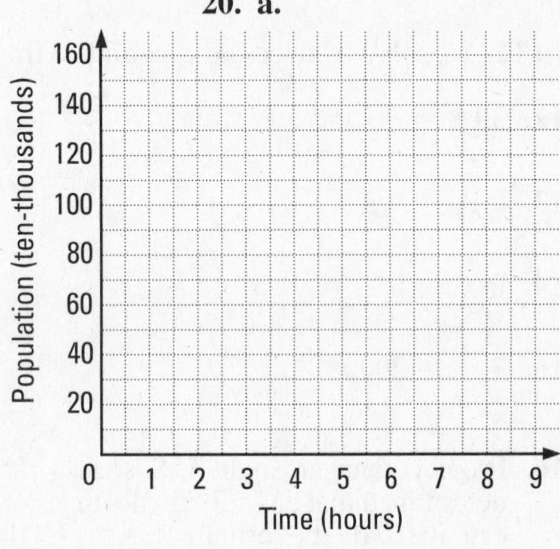

b. Fit an exponential model to these data. **b.** ____________

c. Use your model to predict the bacteria population after nine hours. **c.** ____________

21. *True or false.* $\ln(3x \cdot y^3) = (\ln 3) \cdot (\ln x) \cdot (3 \ln y)$ **21.** ____________

In 22 and 23, refer to the following situation. Suppose $3000 is invested at an annual interest rate of 4.8% compounded continuously. Assume that there are no other deposits or withdrawals in this account.

22. What is the amount in the account after sixteen years? **22.** ____________

23. How long would it take for the amount in the account to triple? **23.** ____________

Check all your work carefully.

Name

CHAPTER 9 TEST, Form C

1. How are the following three equations alike? How are they different? What is the solution of each?

   $\log x = 3$ $\log_4 x = 3$ $\ln x = 3$

2. Name two properties of logarithms that you studied in this chapter. State each property in your own words. Then give an example to illustrate each property that you chose.

3. $\log_2 2^x = \log_2 10$ $\log 2^x = \log 10$ $\ln 2^x = \ln 10$

   Which of the equations above could you use to solve $2^x = 10$? Explain your reasoning. Then show how to find the solution.

4. Do you agree or disagree with this statement?

   If successive units on a scale are unequally spaced, then the scale is logarithmic.

   Justify your answer. Give an example of a logarithmic scale and describe how it illustrates your answer.

5. The size N of a certain population over t years is described by this formula.

   $$N = 10{,}000e^{-.045t}$$

   State as many facts as you can about the growth of this population. Then make a prediction about the future size of this population.

6. Suppose your friend was ill and missed some math classes. You offer to prepare a study sheet about exponential and logarithmic functions. Write a brief paragraph that could accompany this figure on your study sheet.

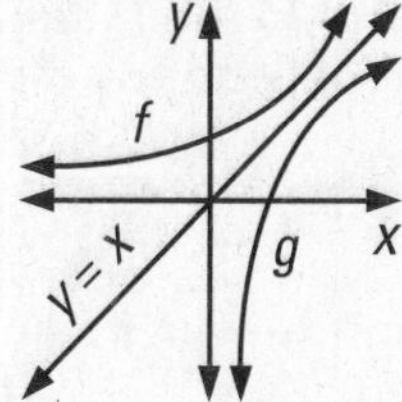

Name

CHAPTER 9 TEST, Form D

The table at the right gives data about the population of the United States by region from 1790 to 1990.

Population of the United States (millions)					
Year	Northeast	Midwest	South	West	Total
1790	2.0		2.0		3.9
1800	2.6	0.1	2.6		5.3
1810	3.5	0.3	3.5		7.2
1820	4.4	0.9	4.4		9.6
1830	5.5	1.6	5.7		12.9
1840	6.8	3.4	7.0		17.1
1850	8.6	5.4	9.0	0.2	23.2
1860	10.6	9.1	11.1	0.6	31.4
1870	12.3	13.0	12.3	1.0	39.8
1880	14.5	17.4	16.5	1.8	50.2
1890	17.4	22.4	20.0	3.1	62.9
1900	21.0	26.3	24.5	4.3	76.0
1910	25.9	29.9	29.4	7.1	92.0
1920	29.7	34.0	33.1	9.2	105.7
1930	34.4	38.6	37.9	12.3	122.8
1940	36.0	40.1	41.1	14.4	131.7
1950	39.5	44.5	47.2	20.2	150.7
1960	44.7	51.6	55.0	28.1	178.5
1970	49.0	56.6	62.8	34.8	203.3
1980	49.1	58.9	75.4	43.2	226.5
1990	50.8	60.0	85.4	52.8	248.7

a. A student who was studying the growth of the population in the northeast made these calculations.

population in 1790: 2.0 million

population in 1800: 2.6 million

decade growth factor: 1.3

annual growth factor for the decade: 1.027

Verify that these calculations are correct.

b. Given the results in Part **a**, the student conjectured that the following equation models the population y (in millions) of the northeast in year x.

$$y = 2.0(1.027)^{x-1790}$$

Use this model to calculate the population of the northeast in 1820 and in 1990. Show your work.

c. Use the model given in Part **b** to tell in what year the population of the northeast would reach 50 million.

d. A second student used a spreadsheet program and the population data for the northeast to create the scatterplot shown at the right. Thinking that the data from 1850 to 1990 might be more linear than exponential, this student entered the data for these years and used the linear regression feature to refine the population model as follows.

$$\begin{cases} y = 2.0(1.027)^{x-1790}, \text{ for } 1790 \le x < 1850 \\ y = .334(x - 1850) + 6.179, \text{ for } x \ge 1850 \end{cases}$$

Use this model to calculate the population of the northeast in 1820 and in 1990. Then determine in what year this model projects that the population of the northeast would reach 50 million.

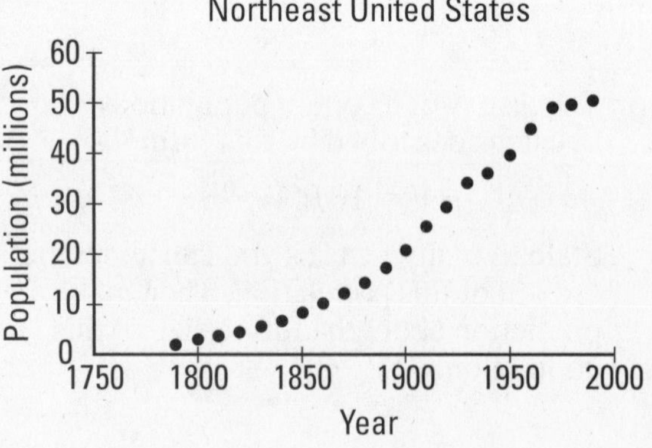

e. Evaluate the models in Parts **b** and **d**. Which do you think is a better model? Do you think that either is a *good* model? Explain your reasoning.

f. Prepare a report in which you analyze the population growth of the midwest, south, or west. Your report should include an algebraic model for the population growth of the region and a prediction for the population of the region in the year 2010. Give a detailed description of how you arrived at your model, and explain why you think your model is appropriate.

Name ____________________

CHAPTER 9 TEST, Cumulative Form

In 1–3, give the exact value of each expression.

1. $\log_2 8$ **1.** ____________

2. $\ln e^{\frac{3}{2}}$ **2.** ____________

3. $\sqrt[5]{-\frac{32}{243}}$ **3.** ____________

4. Consider the sequence defined as follows.

$$\begin{cases} t_1 = 8 \\ t_n = 3t_{n-1}, \text{ for integers } n \geq 2 \end{cases}$$

a. Write the first four terms of the sequence. **4. a.** ____________

b. Find an explicit formula for the sequence. **b.** ____________

c. Is the sequence geometric? Justify your answer.

____

____

5. *True or false.* **5.** ____________

$$\sqrt{a} \cdot \sqrt{b} = a^{\frac{1}{2}} \cdot b^{\frac{1}{2}} = (a \cdot b)^{\frac{1}{2}+\frac{1}{2}} = ab^1 = ab$$

In 6 and 7, solve. If necessary, round to the nearest hundredth.

6. $2 \log_5 x = 4.2$ **6.** ____________

7. $10.8^w = 9.3$ **7.** ____________

8. Consider the function with equation $y = 9x + 2$.

a. Give an equation for the inverse of this function. **8. a.** ____________

b. Is the inverse a function? Why or why not?

Name

9. Evaluate $256^{\frac{3}{4}}$ **9.** ____________

10. Solve $3w^2 - 5w + 4 = 0$. **10.** ____________

11. In 1991, the population of Shanghai, China, was about 6.9 million. It is estimated that the population is growing at a rate of about .9% annually. If this growth rate continues, what would be the population of Shanghai in the year 2000? **11.** ____________

12. The relative intensity of one sound is 25 dB higher than that of a second sound. The first sound is how many times as loud as the second? **12.** ____________

13. Simplify $\sqrt[4]{48c^8d^{17}}$. Assume $c > 0$ and $d > 0$. **13.** ____________

14. On the coordinate axes at the right, graph the feasible set of the system $\begin{cases} y \geq 3x - 5 \\ y \leq -2x \end{cases}$ **14.**

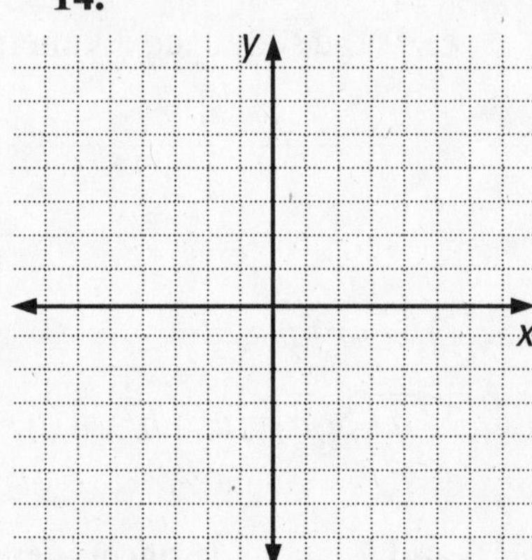

15. Let $f(x) = 2x^3 + 1$ and $g(x) = 4x^2 - 3$.

a. Evaluate $f(g(1))$. **15. a.** ____________

b. Evaluate $g \circ f(1)$. **b.** ____________

16. Rewrite $3 \log 5 + \log 7$ as the logarithm of a single number. **16.** ____________

17. *Multiple choice.* Which of the following graphs represents a function whose inverse also is a function? **17.** ____________

(a)
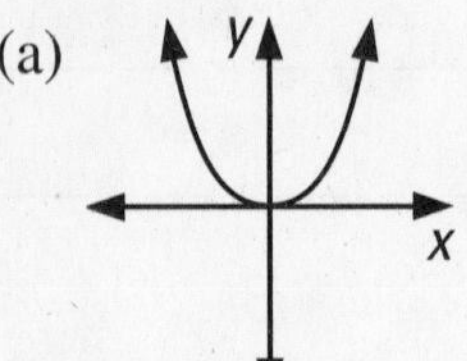

(b)
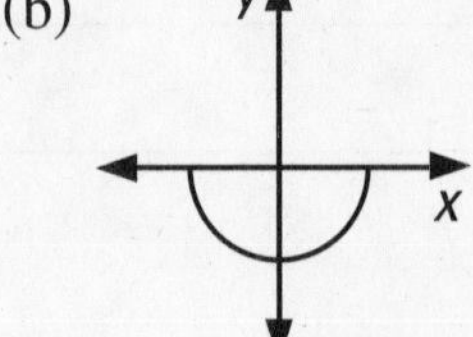

(c)
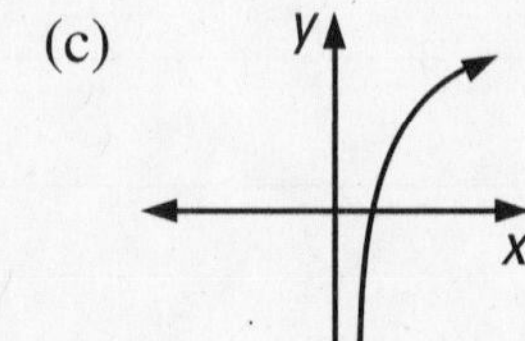

(d)
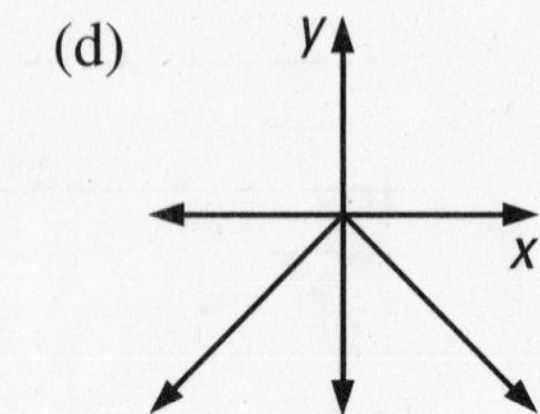

Name

18. The matrix below lists active volcanoes in South America along with the country in which the volcano is located, the year of latest activity, and the height of the volcano.

	Country	Year of Latest Activity	Height (in feet)
Guallatiri	Chile	1987	19,882
Lascar	Chile	1991	19,652
Cotopaxi	Ecuador	1975	19,347
Tupungatito	Chile	1986	18,504
Ruiz	Colombia	1992	17,716
Sangay	Ecuador	1988	17,159
Guagua Pichincha	Ecuador	1988	15,696
Purace	Colombia	1977	15,601
Galeras	Colombia	1993	13,996
Llaima	Chile	1990	10,239
Villarrica	Chile	1992	9,318
Hudson	Chile	1991	8,580
Alcedo	Galapagos Is. (Ecuador)	1970	3,599

a. What are the dimensions of this matrix? **18. a.** ____________

b. Which volcano was last active in 1970? **b.** ____________

c. What does the entry in row 2, column 3 represent? **c.** ____________

19. a. At the right are the graphs of $y = 2^x$ and $y = 4^x$. Which equation corresponds to the graph of f? **19. a.** ____________

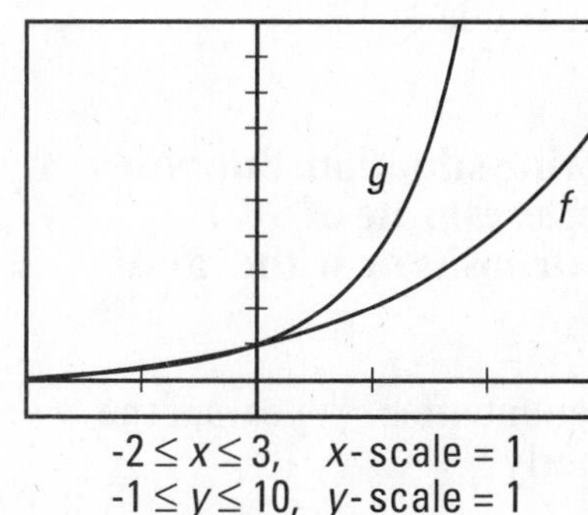

$-2 \le x \le 3$, x-scale = 1
$-1 \le y \le 10$, y-scale = 1

b. Describe how the graph of $y = e^x$ is related to the graphs of f and g.

____

____

Name

20. A ball is thrown upward from a height of 5 feet with an initial velocity of 40 feet per second.

a. What is the height of the ball after two seconds? **20. a.** ______________

b. When does the ball hit the ground? **b.** ______________

21. *Multiple choice.* Which could be the graph of $y = \log_8 x$? **21.**

(a)

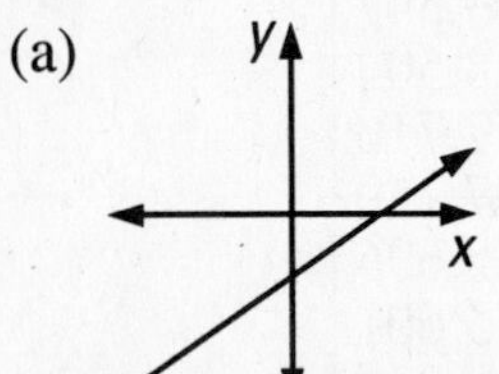

(b)

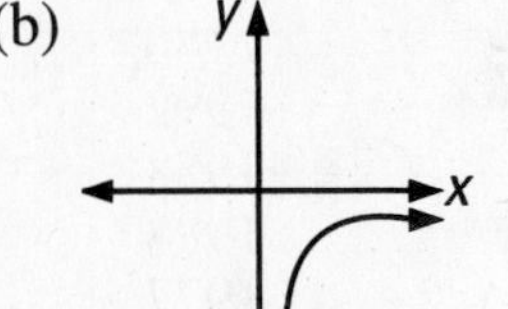

(c)

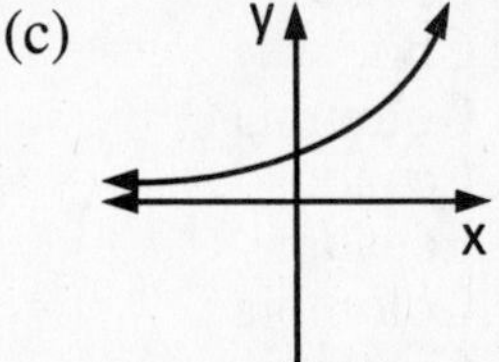

(d)

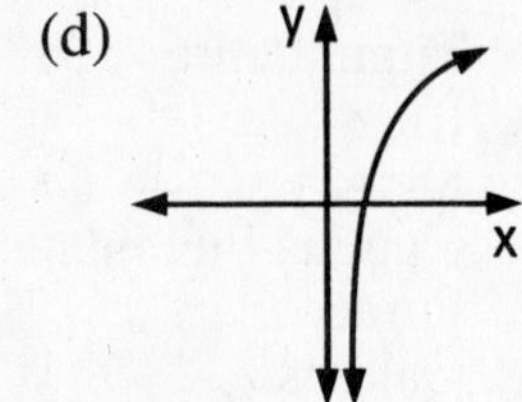

22. Consider the function h defined by $h(x) = e^x$.

a. What is the domain of h? **22. a.** ______________

b. What is the range of h? **b.** ______________

23. The *limiting magnitude* of a telescope is the magnitude of the faintest star that can be seen with the telescope. The formula $L = 17.1 + 5.1 \log D$ relates the limiting magnitude L to the diameter D of the lens in meters. What lens diameter would result in a limiting magnitude of 19? **23.** ______________

In 24 and 25, consider the following situation. Suppose \$1000 is invested at an annual interest rate of 5%. Assume that there are no other deposits or withdrawals in this account.

24. What is the amount in the account after six years if the interest is compounded quarterly? **24.** ______________

25. What is the amount in the account after six years if the interest is compounded continuously? **25.** ______________

Check all your work carefully.

Name

COMPREHENSIVE TEST, CHAPTERS 1-9

***Multiple choice.* Give the letter of the correct answer.**

1. The feasible set of a linear-programming situation is graphed at the right. Which point maximizes the profit equation $P = 30x + 40y$? **1.** ________

(a) A (b) B

(c) C (d) D

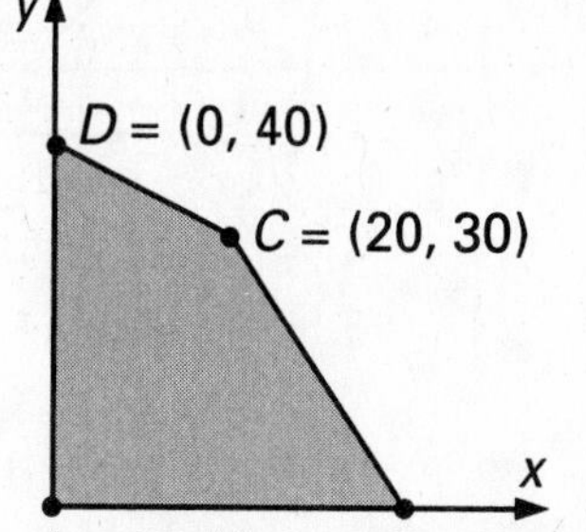

2. The table at the right gives data about workers in farm occupations in the United States as a percent of the total workers in the United States. The data covers selected years from 1820 to 1990. Which of the following could be an exponential model for these data? **2.** ________

(a) $P = -.456t + 82.7$

(b) $P = 214(.979)^{t-50}$

(c) $P = 214(.979)^{t}$

(d) $P = 0.000424t^2 - .547t + 86.4$

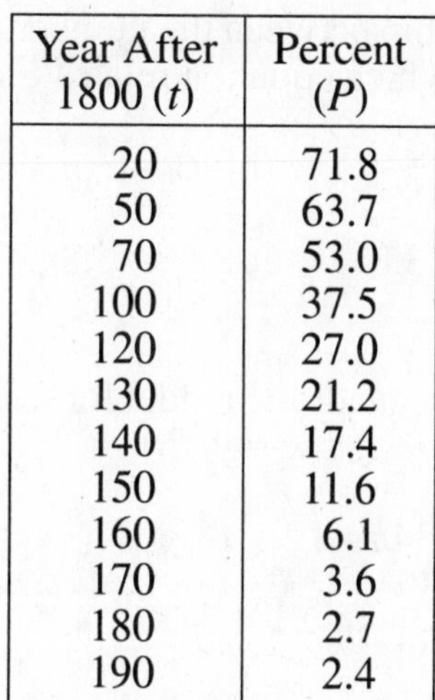

Year After 1800 (t)	Percent (P)
20	71.8
50	63.7
70	53.0
100	37.5
120	27.0
130	21.2
140	17.4
150	11.6
160	6.1
170	3.6
180	2.7
190	2.4

3. To what single transformation is $r_y \circ R_{180}$ equivalent? **3.** ________

(a) r_x (b) r_y (c) $r_{y=x}$ (d) R_{180}

4. What is the number of x-intercepts of the parabola with equation $y = 5x^2 - 3x - 2$? **4.** ________

(a) 0 (b) 1 (c) 2 (d) 3

5. Which of the following is equivalent to $25^{1.5} = 125$? **5.** ________

(a) $\log_{25} 125 = 1.5$ (b) $\log_{25} 1.5 = 125$

(c) $\log_{125} 25 = 1.5$ (d) $\log_{1.5} 25 = 125$

6. Which of the following equations is graphed at the right? **6.** ______

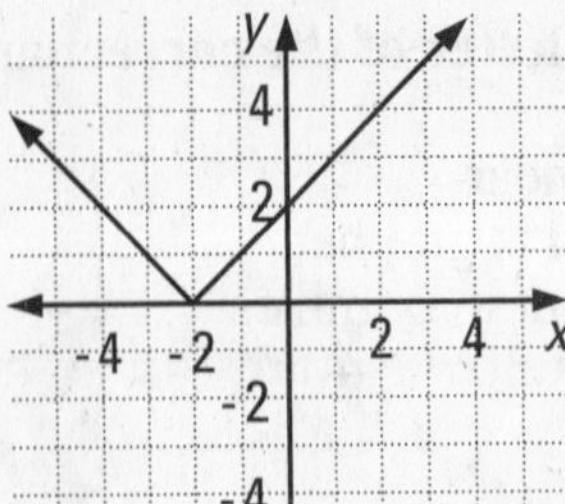

(a) $y = |x - 2|$

(b) $y = |x + 2|$

(c) $y = |x| - 2$

(d) $y = |x| + 2$

7. At Sweet Dreams Bakery, it costs \$410 to make 75 cakes, and it costs \$999 to make 230 cakes. Assume that there is a linear relationship between the number of cakes made n and the cost C. Which equation relates C and n? **7.** 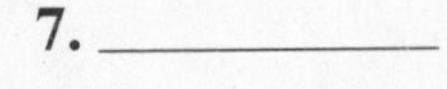

(a) $C = 125n + \frac{5}{19}$ (b) $C = \frac{5}{19}n + 125$

(c) $C = 125n + 3.8$ (d) $C = 3.8n + 125$

8. Which could be a quadratic model for the data in the table at the right? **8.** ______

n	S
1	-1
2	-15
3	-35
4	-61
5	-93
6	-131

(a) $S = -16n^2 + 34n - 19$

(b) $S = -3.5n^2 - 3.5n + 6$

(c) $S = 7n^2 - 55n + 47$

(d) $S = -3n^2 - 5n + 7$

9. If $\begin{bmatrix} 5 & -3 & 6 \\ -2 & 1 & 0 \end{bmatrix} - \begin{bmatrix} b & a & -7 \\ 1 & -5 & 8 \end{bmatrix} = \begin{bmatrix} 2 & -4 & 13 \\ -3 & 6 & -8 \end{bmatrix}$, then $a + b =$ ___?___. **9.** ______

(a) 1   (b) 2   (c) 3   (d) 4

10. A truck weighs 11,000 pounds when empty. It is used for carrying bags of bird seed, each weighing 80 pounds. Which of the following sentences can be used to determine the number of bags n that the driver can transport safely over a bridge with a weight limit of 16,000 pounds? **10.** 

(a) $80n + 11{,}000 \geq 16{,}000$ (b) $80n + 11{,}000 \leq 16{,}000$

(c) $11{,}000 \leq 16{,}000 + 80n$ (d) $80n - 11{,}000 \leq 16{,}000$

Name ____________________

11. Choose the word or phrase that makes the following a true statement: If a group of people is sharing the cost of a magazine subscription, the amount that each person pays varies __?__ as the number of people in the group. **11.** ________

(a) directly (b) inversely

(c) both directly and inversely (d) neither directly nor inversely

12. Which of the following represents a function whose inverse is *not* a function? **12.** 

(a)

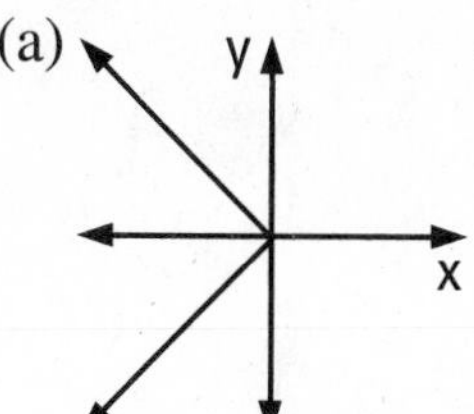

(b)

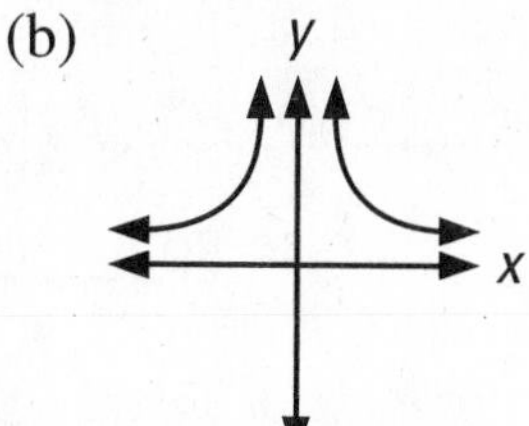

(c)

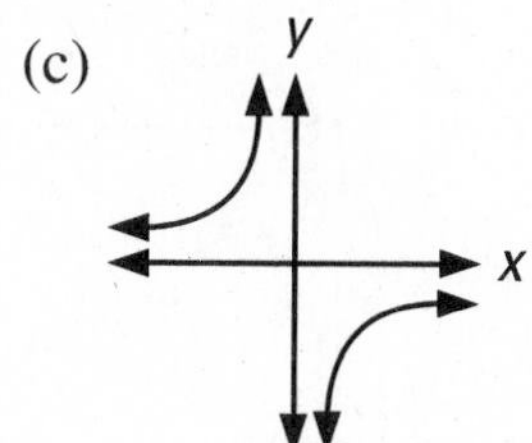

(d)

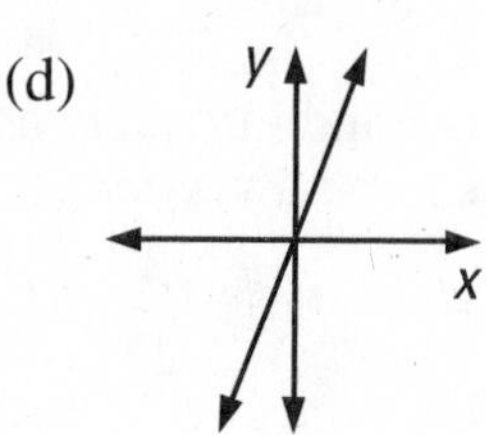

13. $\left(\frac{4}{3}\right)^{-3} =$ __?__. **13.** ________

(a) $\frac{64}{27}$ (b) $\frac{27}{64}$ (c) $-\frac{12}{9}$ (d) $\frac{12}{9}$

14. Jorge invested money in several different ways. He put $\frac{1}{3}$ of his money into ABC Company stock, $\frac{1}{4}$ of his money into XYZ Company stock, $\frac{1}{6}$ of his money into a mutual fund, and $6600 into a certificate of deposit. How much money did he invest altogether? **14.** ________

(a) $8800 (b) $6600 (c) $4400 (d) $26,400

15. In which of the following is y *not* a function of x? **15.** ________

(a)

x	-3	1	e	4	8
y	7	2	6	9	3

(b) $xy = 5000$ (c) $y^2 = x$ (d) $y = 7$

Name ______________________________

16. Let $f(x) = 2x^2$ and $g(x) = 8x + 1$. What is the value of $f(g(-1))$? **16.** __________

(a) 98 (b) 17 (c) -98 (d) -17

17. Which is the graph of $3x - 5y \leq 15$? **17.** __________

(a)

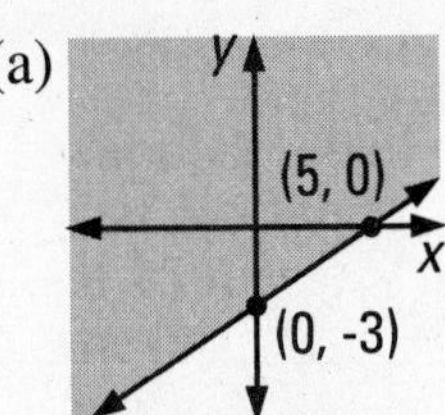

(b)

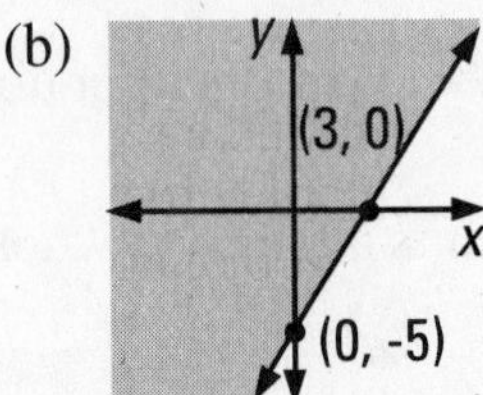

(c)

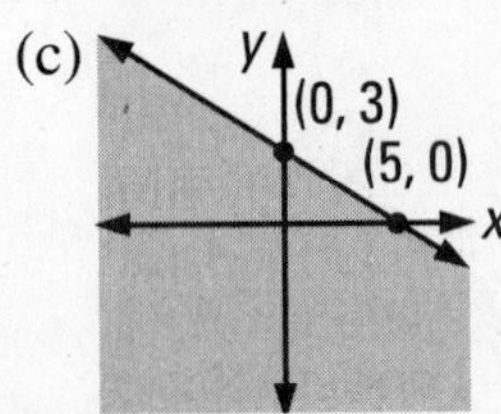

(d)

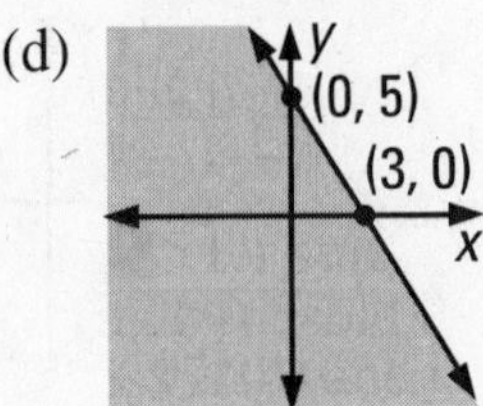

18. Suppose that y varies directly as x and inversely as the square of z. When $x = 3$ and $z = 5$, $y = 4.5$. Find y when $x = -2$ and $z = 3$. **18.** __________

(a) $-\frac{25}{3}$ (b) $\frac{25}{3}$ (c) $-\frac{3}{25}$ (d) $\frac{3}{25}$

19. What type of situation does the function $y = e^{x-3}$ describe? **19.** __________

(a) constant increase (b) constant decrease

(c) exponential growth (d) exponential decay

20. Assume $Q > 0$, $x \neq 0$, $y \neq 0$, and n is an integer. Which property is illustrated by the statement $7^{-\frac{1}{2}} = \frac{1}{7^{\frac{1}{2}}}$? **20.** __________

(a) $Q^0 = 1$ (b) $Q^{-x} = \frac{1}{Q^x}$

(c) $Q^{\frac{1}{x}} = \sqrt[x]{Q}$ (d) $Q^{\frac{y}{x}} = \sqrt[x]{Q^y}$

21. $(\sqrt{29} - \sqrt{52})(\sqrt{29} + \sqrt{52}) =$ ___?___. **21.** __________

(a) -23 (b) 23 (c) 81 (d) 9

22. In the function with the equation $y = \frac{8}{x}$, what is the rate of change from $x = 1$ to $x = 2$? **22.** __________

(a) $\frac{1}{4}$ (b) $-\frac{1}{4}$ (c) 4 (d) -4

▶ COMPREHENSIVE TEST, Chapters 1-9 *page 5*

23. Suppose that matrix A has dimensions $m \times n$ and matrix B has dimensions $n \times p$. Which of the following statements is true?

23. ______

(a) The product AB exists and has dimensions $m \times n$.

(b) The product AB exists and has dimensions $m \times p$.

(c) The product BA exists and has dimensions $m \times n$.

(d) The product BA exists and has dimensions $m \times p$.

24. At the Spic-and-Span Car Wash, the charge is \$10 to wash the exterior of a car and \$5 to clean the interior. To make a profit, the total revenue from washing exteriors and cleaning interiors on a given day should be at least \$800. Let E be the number of exteriors washed and I be the number of interiors cleaned in one day. Which of the following describes this situation?

24. ______

(a) $E + I \geq 800$ (b) $5E + 10I \geq 800$

(c) $10E + 5I \leq 800$ (d) $10E + 5I \geq 800$

25. The scale of an architect's model of a building is 1 to 100. Suppose that the height of a window on the model is x cm. What is the actual height of the window?

25. ______

(a) $100x$ (b) $\frac{100}{x}$ (c) $\frac{x}{100}$ (d) $100 + x$

Check all your work carefully.

Name

QUIZ

Lessons 10-1 Through 10-3

In 1–3, use the triangle at the right.

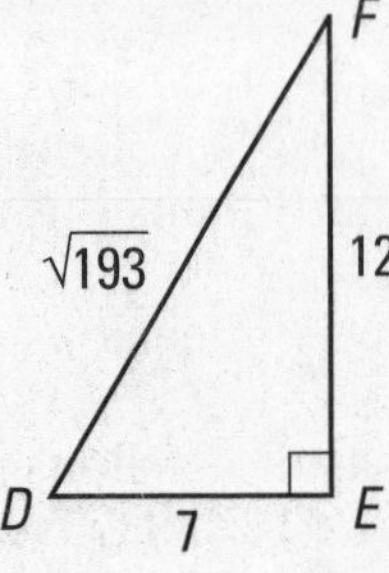

1. Approximate tan F to the nearest thousandth. 1. ____________

2. Fill in the blank with cos, sin, or tan. 2. ____________

   $\sin F =$ __?__ D

3. Find the value of $(\sin D)^2 + (\cos D)^2$. 3. ____________

In 4 and 5, give the exact value.

4. cos 60° 4. ____________

5. tan 45° 5. ____________

6. *True or false.* $\sin(90° - \theta) = \cos \theta$ 6. ____________

In 7 and 8, find x to the nearest tenth.

7. 7. ____________

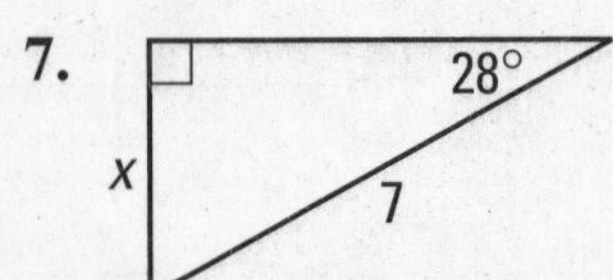

8. 8. ____________

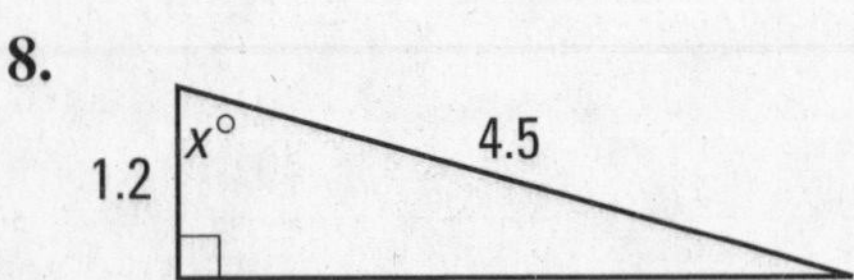

9. An airplane is flying at an altitude of 10,000 feet. The pilot wants to make a smooth final descent to the runway at a constant angle of depression of 4°. How far from the runway should the pilot begin the descent? 9. ____________

Name

QUIZ

Lessons 10-4 Through 10-7

1. *Multiple choice.* Which equation illustrates the Law of Sines for ΔABC at the right? 1. ________

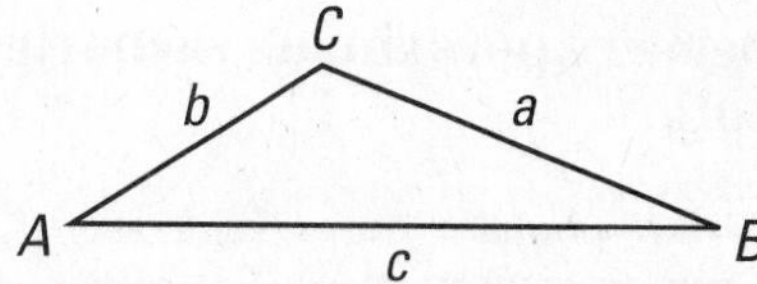

(a) $\sin A = \frac{a}{c}$ (b) $(\sin A)(\sin B)(\sin C) = 1$

(c) $\frac{a}{\sin A} \cdot \frac{b}{\sin B} \cdot \frac{c}{\sin C} = 1$ (d) $\frac{a}{\sin A} = \frac{b}{\sin B} = \frac{c}{\sin C}$

In 2–5, give the exact value.

2. tan 510° 2. ________

3. sin (-315°) 3. ________

4. cos 90° 4. ________

5. sin 750° 5. ________

6. Find two values of θ such that 0° < θ < 360° and $\sin\theta = -\frac{\sqrt{3}}{2}$. 6. ________

7. On the unit circle at the right, approximate the location of $P = (\cos 300°, \sin 300°)$. 7.

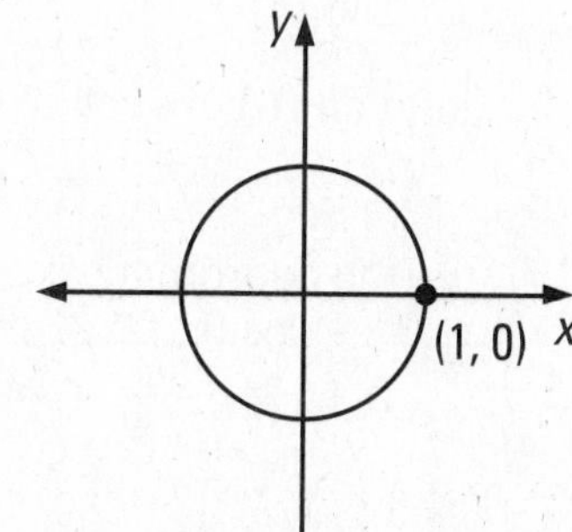

8. Is sin 295° positive, zero, or negative? 8. ________

In 9 and 10, find *x* to the nearest tenth.

9.

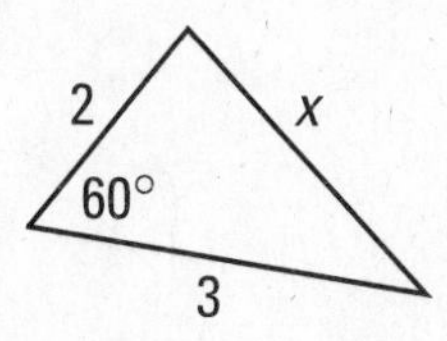

10.

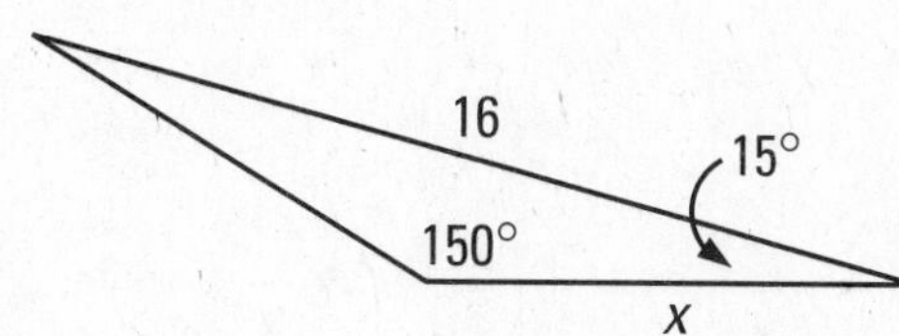

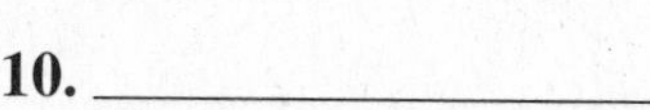

9. ________

10. ________

Name

CHAPTER 10 TEST, Form A

In 1 and 2, use the triangle below. Approximate each trigonometric value to the nearest thousandth.

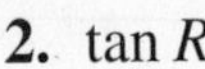

1. sin A 1. ______________

2. tan R 2. ______________

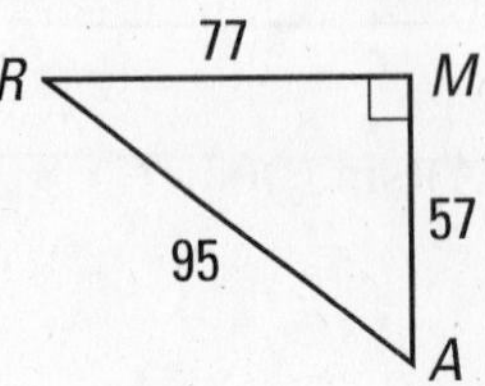

3. An airplane that is flying at an altitude of 6 miles begins a smooth final descent to the runway when it is 28 miles away. At what angle of depression will the plane descend?   3. ______________

In 4 and 5, use the graph of the sine function below.

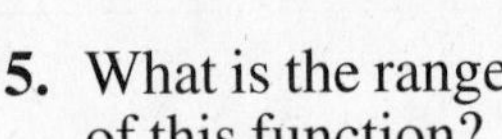

4. What is the period of this function?   4. ______________

5. What is the range of this function?   5. ______________

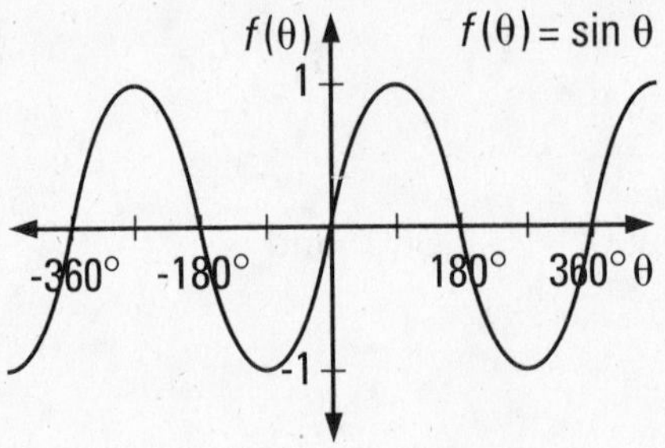

6. Find all θ between 0° and 180° for which $\sin\theta = \frac{1}{2}$.   6. ______________

7. On the coordinate axes at the right, graph $g: \theta \rightarrow \cos\theta$, for $-180° \le \theta \le 180°$.   7.

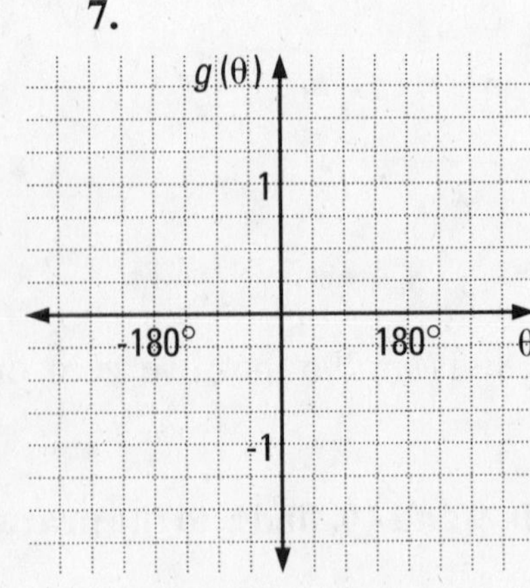

Name ____________________

8. Explain why tan 270° is undefined.

____

____

In 9 and 10, use the unit circle below. Which letter stands for the given number?

9. cos (-300°) **9.** ______

10. $\sin \frac{5\pi}{4}$ **10.** ______

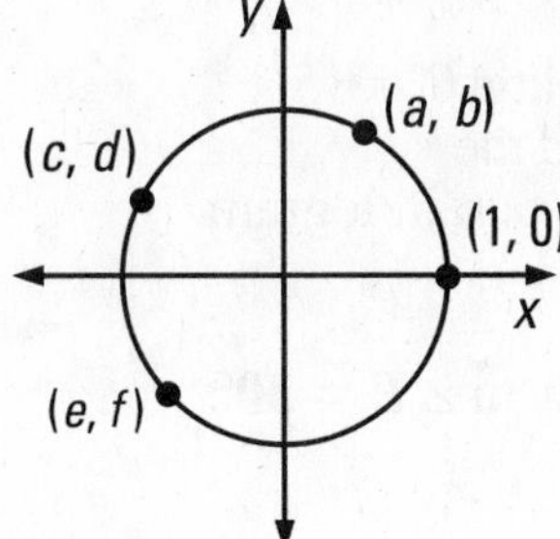

11. Find two values of sin θ when cos θ = .5. Show your work. **11.** ______

12. Convert $-\frac{2\pi}{3}$ radians to degrees. **12.** ______

13. Convert 315° to its exact radian equivalent. **13.** ______

In 14 and 15, find *x* to the nearest tenth.

14.

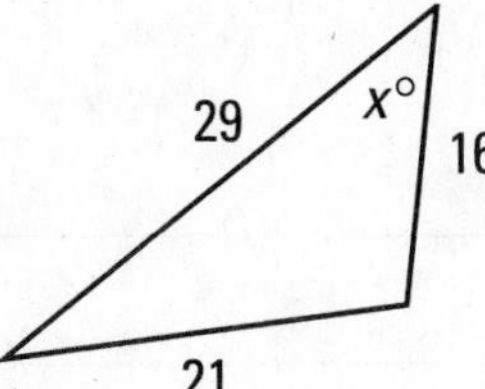

15.

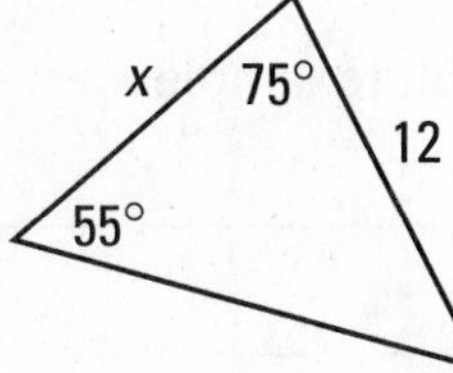

14. ______

15. ______

In 16 and 17, find the exact value.

16. sin 630° **16.** ______

17. $\tan \frac{\pi}{3}$ **17.** ______

Name

18. Two ships are 6 miles apart. The navigator of the first ship spots a life raft at an angle of 49° to the line between the ships. The navigator of the second ship spots the same life raft at an angle of 57°. How far is the second ship from the life raft?

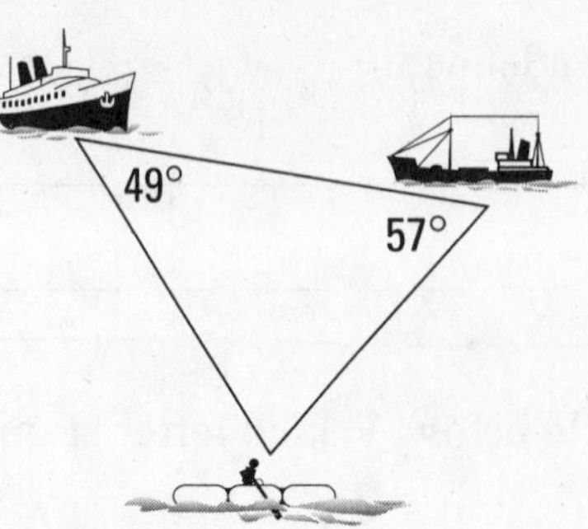

18. ________

19. In parallelogram $ABCD$, suppose that $AB = 15$, $BC = 23$, and $m\angle ABC = 51°$. Find the length of the shorter diagonal of the parallelogram.

19. ________

In 20 and 21, consider ΔTOP, in which $m\angle P = 30°$, $TP = 6$, and $TO = 5$.

20. Find $m\angle O$ if $\angle O$ is acute.

20. ________

21. Is there another possible measure of $\angle O$? If yes, give it. If no, explain why not.

____

____

22. a. *Multiple choice.* Which of these statements is *not* true for all values of θ ?

22. a. ________

(i) $\sin\theta = \cos(90° + \theta)$

(ii) $(\cos\theta)^2 + (\sin\theta)^2 = 1$

(iii) $\dfrac{\sin\theta}{\cos\theta} = \tan\theta$

(iv) $\cos\theta = \sin(90° - \theta)$

b. Justify your answer by giving a counterexample.

____

____

Check all your work carefully.

Name

CHAPTER 10 TEST, Form B

In 1 and 2, use the triangle below. Approximate each trigonometric value to the nearest thousandth.

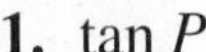

1. tan P

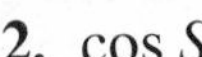

2. cos S

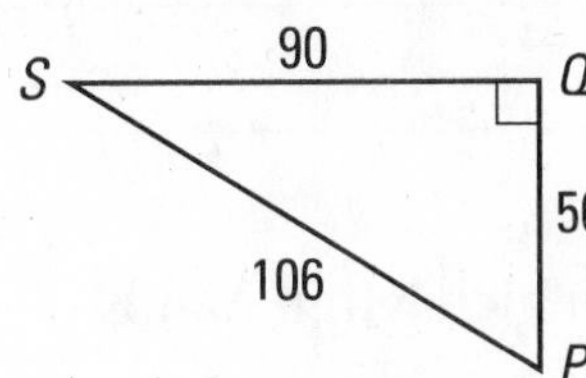

1. ______

2. ______

3. A wheelchair ramp is to be built with a slope of $\frac{2}{27}$. What angle will the ramp make with the horizontal?

3. ______

In 4 and 5, use the graph of the cosine function below.

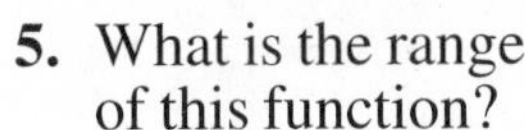

4. What is the period of this function?

5. What is the range of this function?

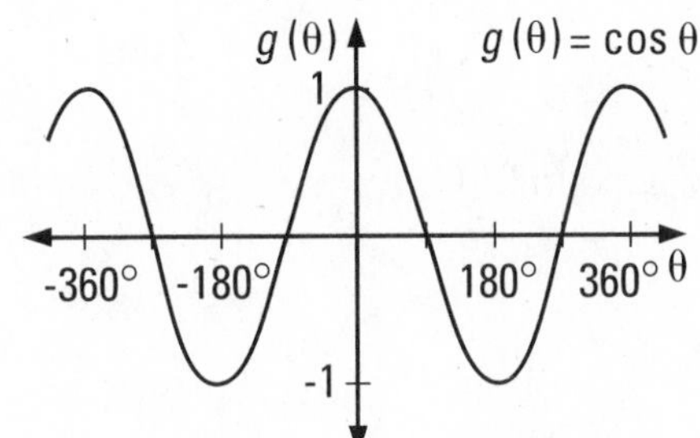

4. ______

5. ______

6. Find all θ between 0° and 180° for which $\cos\theta = -\frac{\sqrt{2}}{2}$.

6. ______

7. On the coordinate axes at the right, graph $f: \theta \rightarrow \sin\theta$, for $-180° \leq \theta \leq 180°$.

7.

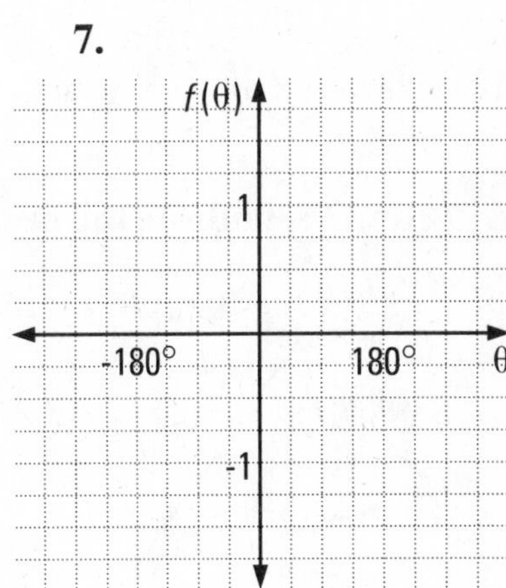

Name

8. Explain why $\tan(-90°)$ is undefined.

In 9 and 10, use the unit circle below. Which letter stands for the given number?

9. $\sin 420°$ 9. ____

10. $\cos \frac{7\pi}{4}$ 10. ____

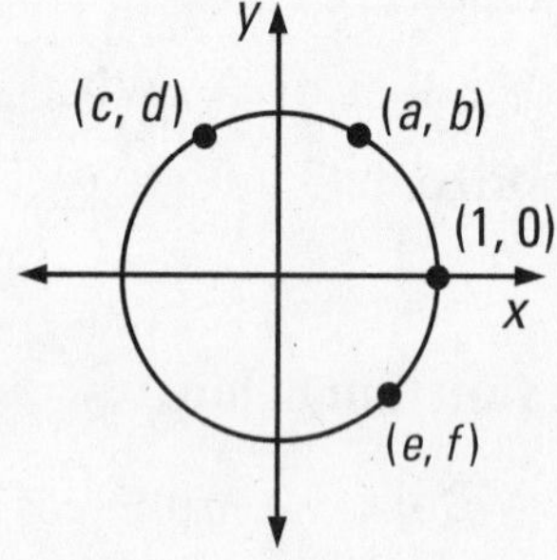

11. Find two values of $\cos \theta$ when $\sin \theta = .6$. Show your work. 11. ____

12. Convert $\frac{5\pi}{4}$ radians to degrees. 12. ____

13. Convert 810° to its exact radian equivalent. 13. ____

In 14 and 15, find *x* to the nearest tenth.

14. 14. ____

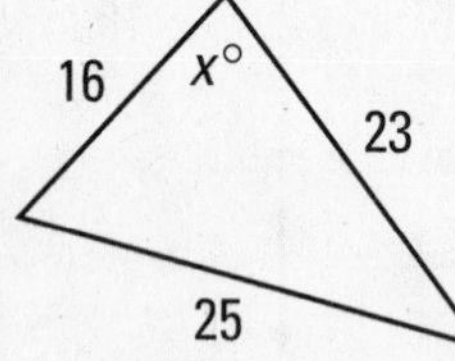

15. 15. ____

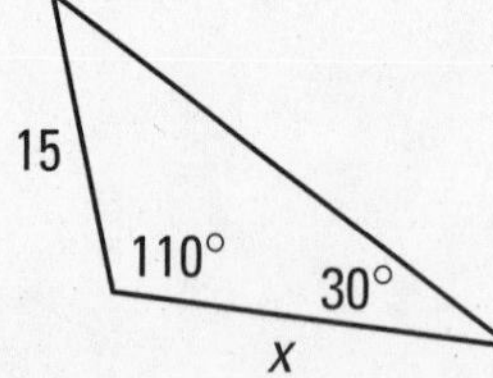

In 16 and 17, find the exact value.

16. $\cos 540°$ 16. ____

17. $\sin \frac{\pi}{4}$ 17. ____

Name

18. A surveyor needs to find the distance between two trees that lie on opposite sides of a small lake. Using a surveyor's transit and a measuring tape, the surveyor made the measurements shown in the figure at the right. What is the distance between the two trees?

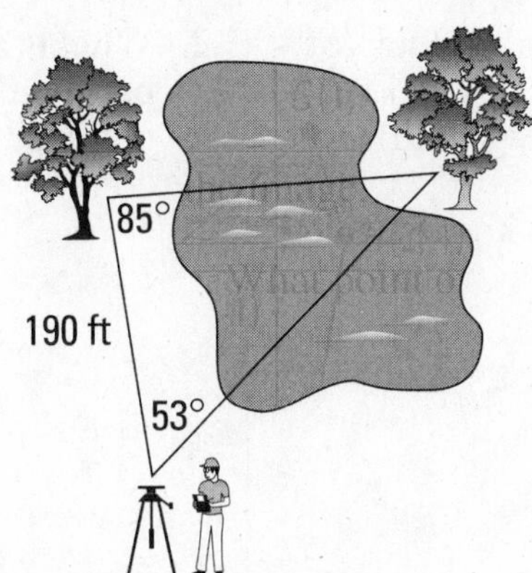

18. ________

19. In parallelogram $ABCD$, suppose that $AB = 10$, $BC = 15$, and $m\angle ABC = 45°$. Find the length of the shorter diagonal of the parallelogram.

19. ________

In 20 and 21, consider ΔPAN, in which $m\angle N = 25°$, $PN = 8$, and $PA = 9$.

20. Find $m\angle A$ if $\angle A$ is acute.

20. ________

21. Is there another possible measure of $\angle A$? If yes, give it. If no, explain why not.

____

____

22. a. *Multiple choice.* Which of these statements is *not* true for all values of θ?

22. a. ________

(i) $\cos\theta = \sin(90° - \theta)$

(ii) $\cos\theta + \sin\theta = 1$

(iii) $\tan\theta = \dfrac{\sin\theta}{\cos\theta}$

(iv) $\sin\theta = \cos(90° - \theta)$

b. Justify your answer by giving a counterexample.

____

____

Check all your work carefully.

Name

CHAPTER 10 TEST, Form C

1. Suppose the [cos] key on your calculator is broken, so the *cos* and cos^{-1} functions are not available to you. How could you use your calculator to find cos 37°? How could you find θ if you know $\cos \theta = .25$? (Assume θ is between 0° and 90°.)

2. What is a *radian*? How can you convert back and forth between degrees and radians? Give an example of each kind of conversion.

3. Write a real-world problem that can be solved using either the Law of Sines or the Law of Cosines. Then show how to solve your problem.

4. Dan was absent for a day in the middle of studying Chapter 10. On the day before his absence, the class was studying trigonometry and right triangles. When he returned, he was surprised that the class was discussing circles. How would you explain this to Dan?

5. Identify the trigonometric function that is graphed below. Then state as many facts as you can about the function.

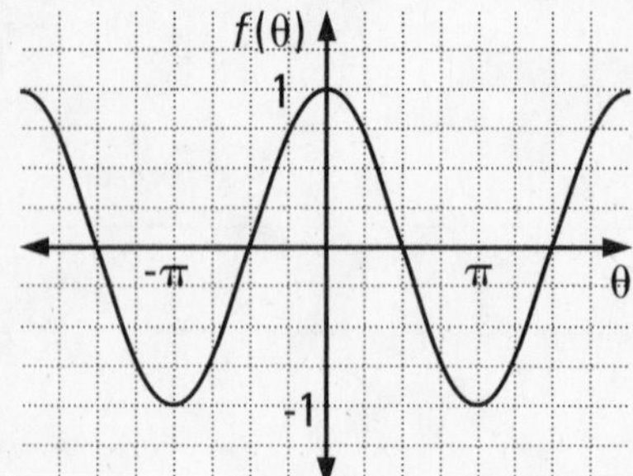

6. Add one reasonable measure to the triangle below that would enable you to solve the triangle. Then show how to find all the missing measures.

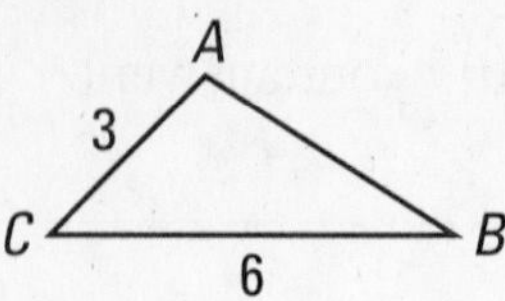

Name

CHAPTER 10 TEST, Form D

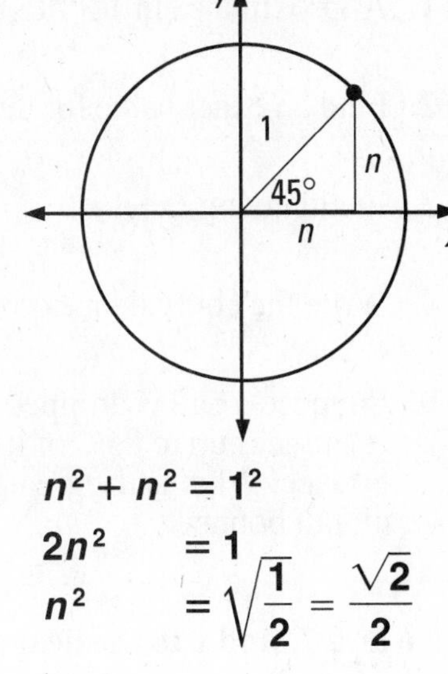

A friend's older brother has said that you need to know the basic trigonometry you learned in this chapter in several future math and science classes. He suggested that you make a summary of the basic concepts so you will have them handy for future reference.

Your friend's brother especially recommended diagrams as a way of summarizing the information. "You know the old saying," he remarked. "One picture is worth a thousand words."

a. Your friend's brother showed you the diagram and the equations at the right, which he uses to help him remember two important facts in trigonometry. What are they? Explain how you think the diagram might help him remember them.

$$n^2 + n^2 = 1^2$$
$$2n^2 = 1$$
$$n^2 = \sqrt{\frac{1}{2}} = \frac{\sqrt{2}}{2}$$

b. You have learned that it is important to remember the relationship between degrees and radians. What is that relationship? Create a diagram that you might use to help you remember it.

c. A student created the diagram below. Study the diagram carefully. What relationship does the diagram picture? Explain how the diagram illustrates the relationship.

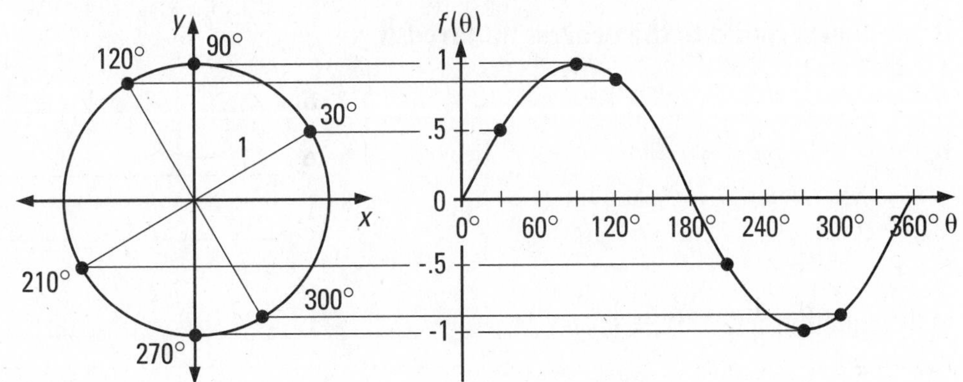

d. Design a diagram that will help someone remember the Law of Sines and the Law of Cosines and how to use them.

Name

CHAPTER 10 TEST, Cumulative Form

1. Approximate sin 140° to the nearest thousandth. **1.** ________

2. Find an exact value for $\tan \frac{9\pi}{4}$. **2.** ________

3. Evaluate $\log_6 \frac{1}{216}$. **3.** ________

4. Write the equivalent exponential form for $\ln 53 \approx 3.97$. **4.** ________

5. Suppose a ball is dropped from a height of 12 feet, and it bounces up to 85% of its previous height after each bounce. What is the greatest height of the ball after the eighth bounce? **5.** ________

In 6 and 7, find *x* to the nearest tenth.

6.

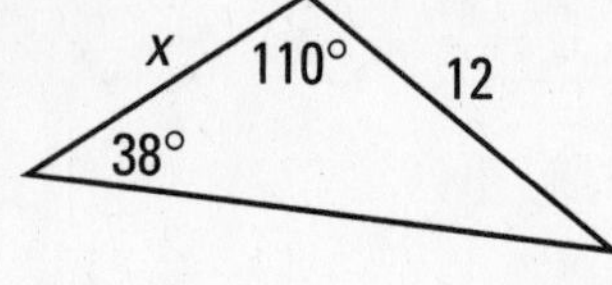

7.

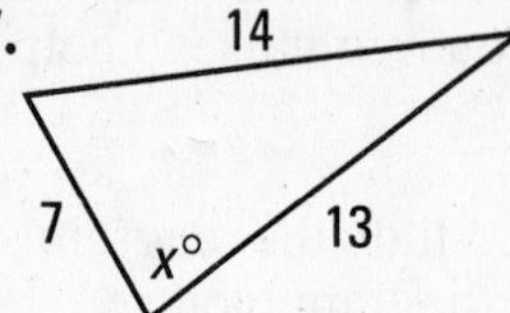

6. ________

7. ________

In 8–10, solve. If necessary, round to the nearest hundredth.

8. $3^r = 19.6$ **8.** ________

9. $\log_4 m = -.75$ **9.** ________

10. $3j^{\frac{2}{3}} = 48$ **10.** ________

11. Solve for *x* in the equation $\frac{4}{5}x - 3y = 12$. **11.** ________

12. Rewrite the equation $y = 2x^2 - 8x + 4$ in vertex form. **12.** ________

13. A 5-ft-tall person is standing 36 feet from a tree. The person finds that the angle of elevation to the top of the tree is 42°. How tall is the tree? **13.** ________

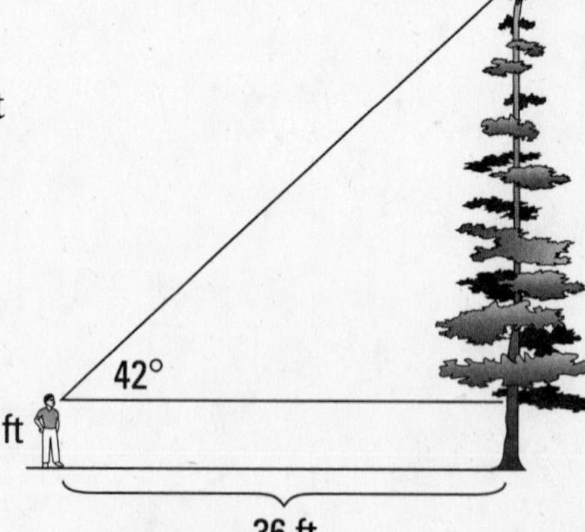

Name

14. a. On the coordinate axes at the right, sketch $f: \theta \rightarrow \cos\theta$, for $-90° \leq \theta \leq 360°$.

14. a.

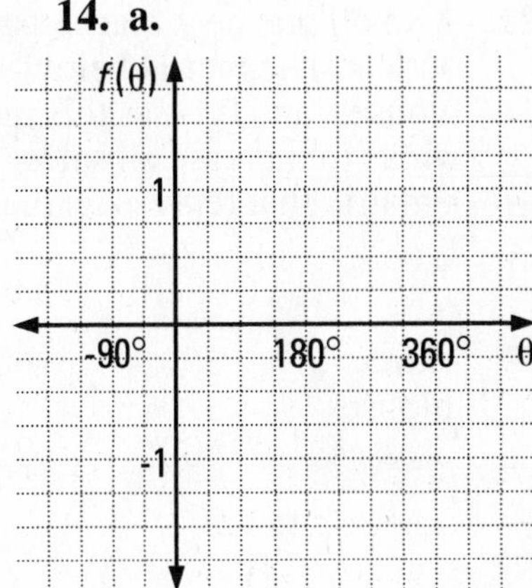

b. Name all the x-intercepts of the curve that you sketched. **b.** ______

15. Two ships are spotted by an observer in a lighthouse. Ship A is 25 miles from the lighthouse, and ship B is 46 miles from the lighthouse. The angle between the two sightings is 60°. How far is ship A from ship B? **15.** ______

16. *Multiple choice.* sin 120° = __?__ **16.** ______

(a) cos 120° (b) cos 60° (c) sin 60° (d) sin 30°

17. Use the unit circle at the right. Find θ to the nearest degree. **17.** ______

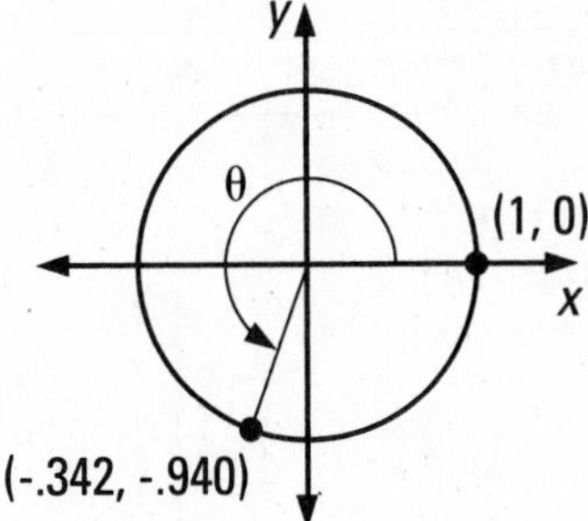

18. Find all θ between 0° and 360° for which sin θ = -.88. **18.** ______

19. Convert to an exact radian equivalent.

a. 24° **19. a.** ______

b. -665° **b.** ______

20. Let $f(x) = 3x^2 - 2$ and $g(x) = -4x + 1$.

a. Find $g \circ f(3)$. **20. a.** ______

b. Find $f(g(-1))$. **b.** ______

Name

21. A small business that sells women's clothing has two outlets. The matrix below summarizes sales of skirts, blouses, and dresses this month. Suppose the owner wants to increase all sales by 50% next month. Write a matrix that represents the desired amount of sales.

21. ________________

	Outlet 1	Outlet 2
skirts	550	600
blouses	320	400
dresses	600	350

In 22 and 23, refer to the following situation. Suppose that, $5\frac{1}{2}$ years ago, \$2000 was invested at an annual interest rate of 3.7%. Assume that there were no other deposits or withdrawals in the account. How much would be in the account now under the given conditions?

22. The interest was compounded quarterly.

22. ________________

23. The interest was compounded continuously.

23. ________________

24. The table below gives the population of Maryland in twenty-year intervals from 1790 to 1990.

Year After 1790	t	0	20	40	60	80	100	120	140	160	180	200
Population (millions)	P	.32	.38	.45	.58	.78	1.04	1.30	1.63	2.34	3.92	4.78

a. Make a scatterplot of the data on the coordinate axes at the right.

24. a.

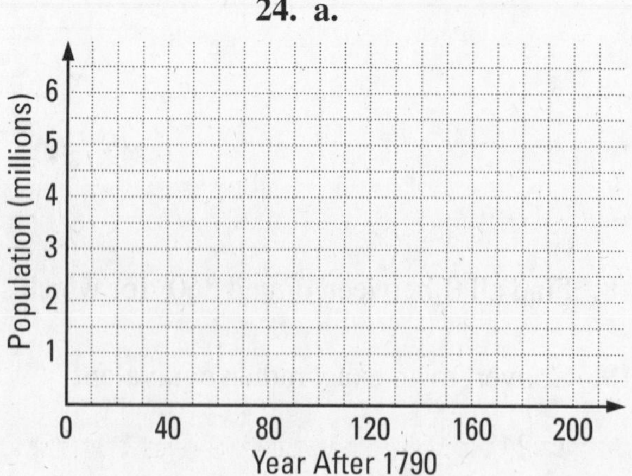

b. Fit an exponential model to these data.

b. ________________

c. Use your model to predict the population of Maryland in the year 2050.

c. ________________

Check all your work carefully.

Name

QUIZ

Lessons 11-1 Through 11-3

In 1–3, consider the polynomial function P with equation $P(x) = 15x^5 - 21x + 13x^7$.

1. What is the degree of the polynomial? 1. ____

2. What is the leading coefficient of the polynomial? 2. ____

3. Sketch a graph of P on the coordinate axes at the right. 3.

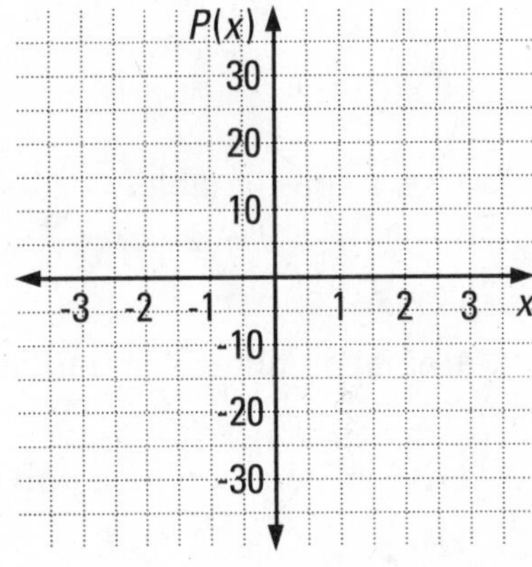

In 4 and 5, expand and write in standard form.

4. $(4m - 6)(3m^2 + 2m + 1)$ 4. ____

5. $3w(6w - 1)(2w - 5)$ 5. ____

In 6 and 7, factor completely over the set of polynomials with integer coefficients.

6. $6x^4y - 9x^3y^2 - 18x^2y^3$ 6. ____

7. $16m^4 - 289$ 7. ____

8. Is $12n^2 + 12n + 1$ prime over the set of polynomials with rational coefficients? Explain your reasoning.

____

____

9. If the length of each edge of a cube is $x + 2$, find a polynomial formula for the volume $V(x)$ of the cube. 9. ____

10. Jorge's aunt gave him \$30, \$50, and \$75 on his 13th, 14th, and 15th birthdays, respectively. All the money was put into an account paying $r\%$ interest, compounded annually. No additional money was added or withdrawn. Let $x = 1 + r$. Write a polynomial expression in x to give the total amount in the account on Jorge's 15th birthday. 10. ____

Name

QUIZ

Lessons 11-4 Through 11-7

1. The table at the right gives some values of the polynomial function P with equation $P(x) = 3x^3 + 5x^2 - 7x - 7$. According to the table, between what pairs of consecutive integers must the zeros of P be located?

x	$P(x)$
-4	-91
-3	-22
-2	3
-1	2
0	-7
1	-6
2	23
3	98
4	237

1. __________

2. Use graphs or tables to solve the following system.

$$\begin{cases} y = 4x^3 - 7x^2 + 15x + 1 \\ y = 2x^2 - 5 \end{cases}$$

Round noninteger solutions to the nearest tenth.

2. __________

3. Give an equation for a polynomial function P with zeros 2, $-\frac{3}{2}$, and -1.

3. __________

4. Use the function f, where $f(x) = 10x^3 - 3x^2 - x$.

a. Factor $f(x)$.

b. Find the zeros of f.

4. a. __________

b. __________

In 5–7, factor completely over the set of polynomials with integer coefficients.

5. $8x^2 + 34x + 21$

5. __________

6. $m^2 + 2m - 575$

6. __________

7. $6z - 4z^2 - 16z^3$

7. __________

In 8 and 9, list all the possible rational zeros (according to the Rational-Zero Theorem) of the function described.

8. $f(x) = x^3 - 5x^2 + 7x + 8$

8. __________

9. $g(x) = 3x^4 - 5x^2 + 4x + 4$

9. __________

10. Find all rational zeros of P, when $P(x) = 6x^3 - 7x^2 - 41x - 28$.

10. __________

Name

CHAPTER 11 TEST, Form A

In 1 and 2, use the following information: Johari's uncle gave her \$100, \$125, \$150, and \$200 when she started 9th, 10th, 11th, and 12th grades, respectively. She placed all this money into an account paying r% interest, compounded annually. No additional money was added or withdrawn.

1. Write a polynomial in x, where $x = 1 + r$, that represents the total amount in the account immediately after Johari started 12th grade. **1.** ____________

2. If the account pays 5.25% interest annually, calculate the total amount in the account immediately after Johari started 12th grade. **2.** ____________

In 3–5, consider the polynomial function P, where $P(x) = x^3 + 2x^2 - 10x - 8$.

3. How many zeros does P have? **3.** ____________

4. According to the Rational-Zero Theorem, what are the possible rational zeros of P? **4.** ____________

5. The table at the right gives some values of P. Identify the integer zeros of P, if any. Between what pairs of consecutive integers must the noninteger zeros be located? **5.** ____________

x	$P(x)$
-6	-92
-5	-33
-4	0
-3	13
-2	12
-1	3
0	-8
1	-15
2	-12
3	7
4	48

6. A rectangular piece of cardboard is 20 cm by 28 cm. Squares of side x are cut out of the corners, and an open box is made by folding the remaining cardboard.

a. Make a sketch of this situation. **6. a.**

b. Write a polynomial formula for the surface area $S(x)$ of the box. **b.** ____________

Name

In 7–10, consider the function f with $f(x) = 2x^4 - 8x^3 - 10x^2$.

7. Factor $2x^4 - 8x^3 - 10x^2$ completely. **7.** ____________

8. Find all the zeros of f. **8.** ____________

9. Sketch a graph of f on the coordinate axes at the right. **9.**

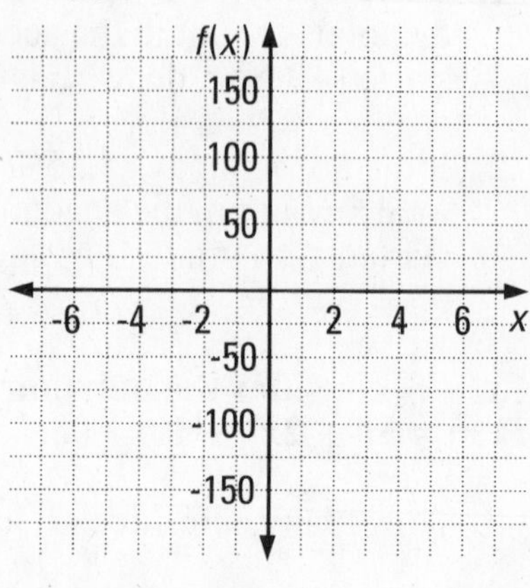

10. Give an equation for a different function g that has the same zeros as f. **10.** ____________

In 11–13, the polynomial function $P(x) = x^3 + a_2x^2 + a_1x + a_0$ with integer zeros is graphed below.

11. What is the value of a_0? **11.** ____________

12. Write an equation for $P(x)$ in factored form. **12.** ____________

13. Write an equation for $P(x)$ in standard form. **13.** ____________

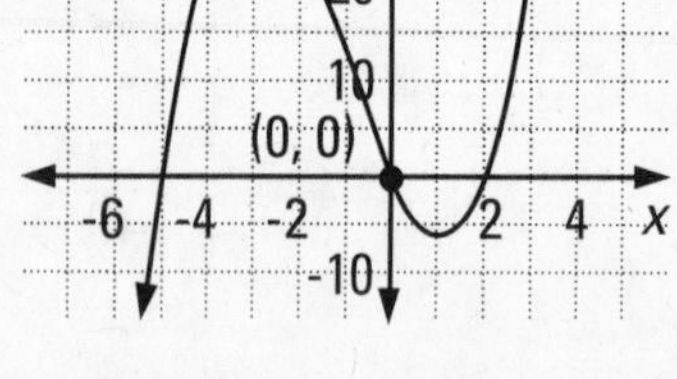

In 14–16, refer to the following sequence.

n:	1	2	3	4	5
$f(n)$:	•••	•••• / ••••	3 rows of 5 dots	4 rows of 6 dots	5 rows of 7 dots
	3	8	15	24	35

14. f is a polynomial function of degree __?__. **14.** ____________

15. Find a formula for $f(n)$. **15.** ____________

16. How many dots make up the twelfth figure in the sequence? **16.** ____________

Name

17. Can the data points in the table below be described by a polynomial function of degree ≤ 5? Justify your answer.

x	1	2	3	4	5	6	7	8
y	.25	1	4	16	64	256	1024	4096

18. Factor $18r^3s^4 - 128r^5s^2$ completely over the set of polynomials with integer coefficients. **18.** ____________

19. Factor $3q^2 - 12q + 4$ into linear factors. **19.** ____________

In 20 and 21, expand and write in the standard form of a polynomial.

20. $(5x + 1)^3$ **20.** ____________

21. $(c + 1)(c - 1)(c + 3)$ **21.** ____________

22. Consider the polynomial $-5x^2 + 8x^3 - 2$.

a. What is the degree of the polynomial? **22. a.** ____________

b. Classify the polynomial according to its number of terms. **b.** ____________

c. What is the leading coefficient of the polynomial? **c.** ____________

23. *Multiple choice.* Who first proved the Fundamental Theorem of Algebra? **23.** ____________

(a) Niels Abel

(b) Ludovico Ferrari

(c) Karl Friedrich Gauss

(d) Omar Khayyam

Check all your work carefully.

Name

CHAPTER 11 TEST, Form B

In 1 and 2, use the following information. Robert deposited \$1000, \$2500, \$1750, \$1500, and \$3000 into an account on his 21st, 22nd, 23rd, 24th, and 25th birthdays, respectively. The account paid r% interest, compounded annually. No additional money was added or withdrawn.

1. Write a polynomial in x, where $x = 1 + r$, that represents the total amount in the account immediately after Robert's 25th birthday. **1.** ________________

2. If the account pays 4.75% interest annually, calculate the total amount in the account immediately after Robert's 25th birthday. **2.** ________________

In 3–5, consider the polynomial function P, where $P(x) = x^3 - 6x^2 + 4x + 15$.

3. How many zeros does P have? **3.** ________________

4. According to the Rational-Zero Theorem, what are the possible rational zeros of P? **4.** ________________

5. The table at the right gives some values of P. Identify the integer zeros of P, if any. Between what pairs of consecutive integers must the noninteger zeros be located? **5.** ________________

x	$P(x)$
-4	-161
-3	-78
-2	-25
-1	4
0	15
1	14
2	7
3	0
4	-1
5	10
6	39

6. A rectangular piece of cardboard is 28 cm by 36 cm. Squares of side x are cut out of the corners, and an open box is made by folding the remaining cardboard.

a. Make a sketch of this situation. **6. a.**

b. Write a polynomial formula for the surface area $S(x)$ of the box. **b.** ________________

Name ____________________

In 7–10, consider the function g with $g(x) = 3x^4 + 3x^3 - 36x^2$.

7. Factor $3x^4 + 3x^3 - 36x^2$ completely. **7.** ____________

8. Find all the zeros of g. **8.** ____________

9. Sketch a graph of g on the coordinate axes at the right. **9.**

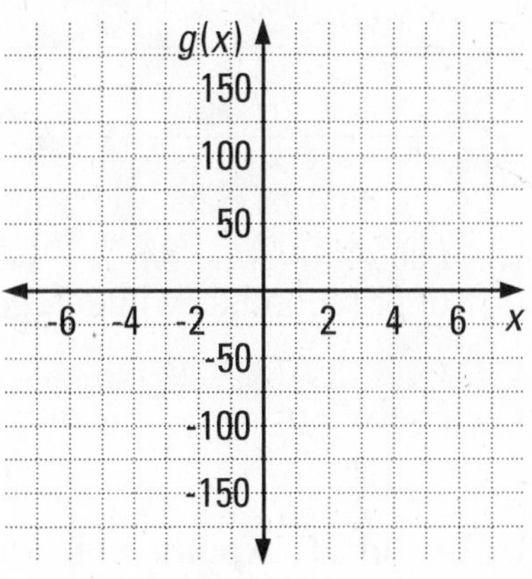

10. Give an equation for a different function f that has the same zeros as g. **10.** ____________

In 11–13, the polynomial function $P(x) = x^4 + a_3x^3 + a_2x^2 + a_1x + a_0$ with integer zeros is graphed at the right.

11. What is the value of a_0? **11.** ____________

12. Write an equation for $P(x)$ in factored form. **12.** ____________

13. Write an equation for $P(x)$ in standard form. **13.** ____________

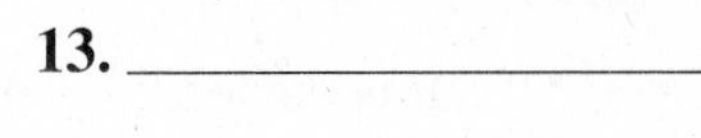

In 14–16, refer to the following sequence.

n:	1	2	3	4	5
$f(n)$:	1	5	11	19	29

14. f is a polynomial function of degree ___?___. **14.** ____________

15. Find a formula for $f(n)$. **15.** ____________

16. How many dots make up the twelfth figure in the sequence? **16.** ____________

Name ____________________

17. Can the data points in the table below be described by a polynomial function of degree ≤ 5? Justify your answer.

x	1	2	3	4	5	6	7	8
y	-3	-13	-3	45	149	327	597	977

____

____

18. Factor $4m^3n + 8m^2n^2 + 4mn^3$ completely over the set of polynomials with integer coefficients. **18.** ____________

19. Factor $8p^2 - 7p - 3$ into linear factors. **19.** ____________

In 20 and 21, expand and write in the standard form of a polynomial.

20. $(3x - 2)^3$ **20.** ____________

21. $(c^2 + 2c + 4)(c - 2)$ **21.** ____________

22. Consider the polynomial $15x^3 - 7x^4 + 3$.

a. What is the degree of the polynomial? **22. a.** ____________

b. Classify the polynomial according to its number of terms. **b.** ____________

c. What is the leading coefficient of the polynomial? **c.** ____________

23. Name a mathematician mentioned in this chapter and tell what contribution this person made regarding the Fundamental Theorem of Algebra.

____

____

Check all your work carefully.

Name

CHAPTER 11 TEST, Form C

1. Consider the trinomial $x^2 + bx + 16$.

a. Name a value of b for which the trinomial is factorable into linear factors with integer coefficients. Give the factorization.

b. Name a value of b for which the trinomial is prime over the set of rational numbers. Justify your answer.

2. Let $f(x) = 6x^3 - 9x^2 - 6x$. Give an equation for a polynomial function g having the same zeros as f, plus one additional zero. Your equation should *not* have any double roots. Write your polynomial in standard form and identify the zeros of your function.

3. Complete the table below so the set of data can be modeled by a polynomial function of degree two or higher. Identify your function. Then explain how, given this set of data, a person could work backward from the table to determine your function.

x	1	2	3	4	5	6
y						

4. The diagram at the right shows a pattern for a cardboard box. Explain how the surface area and volume of the box are related to polynomial functions.

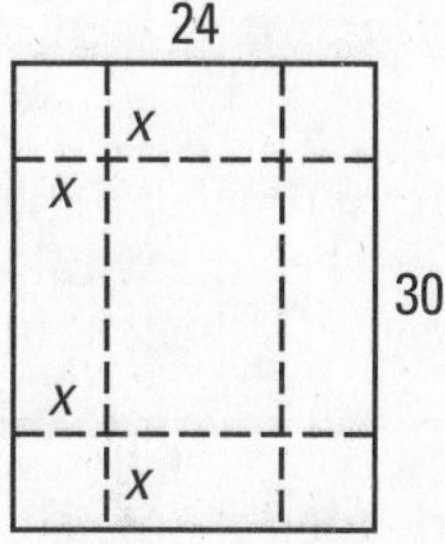

5. Andi graphed $y = x^4 - 9x^3 - 37x^2 + 9x + 36$ on an automatic grapher and obtained the display shown at the right. She concluded that the equation has exactly three rational roots: -3, -1, and 1.

Do you agree or disagree? If you agree, justify your answer. If you disagree, explain how you would correct Andi's work.

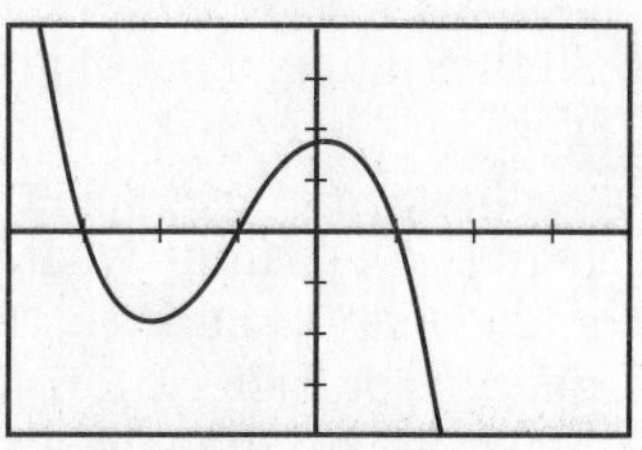

$-4 \le x \le 4$, x-scale = 1
$-80 \le y \le 80$, y-scale = 20

Name

CHAPTER 11 TEST, Form D

As a summer job, you are working as an assistant to an industrial design technician. You have been asked to help in preparing specifications for cardboard packing cartons like the one shown at the right.

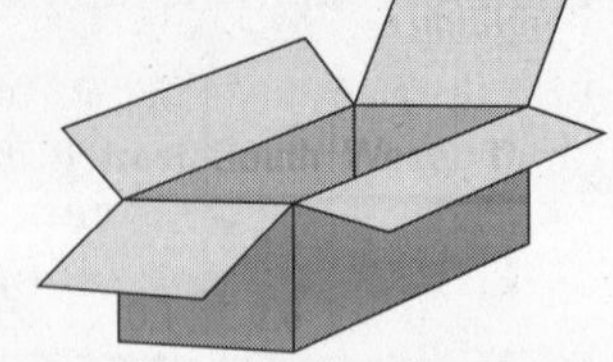

The technician gave you the following sketch as a pattern for a packing carton that is made from a 24-inch by 48-inch sheet of cardboard.

2 in.

x in.

6 in.	top flap A	top flap B	top flap C	top flap D
12 in.	gluing flap / back	side	front	side
6 in.	bottom flap A	bottom flap B	bottom flap C	bottom flap D

48 in.

waste

fold line

cut line

Note: Width of top and bottom flaps must equal half the height of the carton.

a. Explain what each of the following measures in the pattern represents.
i. 12 inches **ii.** 6 inches **iii.** 2 inches **iv.** x inches

b. Write a variable expression to represent each of the following.
i. the width of the back of the carton
ii. the length of each side of the carton

c. Write a polynomial $V(x)$ to represent the volume of the carton.

d. Identify the zeros of the function V from Part **c**. Explain the meaning of the zeros as they relate to the carton.

e. Suppose a client asks for a carton with a volume of at least 1800 cubic inches. Graph your function from Part **c** and use the graph to explain why the pattern above will not satisfy this requirement.

f. Suppose another client asks for a carton with a volume that is approximately 1000 cubic inches. Use your graph from Part **e** to determine what value of x will give you a carton that satisfies this requirement. Using this value of x, identify all the dimensions of the carton. Do you think the shape of this carton is reasonable?

g. At the right is a list of all the sizes of cardboard available to you. You have been asked to plan a set of five packing cartons with volumes of approximately 600, 1000, 1500, 1800, and 2800 cubic inches. Determine what size of cardboard you think would make a reasonably shaped carton for each volume. Then present a pattern for each carton. (Each pattern should fill the entire sheet of cardboard, like the pattern shown above.) Identify the dimensions and volume of the carton obtained from each of your patterns.

Cardboard Sizes
18″ × 36″
20″ × 30″
24″ × 38″
28″ × 48″
30″ × 40″
36″ × 42″
36″ × 50″
40″ × 54″

Name

CHAPTER 11 TEST, Cumulative Form

1. *Multiple choice.* If $ab = 0$, then which of the following must be true? 1. ________

   (a) $a = 0$ (b) $b = 0$

   (c) $a = 0$ or $b = 0$ (d) $a = 0$ and $b = 0$

2. Give an example of a quadratic trinomial. 2. ________

3. Find the exact value of sin 210°. 3. ________

4. Find all θ between 0° and 360° for which $\cos \theta = -\frac{\sqrt{3}}{2}$. 4. ________

5. Graph the function with equation $y = \log_2 x$ on the coordinate axes at the right. Label four points on your graph. 5.

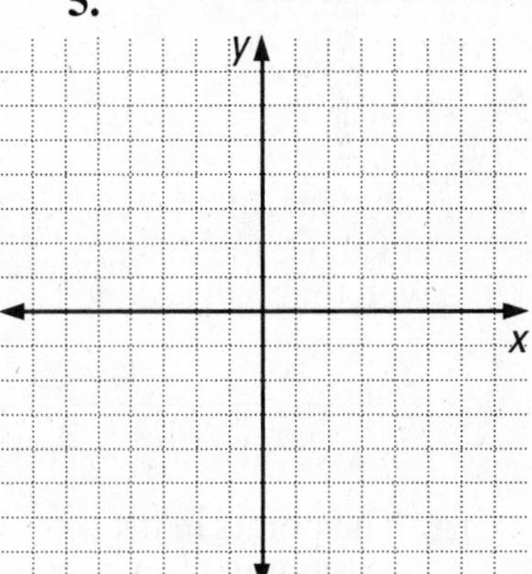

6. With each stroke of a vacuum pump, 5% of the air is removed from a chamber. How many strokes are needed to remove at least 80% of the air from the chamber? 6. ________

7. Expand and write in standard form: $(4a^2 - 3)(2a^2 + 5a - 3)$ 7. ________

In 8 and 9, factor completely over the set of polynomials with integer coefficients.

8. $x^2 - 81y^2$ 8. ________

9. $4p^2 - 28p - 120$ 9. ________

10. Find the exact zeros of the polynomial function f with equation $f(x) = 9x^3 - 289x$. 10. ________

Name ________________________________

11. What is the period of the function graphed at the right?

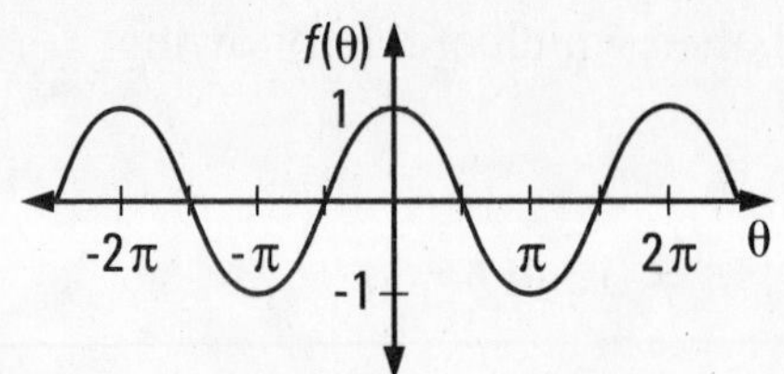

11. ____________

12. Refer to the graph of the polynomial function at the right. Name three pairs of consecutive integers between which a zero of the function must occur.

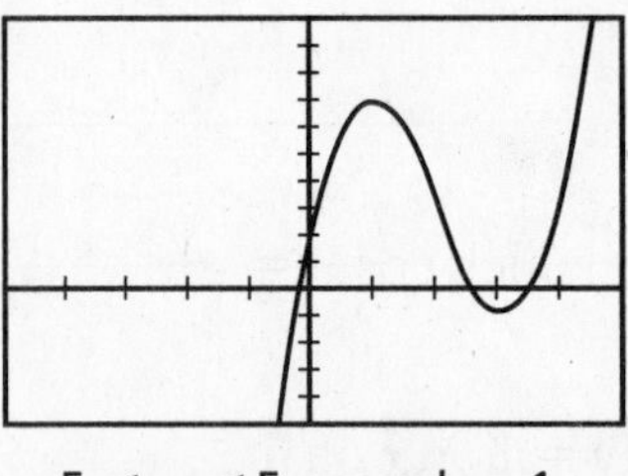

$-5 \le x \le 5$, x-scale = 1
$-5 \le y \le 10$, y-scale = 1

12. ____________

13. A student rolled a ball down a ramp and recorded the following data about the distance d in centimeters that the ball rolled in a given time t in seconds.

t	1	2	3	4	5	6
d	3.6	14.4	32.4	57.6	90.0	129.6

a. The points in the table can be described by a polynomial function of degree ___?___ .

13. a. ____________

b. Find a polynomial function $d = f(t)$ that describes these data.

b. ____________

c. Use your model to predict how far the ball will roll in 10 seconds.

c. ____________

14. Estimate the real zeros of the function with equation $f(x) = 3x^4 - 7x^3 + 5x^2 - 2x - 1$ to the nearest tenth.

14. ____________

15. Find ME in the triangle at the right.

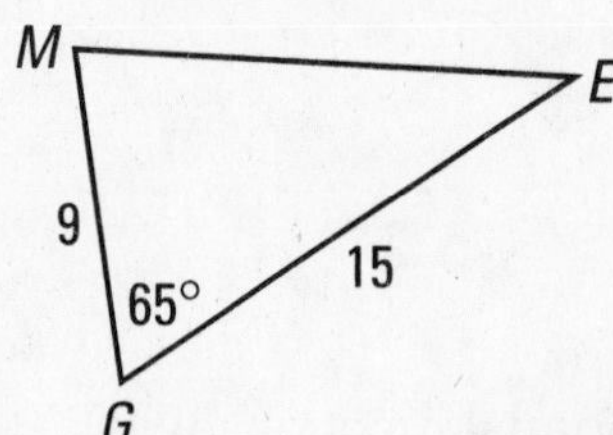

15. ____________

16. A ship sails 426 miles on a bearing of 10°. How far east of its original position is the ship?

16. ____________

Name ____________________

17. Consider the function with equation $y = x^4$.

a. Give an equation for the inverse of this function. **17. a.** ____________

b. Is the inverse a function? Why or why not?

____

____

18. Does the set $\{(-1, 1), (3, 1), (-1, 4), (0, 6)\}$ describe a function? Why or why not?

____

____

19. Rectangle $ABCD$ is shown at the right. What is its area? **19.** ____________

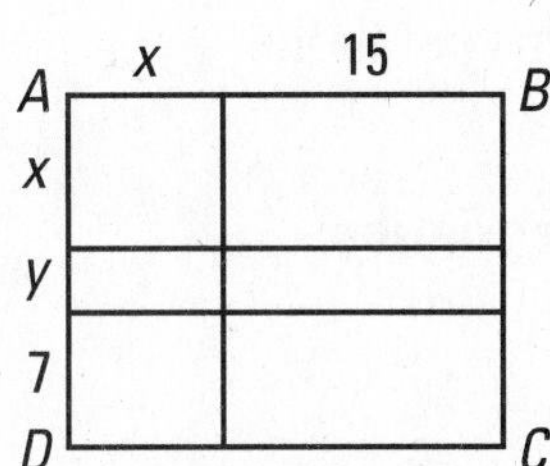

20. The table below gives the number of students with learning disabilities served by special programs in the United States in academic years from 1982 to 1990.

Year	1982	1983	1984	1985	1986	1987	1988	1989	1990
Students (millions)	1.74	1.81	1.83	1.86	1.91	1.93	1.99	2.05	2.13

a. Make a scatterplot of the data on the coordinate axes at the right. **20. a.**

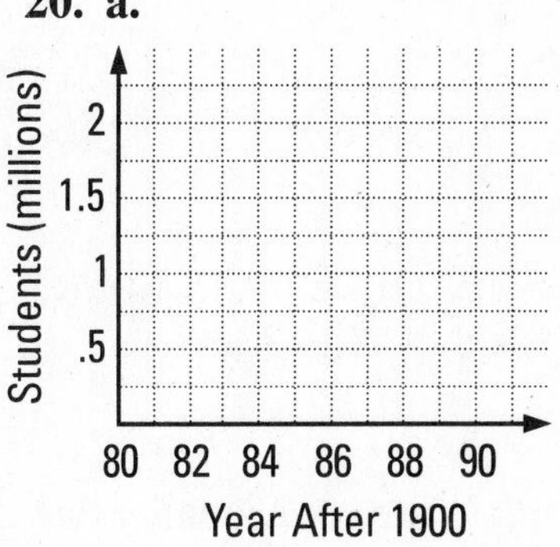

b. Find an equation of the regression line. **b.** ____________

c. Use your equation to predict the number of students with learning disabilities who will be served in 1999. **c.** ____________

Check all your work carefully.

Name

QUIZ

Lessons 12-1 Through 12-3

In 1–5, refer to the parabola below with focus $F = (3, 4)$.

1. Give the coordinates of the vertex of this parabola.   1. ________

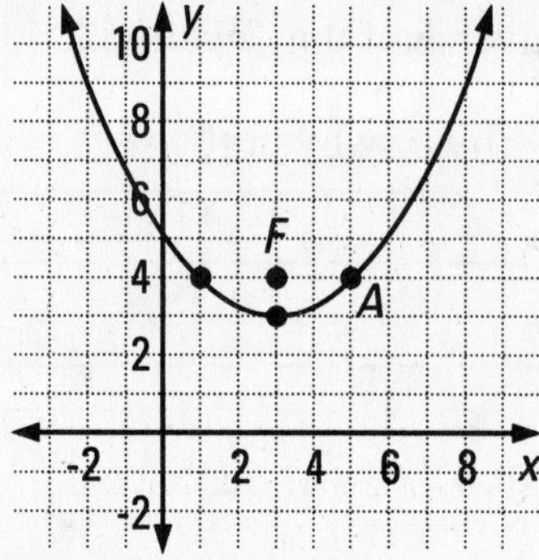

2. This parabola is a translation image of the parabola with equation $y = \frac{1}{4}x^2$. Write an equation for this parabola.   2. ________

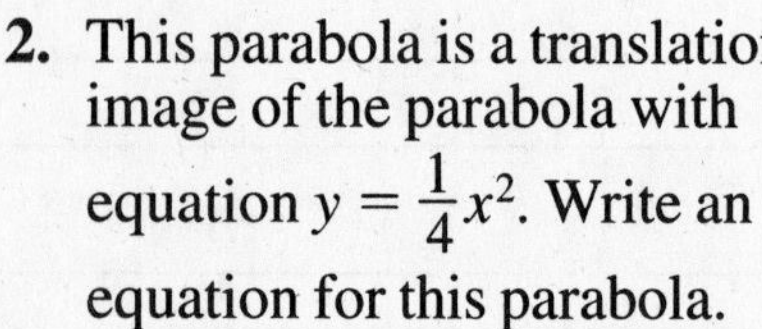

3. Give an equation for the directrix of this parabola.   3. ________

4. The distance from point A to point F is equal to the distance from point A to the point on the directrix with coordinates __?__.   4. ________

5. The point (4, __?__) is on this parabola.   5. ________

In 6–9, consider the circle with equation $(x + 1)^2 + (y - 3)^2 = 16$.

6. What is the center of the circle?   6. ________

7. What is the radius of the circle?   7. ________

8. Graph the circle on the coordinate axes at the right.   8.

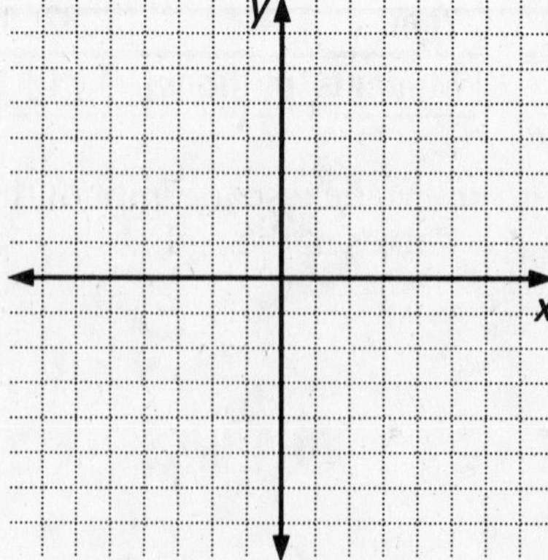

9. Write an inequality that describes the exterior of the circle.   9. ________

10. Eric and Erin built a fort that had a semicircular entrance with radius .9 m. How high is the entrance at a point that is .5 m from the center?   10. ________

Name

QUIZ

Lessons 12-4 Through 12-7

1. Find the area of the ellipse with equation $\frac{x^2}{36} + \frac{y^2}{64} = 1$. **1.** ____________

2. Name the vertices of the hyperbola with equation $xy = 32$. **2.** ____________

3. On the conic graph paper at the right, draw the set of points P such that $PF_1 + PF_2 = 14$. **3.**

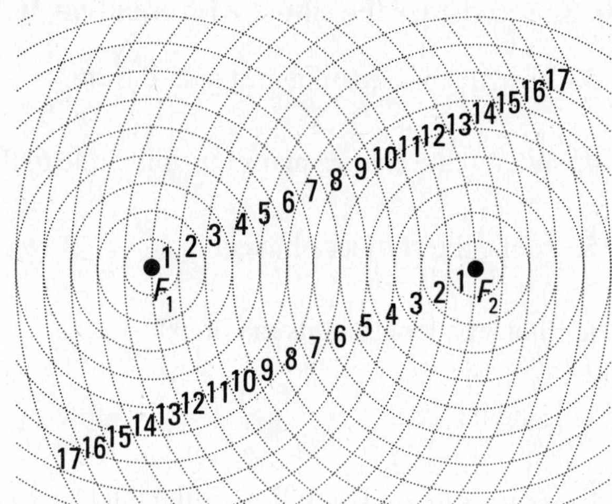

4. Write an equation for the image of $x^2 + y^2 = 1$ under the scale change $S_{5,2}$. **4.** ____________

5. Write an equation for the ellipse with foci (-10, 0) and (10, 0) and focal constant 25. **5.** ____________

In 6 and 7, consider the hyperbola with equation $\frac{x^2}{16} - \frac{y^2}{9} = 1$.

6. Give equations for its asymptotes. **6.** ____________

7. Graph the hyperbola on the coordinate axes at the right. **7.**

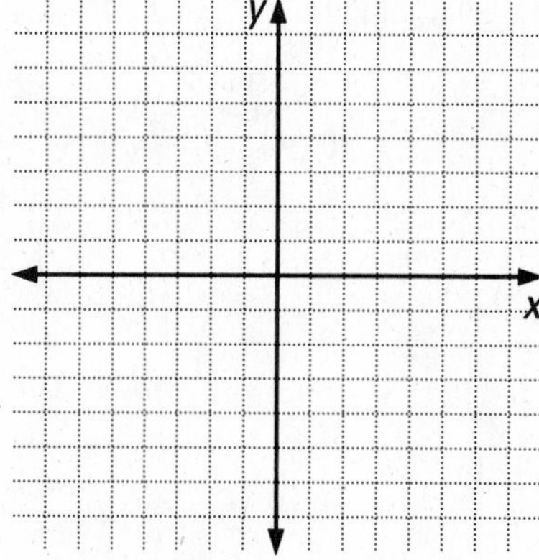

Name

CHAPTER 12 TEST, Form A

1. *True or false.* All circles are ellipses. 1. ______

2. Find equations for the asymptotes of the hyperbola with equation $\frac{x^2}{9} - \frac{y^2}{100} = 1$. 2. ______

In 3–8, consider the ellipse with equation $36x^2 + 49y^2 = 1764$.

3. Rewrite the equation in standard form. 3. ______

4. What scale change maps the unit circle to this ellipse? 4. ______

5. Name the vertices of the ellipse. 5. ______

6. State the length of its major axis. 6. ______

7. Find its area. 7. ______

8. *True or false.* This ellipse is the intersection of a plane and a cone. 8. ______

9. Find the point(s) of intersection of the line $y = x - 1$ and the parabola $y = \frac{1}{4}x^2$. 9. ______

In 10 and 11, give an equation for the quadratic relation that is graphed on the coordinate axes.

10.

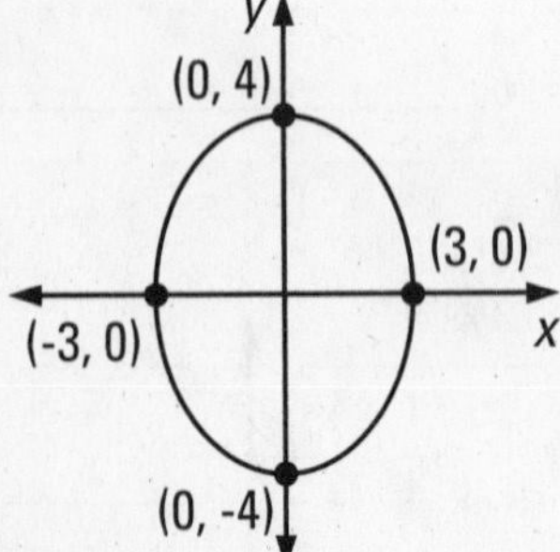

11.

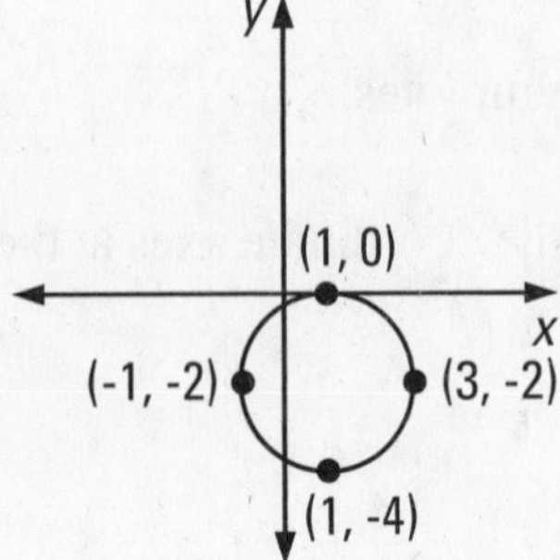

10. ______

11. ______

Name

In 12 and 13, find an equation for a quadratic relation that satisfies the given conditions.

12. a hyperbola with foci (-6, 0) and (6, 0) and focal constant 10 — **12.** ______

13. the interior of a circle with center (-1, 6) and radius 5 — **13.** ______

14. a. Graph the system $\begin{cases} y = x^2 + 4 \\ xy = 6 \end{cases}$ on the coordinate axes at the right. — **14. a.**

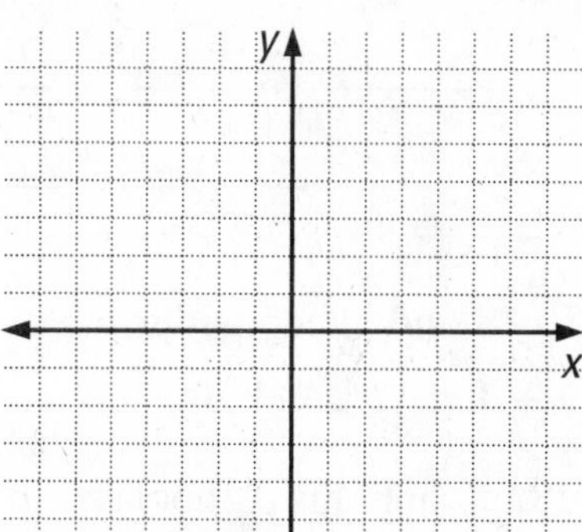

b. Use the graph to estimate the solution(s) to the system to the nearest tenth. — **b.** ______

15. Find the exact solution(s) of the following system. — **15.** ______

$$\begin{cases} y = \frac{1}{4}x^2 - 5 \\ y = -2x^2 + 4 \end{cases}$$

16. On the conic graph paper at the right, draw the set of points P such that $|PF_1 - PF_2| = 4$. — **16.**

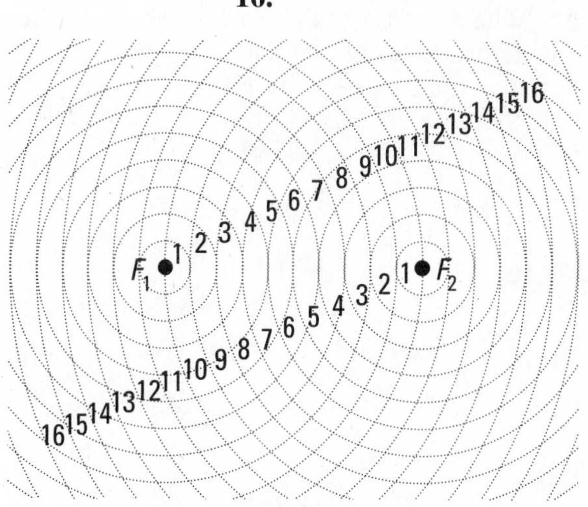

Name ____

17. The figure at the right shows a cross section of a semicircular tunnel with a diameter of 20 feet. Will a truck 8 feet high and 5.5 feet wide fit through this tunnel if it must travel to the right of the center line? Justify your answer.

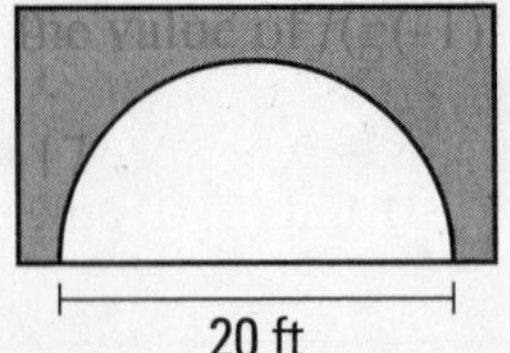

____

____

____

____

In 18 and 19, consider the parabola with equation $y + 1 = \frac{1}{8}x^2$.

18. Graph this parabola on the coordinate axes at the right.

18.

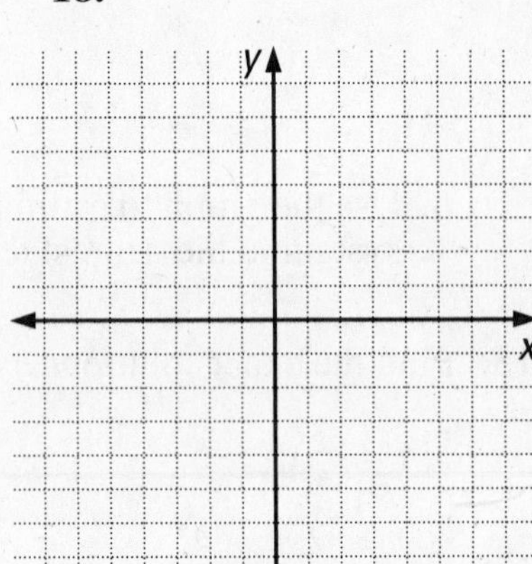

19. The directrix of this parabola is $y = -3$. Find the coordinates of its focus.

19. 

Check all your work carefully.

Name

CHAPTER 12 TEST, Form B

1. *True or false.* All ellipses are circles. 1. __________

2. Find equations for the asymptotes of the hyperbola with equation $\frac{x^2}{36} - \frac{y^2}{144} = 1$. 2. __________

In 3–8, consider the ellipse with equation $25x^2 + 16y^2 = 400$.

3. Rewrite the equation in standard form. 3. __________

4. What scale change maps the unit circle to this ellipse? 4. __________

5. Name the vertices of the ellipse. 5. __________

6. State the length of its major axis. 6. __________

7. Find its area. 7. __________

8. *True or false.* This ellipse is not the intersection of a plane and a cone. 8. __________

9. Find the point(s) of intersection of the line $y = 2x + 1$ and the parabola $y = 3x^2$. 9. __________

In 10 and 11, give an equation for the quadratic relation that is graphed on the coordinate axes.

10.

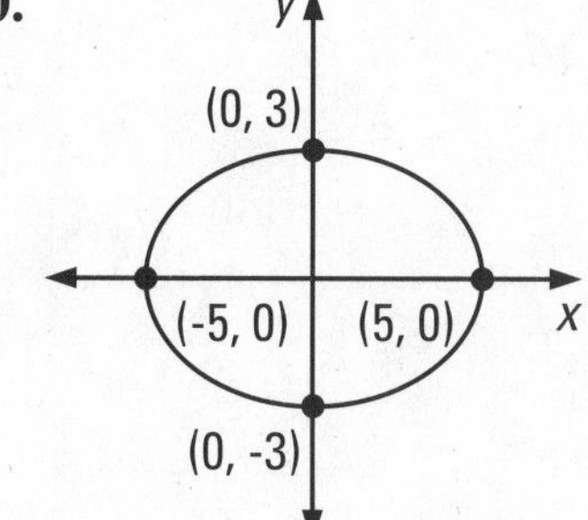

11.

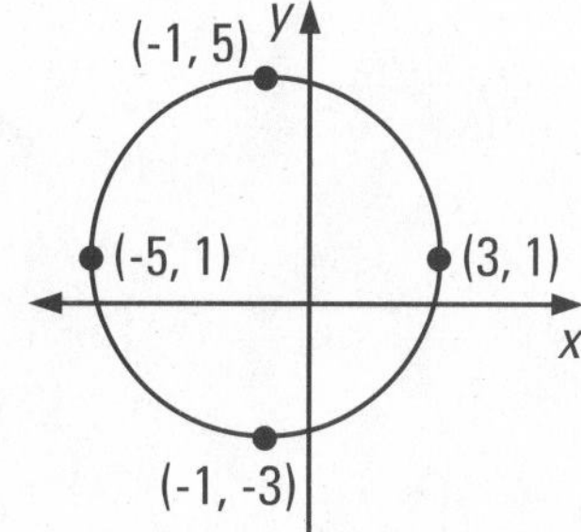

10. __________

11. __________

Name

In 12 and 13, find an equation for a quadratic relation that satisfies the given conditions.

12. a hyperbola with foci (-15, 0) and (15, 0) and focal constant 20 — **12.** ______________

13. the interior of a circle with center (-1, 2) and radius 7. — **13.** ______________

14. a. Graph the system $\begin{cases} y = -x^2 + 2 \\ x + 2y = -8 \end{cases}$ on the coordinate axes at the right. — **14. a.**

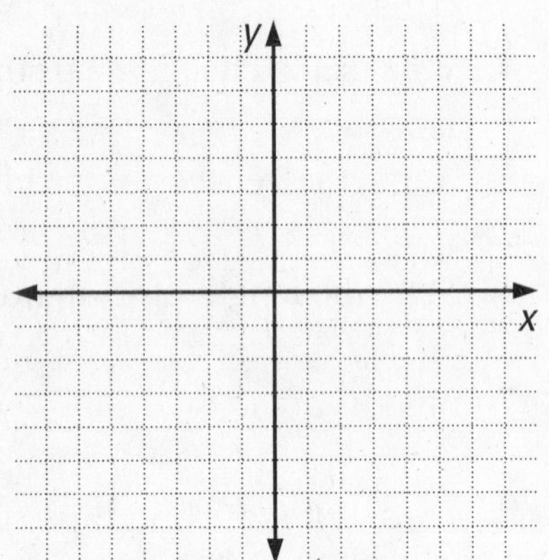

b. Use the graph to estimate the solution(s) to the system to the nearest tenth. — **b.** ______________

15. Find the exact solution(s) of the following system. — **15.** ______________

$$\begin{cases} x^2 + (y-3)^2 = 25 \\ (x-6)^2 + (y-3)^2 = 1 \end{cases}$$

16. On the conic graph paper at the right, draw the set of points P such that $|PF_1 - PF_2| = 6$. — **16.**

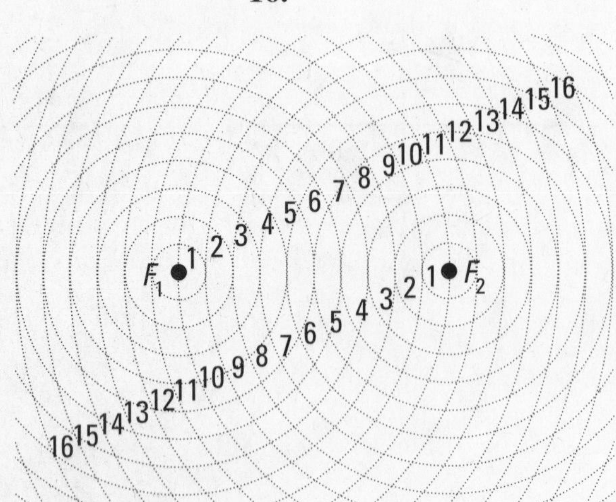

Name ______________________________

17. The figure at the right shows a cross section of a tunnel. The tunnel is constructed so that *ABCD* is a square of side 12 feet, and above it is a semicircular arch. Will a truck 14 feet high and 6 feet wide fit through this tunnel if it is allowed anywhere on the road? Justify your answer.

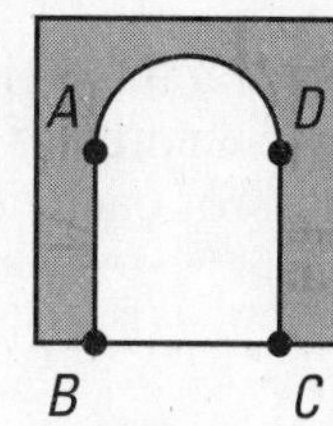

____

____

____

____

In 18 and 19, consider the parabola with equation $y - 4 = -\frac{1}{8}x^2$.

18. Graph this parabola on the coordinate axes at the right.

18.

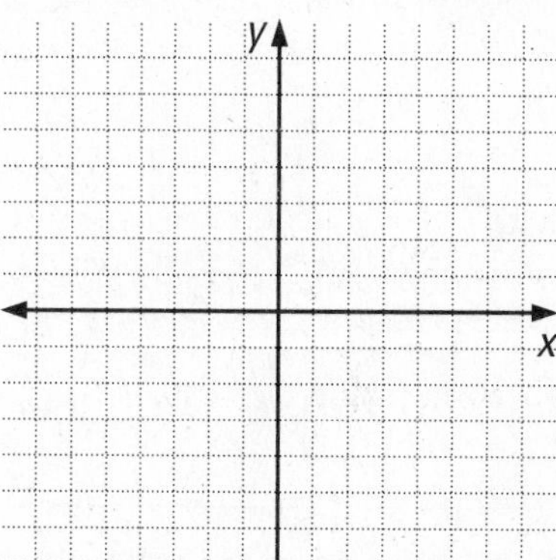

19. The directrix of this parabola is $y = 6$. Find the coordinates of its focus.

19. ______________________________

Check all your work carefully.

Name

CHAPTER 12 TEST, Form C

1. On the coordinate axes at the right, sketch two different ellipses that each have an area of 12π square units. Then give an equation for each ellipse.

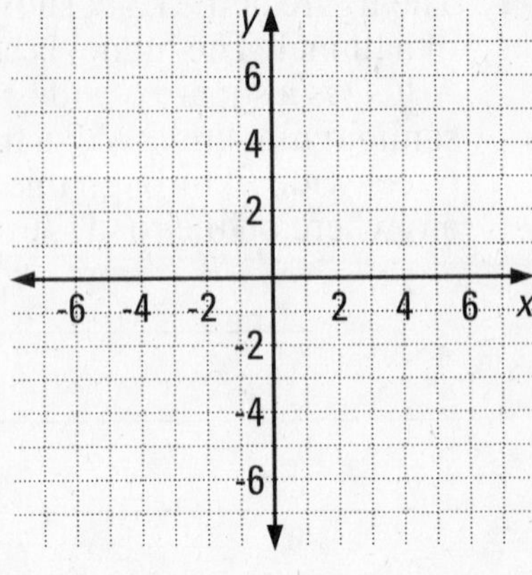

2. Explain how you can describe the parabola shown at the right without giving its equation and without naming any points that it contains.

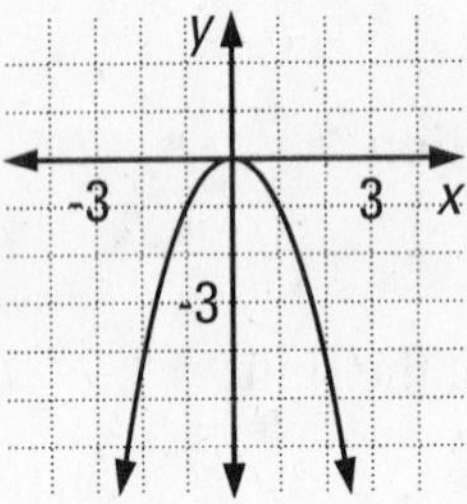

3. How are a hyperbola and an ellipse alike? How are they different? State as many likenesses and differences as you can.

4. Choose from the following equations.

   i. $(x - 2)^2 + (y + 3)^2 = 16$ ii. $xy = 8$

   iii. $\frac{x^2}{4} + \frac{y^2}{36} = 1$ iv. $y = \frac{1}{4}x + 4$

   v. $y = -\frac{1}{4}x^2$

   a. Find two equations that form a system with exactly two solutions.
   b. Find two equations that form a system with exactly one solution.
   c. Find two equations that form an inconsistent system.

   Justify your answers.

5. The curve in the figure below is a semicircle. Describe a real-world situation that this figure might represent. Write a problem about the situation that you could solve by using the equation of the semicircle. Then show how to solve your problem.

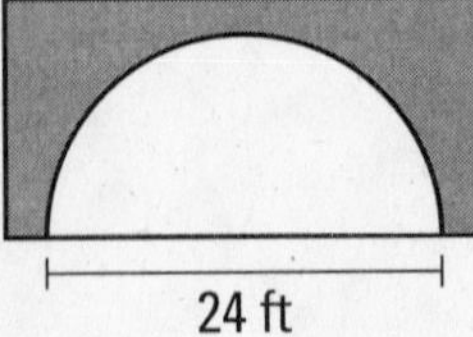

Name

CHAPTER 12 TEST, Form D

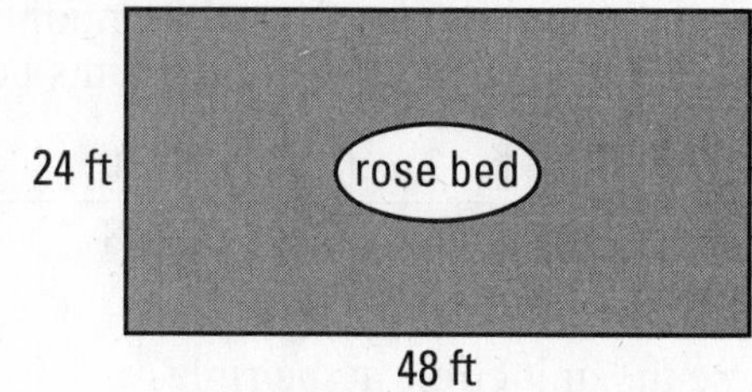

Larry and Althea Conic have moved into a new house. At the back of the house is a large rectangular plot of land. They want to transform this land into a formal garden.

The Conics plan to have a bed of roses at the center of the garden. They want the border of this rose bed to be an ellipse. They made the sketch at the right to show the dimensions of the entire plot and to indicate about how large the rose bed should be in relation to it.

a. What do you think is a reasonable length for the major axis of the ellipse that forms the border of the rose bed? for the minor axis?

b. Describe how you could find an equation for the ellipse determined by your measures in Part **a**. Then give the equation of the ellipse and graph the equation.

c. Name the foci of the ellipse that you identified in Part **b**.

d. The Conics have hired a landscaper who will prepare the area for the rose bed and plant the roses. However, the landscaper needs instructions about how to locate the elliptical border of the bed. The Conics have asked for your assistance. Write a step-by-step set of instructions that will tell the landscaper how to dig out an ellipse whose center is also the center of the plot of land. (You may assume that the plot of land is a perfect rectangle.)

e. The landscaper has said that, as a rule of thumb, you can plant two rose bushes for each square yard of area in your rose bed. About how many rose bushes will the landscaper be able to plant in the Conics' rose bed?

f. The Conics also would like to lay one or more gravel pathways across their garden. Of course, because they are the Conics, any pathway in their garden must have the shape of a conic section. Furthermore, each pathway must be laid out precisely using the appropriate quadratic relation.

Plan a pathway for their garden. Give a set of equations that can be used to determine the pathway, and graph the equations. (*Note:* A pathway should be at least two or three feet wide, so you need more than one equation to describe each one.) Then write a set of instructions that will tell the landscaper how to locate the pathway.

Name

CHAPTER 12 TEST, Cumulative Form

1. Find an equation for the polynomial function of lowest degree described by the data points below. **1.** ______

x	1	2	3	4	5	6
y	7	6	1	-8	-21	-38

2. Use the unit circle at the right. Which letter on the figure stands for the indicated value of the trigonometric function?

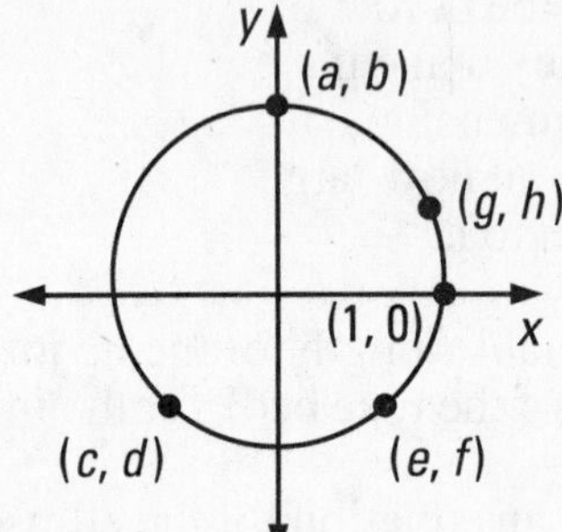

a. sin 225° **2. a.** ______

b. cos (-330°) **b.** ______

3. Rewrite $\frac{x^2}{16} + \frac{y^2}{25} = 1$ in the form $Ax^2 + Bxy + Cy^2 + Dx + Ey + F = 0$. **3.** ______

4. Write an equation for the hyperbola with foci (6, 0) and (-6, 0) and focal constant 8. **4.** ______

In 5 and 6, refer to the figure at the right. It shows a steel hut with each cross section a semiellipse (half an ellipse) having base 36 feet and height 12 feet.

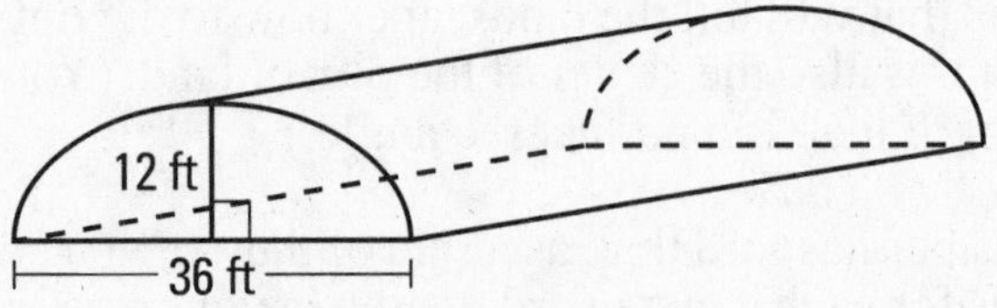

5. Beds that are 3 feet high will be placed in the hut so that the head of each bed is against one of the curved walls. What will be the distance along the floor between the bottom of each headboard and the curved wall that it touches? Justify your answer.

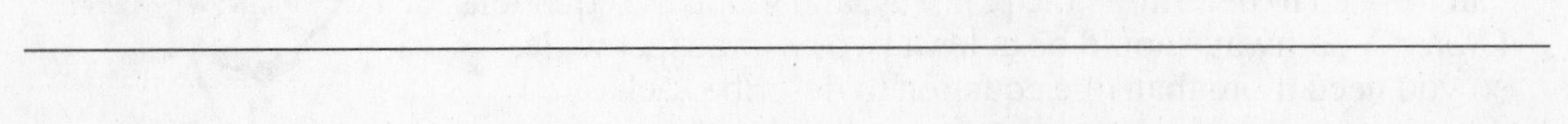

6. The back wall of this hut has no doors or windows. What is the area of this wall, to the nearest square foot? **6.** ______

Name

7. Write an equation in vertex form for the parabola with focus (0, 5) and directrix $y = -3$.

7. 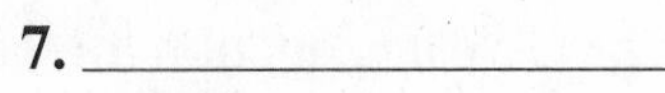

8. The perimeter of a rectangular garden is 456 meters, and its area is 9275 square meters. What are the length and width of the garden?

8. 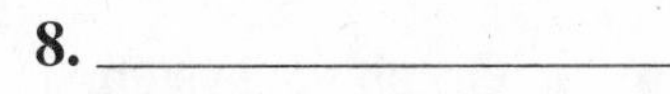

9. Find an equation for the circle that is tangent to the x-axis at (3, 0) and tangent to the y-axis at (0, -3).

9. 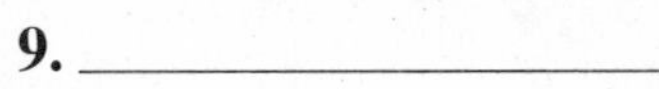

10. On the coordinate axes at the right, graph a polynomial function P of degree 3 whose zeros are -1, 1, and 3.

10.

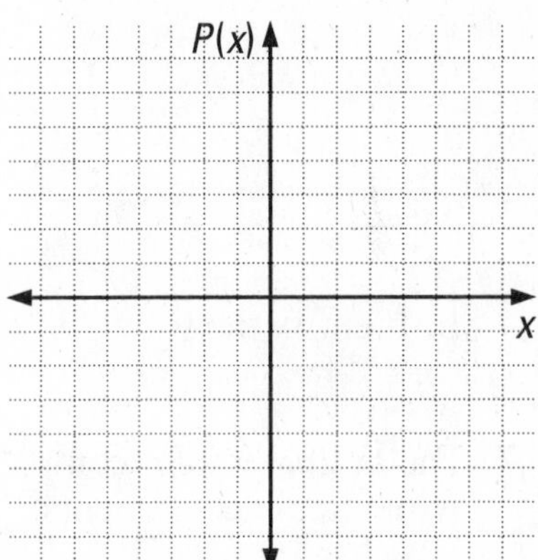

11. Consider the polynomial function P such that $P(x) = 6x^3 - 7x^2 - x + 2$.

a. List all the possible rational zeros of P.

11. a. ____________

b. Find the rational zeros of P.

b. ____________

12. Explain why you cannot apply the Zero-Product Theorem directly to the equation $(2x + 5)(3x - 7) = 15$.

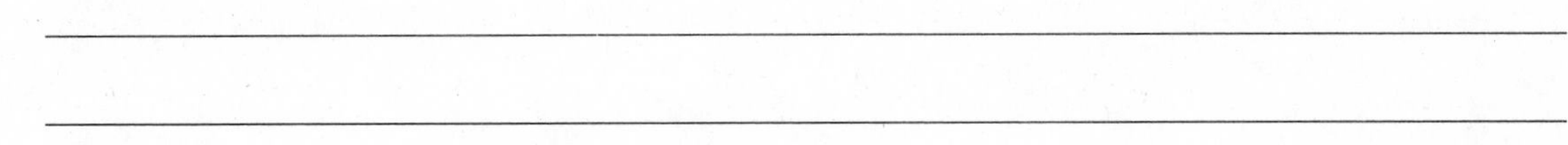

13. Let $f = \{(-3, 6), (-1, 2), (0, 0), (5, -10)\}$. What is the domain of f^{-1}?

13. ____________

14. Solve $(8^4)^{\frac{1}{3}} = 8^{x+\frac{1}{3}}$.

14. ____________

Name

15. Give an equation for the image of $x^2 + y^2 = 1$ under the scale change $S_{7,10}$.

15. 

16. a. Graph the system $\begin{cases} y = 2x^2 - 5 \\ xy = 6 \end{cases}$ on the coordinate axes at the right.

16. a.

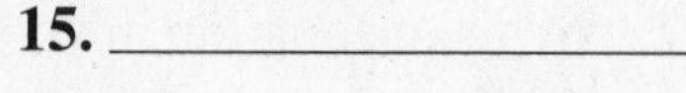

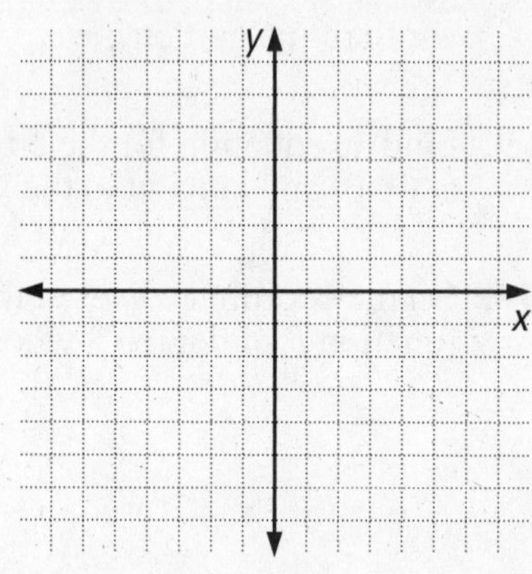

b. Identify the solution(s) to the system.

b. ____________

17. Factor $28t^5 - 63t^3$ completely over the set of polynomials with integer coefficients.

17. 

18. Suppose that, two years ago, $1750 was invested at an annual interest rate of 4.7% compounded monthly. How much will be in this account $3\frac{1}{2}$ years from now? Assume that no other deposits or withdrawals have been made or will be made.

18. ____________

Check all your work carefully.

Name

QUIZ

Lessons 13-1 Through 13-3

1. *Multiple choice.* $\sum_{i=1}^{5} i^2 = \underline{\quad ? \quad}$ 1. ____

   (a) $1^2 + 5^2$ (b) $1 + 2 + 3 + 4 + 5$

   (c) $1 + 4 + 9 + 16 + 25$ (d) $2 + 4 + 6 + 8 + 10$

2. Rewrite $2 + 6 + 10 + 14 + 18 + 22$ using Σ-notation. 2. ____

3. Evaluate $\sum_{i=1}^{50} i$. 3. ____

4. Four miniature statues of warriors from Xi'an, China, are to be placed on a mantel in a line from left to right. How many different arrangements are possible? 4. ____

In 5 and 6, evaluate.

5. $8! + 5!$ 5. ____

6. $\frac{8!}{5!}$ 6. ____

7. Consider the arithmetic sequence 1, 4, 7, 10, 13, ...

   a. Find a_{40}, the 40th term. 7. a. ____

   b. Find S_{40}, the sum of the first 40 terms. b. ____

8. Let S_n be the sum of the first n terms of the sequence defined by $a_n = 5n + 2$, for integers $n \geq 1$. Find the least value of n such that $S_n \geq 500$. 8. ____

9. Find the sum of the first 8 terms of the geometric series with first term 3 and common ratio 2. 9. ____

10. Suppose \$100 is deposited on January 1 of each year from 1995 through 2000, inclusive, and earns an annual yield of 5%. What will be the value of this investment on January 1, 2001? 10. ____

Name

QUIZ

Lessons 13-4 Through 13-7

In 1 and 2, use this information. A store presently has one manager and three employees. The manager earns $33,000 a year. Among the employees, one earns $22,000 a year, one earns $20,000 a year, and one earns $18,000 a year. The manager decides to hire a new employee.

1. If, after the new employee is hired, the mode of all the salaries is $22,000. What is the new employee's salary? **1.** ____________

2. If, after the new employee is hired, the mean of all the salaries is $22,000. What is the new employee's salary? **2.** ____________

In 3 and 4, use this information. The following are the Advanced-Placement Test scores earned by students in a BC calculus class: {3, 4, 5, 5, 4, 5, 5, 5, 4, 5, 5, 5, 3, 4, 5}

3. What is the median of the scores? **3.** ____________

4. What is the standard deviation of the scores? **4.** ____________

5. What element in which row of Pascal's Triangle does $\binom{5}{3}$ represent? **5.** ____________

6. *Multiple choice.* Which has the same value as $\binom{7}{2}$? **6.** ____________

(a) $\binom{2}{7}$ (b) $\binom{7}{5}$ (c) $\binom{5}{2}$ (d) $\binom{7}{3}$

In 7–10, evaluate.

7. $\binom{5}{5}$ **8.** $\binom{16}{0}$

9. $\binom{15}{3} + \binom{15}{4}$ **10.** $\binom{23}{22}$

7. ____________

8. ____________

9. ____________

10. ____________

In 11 and 12, expand.

11. $(x + 2y)^4$ **11.** ____________

12. $(3m^2 - 4n)^3$ **12.** ____________

13. A team of 5 players is to be chosen from a class of 35 students. In how many ways can this be done? **13.** ____________

14. *True or false.* A set with 6 elements has 6^2 subsets. **14.** ____________

Name

CHAPTER 13 TEST, Form A

In 1 and 2, a series is given. a. Identify the series as arithmetic or geometric. b. Rewrite the series using Σ-notation. c. Evaluate the series.

1. $2 + 5 + 8 + \ldots + 302$

1. a. ____________

b. ____________

c. ____________

2. $7 + 7\left(\frac{1}{2}\right) + 7\left(\frac{1}{2}\right)^2 + \ldots 7\left(\frac{1}{2}\right)^{30}$

2. a. ____________

b. ____________

c. ____________

In 3–5, rows 0 through 2 of Pascal's Triangle are shown at the right.

row 0 → 1

row 1 → 1 1

row 2 → 1 2 1

3. Write the next five rows.

row 3 → ____________

row 4 → ____________

row 5 → ____________

row 6 → ____________

row 7 → ____________

4. What is the sum of the numbers in row 13?

4. ____________

5. What element in which row does $\binom{7}{2}$ represent?

5. ____________

In 6 and 7, evaluate.

6. $\binom{52}{5}$

6. ____________

7. $\frac{27!}{24!\,3!}$

7. ____________

Name ______

8. To evaluate the quality of the television sets it manufactured last year, a company is using a sample of sets bought rather than the population.

a. What is the population in this situation?

______

b. Why might a sample be preferred over the population?

______

9. The table at the right lists the number of baseball games won by teams in the American League West Division in 1993.

Team	Games Won
Chicago	94
Texas	86
Kansas City	84
Seattle	82
California	71
Minnesota	71
Oakland	68

a. Find the median number of wins.

b. Find the mode.

9. a. ______

b. ______

10. Joyce scored 3, 11, 10, 12, 7, and 20 points in her first six basketball games. How many points must she score in the seventh game to have a mean of 13 points for all seven games?

10. ______

In 11 and 12, consider that a fair coin is tossed 8 times.

11. How many possible outcomes are there?

11. ______

12. What is the probability of getting 6 heads and 2 tails?

12. ______

13. You have a choice of 10 toppings for your frozen yogurt. How many combinations of 6 toppings are possible?

13. ______

14. Expand $(2x - 3z)^4$.

14. ______

In 15 and 16, use the following information: In the past year, the monthly cost of residential customers' water bills in a particular city had a mean of $13.73 and a standard deviation of $2.41. Assume that the costs were normally distributed.

15. About what percent of the monthly water bills were between $11.32 and $16.14?

15. ______

16. About what percent of the monthly water bills were at least $18.55?

16. ______

Name

17. a. Let $P(n) = \dfrac{\binom{6}{n}}{2^6}$. Complete the table at the right. **17. a.**

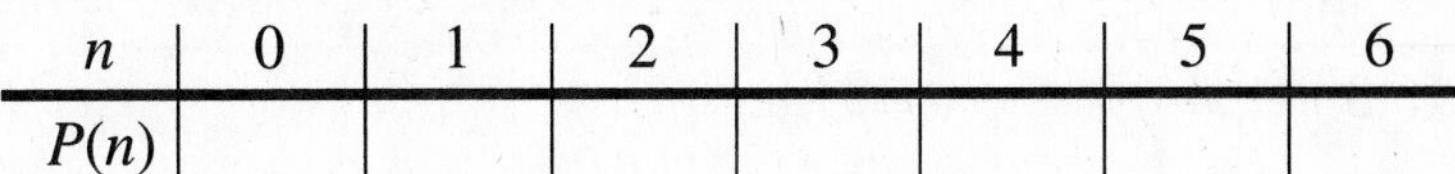

n	0	1	2	3	4	5	6
$P(n)$							

b. Graph the function on the coordinate axes at the right. **b.**

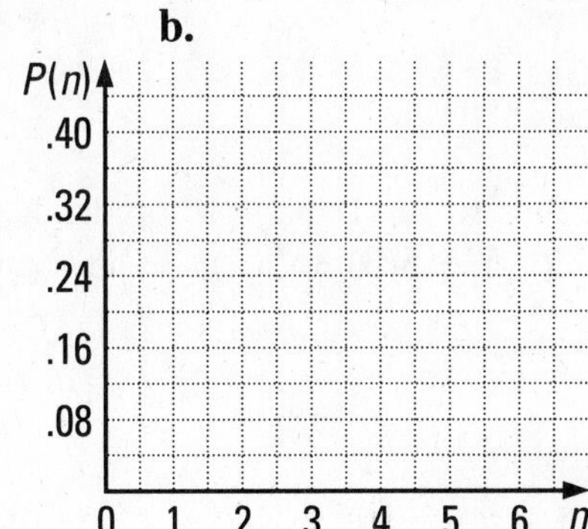

c. *True or false.* This is a graph of a quadratic function. **c.** ____________

18. Job A pays $130 the first week, with a raise of $15 per week beginning the 2nd week. Job B pays biweekly, with $200 on the first paycheck, and a 50% increase every paycheck thereafter. Suppose Paul wants to work for 10 weeks and earn as much money as possible. Which job should he take? Justify your reasoning.

____

____

19. In lottery *A*, a player picks five numbers from 1 through 50 and must match five balls picked randomly from balls numbered 1 through 50. What is the probability of picking all five winning numbers in this lottery? **19.** ____________

20. In lottery *B*, a player picks four numbers from 1 through 40 and must match four balls picked randomly from balls numbered 1 through 40.What is the probability of picking exactly three of the four winning numbers in this lottery? **20.** ____________

Check all your work carefully.

Name

CHAPTER 13 TEST, Form B

In 1 and 2, a series is given. a. Identify the series as arithmetic or geometric. b. Rewrite the series using Σ-notation. c. Evaluate the series.

1. $3 + 8 + 13 + \ldots + 313$

1. a. ____________

b. ____________

c. ____________

2. $5 + 5(3) + 5(3)^2 + \ldots + 5(3)^{19}$

2. a. ____________

b. ____________

c. ____________

In 3–5, rows 0 through 2 of Pascal's Triangle are shown at the right.

row 0 → 1

row 1 → 1 1

row 2 → 1 2 1

3. Write the next six rows.

row 3 → ____________

row 4 → ____________

row 5 → ____________

row 6 → ____________

row 7 → ____________

row 8 → ____________

4. What is the sum of the numbers in row 20?

4. ____________

5. What element in which row does $\binom{8}{5}$ represent?

5. ____________

In 6 and 7, evaluate.

6. $\binom{20}{18}$

6. ____________

7. $\frac{15!}{3!\,12!}$

7. ____________

Name

8. To determine which candidate is favored by voters in an upcoming election, a polling service is using a sample rather than the population.

a. What is the population in this situation?

____

b. Why might a sample be preferred over the population?

____

9. The table at the right lists the number of baseball games won by teams in the American League East Division in 1993.

Team	Games Won
Toronto	95
New York	88
Baltimore	85
Detroit	85
Boston	80
Cleveland	76
Milwaukee	69

a. Find the median number of wins. **9. a.** __________

b. Find the mode. **b.** __________

10. Huan scored 90, 85, 82, 83, and 95 on his first five algebra tests. What score must he get on the sixth test to have a mean score of 88 for all six tests? **10.** __________

In 11 and 12, consider that a fair coin is tossed 9 times.

11. How many possible outcomes are there? **11.** __________

12. What is the probability of getting 6 heads and 3 tails? **12.** __________

13. You have a choice of 8 toppings for your taco. How many combinations of 3 toppings are possible? **13.** __________

14. Expand $(5m - 8n)^4$. **14.** __________

In 15 and 16, use the following information: On an IQ test, the mean score is 100 and the standard deviation is 15. The scores are normally distributed.

15. About what percent of people have IQ scores between 85 and 115? **15.** __________

16. About what percent of people have IQ scores at or above 130? **16.** __________

Name

17. a. Let $P(n) = \dfrac{\binom{5}{n}}{2^5}$. Complete the table at the right. **17. a.**

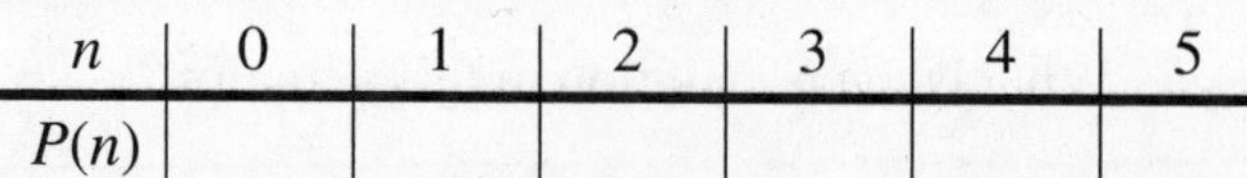

n	0	1	2	3	4	5
$P(n)$						

b. Graph the function on the coordinate axes at the right. **b.**

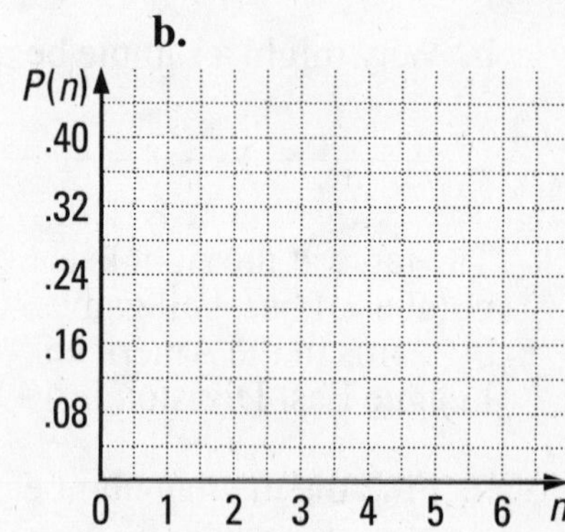

c. *True or false.* This is a graph of a binomial distribution. **c.** __________

18. Job A pays \$115 the first week, with a raise of \$10 per week beginning the 2nd week. Job B pays biweekly, with \$200 on the first paycheck, and a 25% increase every paycheck thereafter. Suppose Shasheena wants to work for 10 weeks and earn as much as possible. Which job should she take? Justify your reasoning.

____

____

19. In lottery *A*, a player picks six numbers from 1 through 25 and must match six balls picked randomly from balls numbered 1 through 25. What is the probability of picking all six winning numbers in this lottery? **19.** __________

20. In lottery *B*, a player picks seven numbers from 1 through 35 and must match seven balls picked randomly from balls numbered 1 through 35. What is the probability of picking exactly six of the seven winning numbers in this lottery? **20.** __________

Check all your work carefully.

Name

CHAPTER 13 TEST, Form C

1. Pat wrote the following statement on a homework assignment.

$$\sum_{i=1}^{10}(2i + 3) = 23$$

Do you agree or disagree with Pat's statement? If you agree, justify your answer. If you disagree, explain how you would correct the statement.

2. Give both a mathematical explanation and a real-world explanation to demonstrate why the expression $\binom{5}{7}$ is not meaningful.

3. State two important properties of Pascal's Triangle. Demonstrate how these properties apply to row 6 of the triangle.

4. Create a set of seven test scores that satisfies all the following conditions.

   The mean is 75.
   The median is 77.
   The mode is 78.

   Find the standard deviation of your scores.

5. Describe a real-world situation that the function at the right might represent. Then graph the function. $P(n) = \dfrac{\binom{8}{n}}{2^8}$

6. Use the Binomial Theorem to show that $(a - b)^4 = (b - a)^4$. Do you think it follows that $(a - b)^n = (b - a)^n$ for all nonnegative integers n? Explain your reasoning.

Name

CHAPTER 13 TEST, Form D

Your town is making plans for its annual Spring Fair. Lotteries are becoming very popular, so a town official suggested that the money raised from adult admissions might be used as the prize in a lottery. To play the lottery, a person would pick numbers from a game card printed on the back of each adult admission ticket. The person would enter the lottery by handing in the ticket at the gate.

You have been asked to make a plan for conducting the lottery. The Spring Fair committee has given you these general guidelines.

- The town hopes to attract between 4000 and 5000 adults to the fair.
- The prize money will consist of the total amount collected from adult admissions.
- The prize money will be shared equally among all the winners.
- It should be most likely that there are two or three winners.
- Each winner should have a chance of receiving $1000 or more.

a. Suppose you conduct the lottery as follows: A player picks three numbers from 1 through 10 and must match three balls picked randomly at the same time from a set of balls numbered 1 through 10. How many different combinations of three numbers are possible? What is the probability that a person will pick the winning combination?

b. Suppose 4000 adults enter the lottery. If you conduct the lottery as described in Part **a**, about how many winners do you think there might be? Explain your reasoning.

c. Suppose that the cost of adult admission is $2. Assume the conditions in Parts **a** and **b**. About how much money might a person expect to win? Explain your reasoning.

d. Explain why conducting the lottery as described in Parts **a** through **c** may or may not meet the guidelines that the committee gave you

e. Suppose that you want to conduct the lottery using the basic procedure of picking numbers and matching balls that is outlined in Part **a**. Explain why you are not likely to meet the guidelines by using just ten balls.

f. Using the committee's guidelines, make a plan for the lottery. (You may use the basic procedure of picking numbers and matching balls that is described above, or you may create your own procedure.) Then write a report in which you present your plan to the committee. Your report should include the following.

- a suggested cost for an adult admission ticket
- a description of the procedure for conducting the lottery
- an analysis of the probability of winning
- a prediction of the amount each winner might get
- a suggested design for the game card that will appear on the back of the admission ticket

Name ______________________

CHAPTER 13 TEST, Cumulative Form

1. Evaluate $\sum_{i=7}^{25}(6i)$. **1.** ________

2. Expand $(3 + 2x)^5$. **2.** ________

3. Evaluate $\binom{95}{92}$. **3.** ________

4. Convert 320° to its exact radian equivalent. **4.** ________

5. a. *Multiple choice.* Which of the following graphs represents a function whose inverse also is a function? **5. a.** ________

(a)

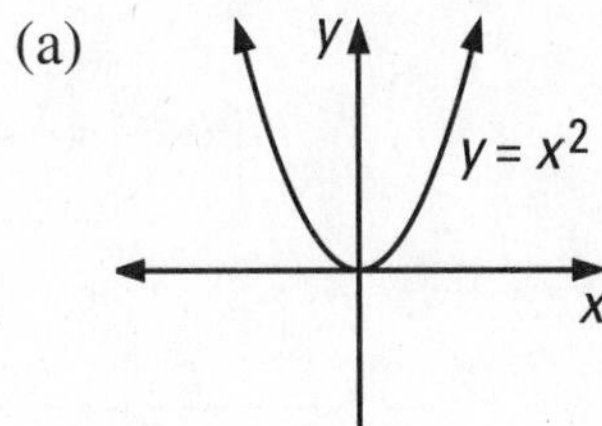

(b)

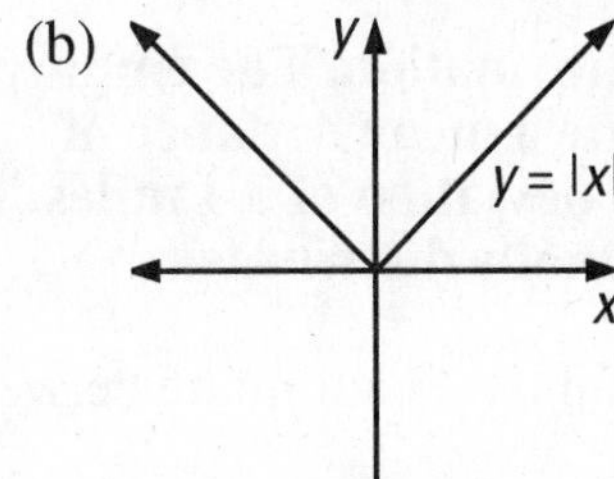

(c)

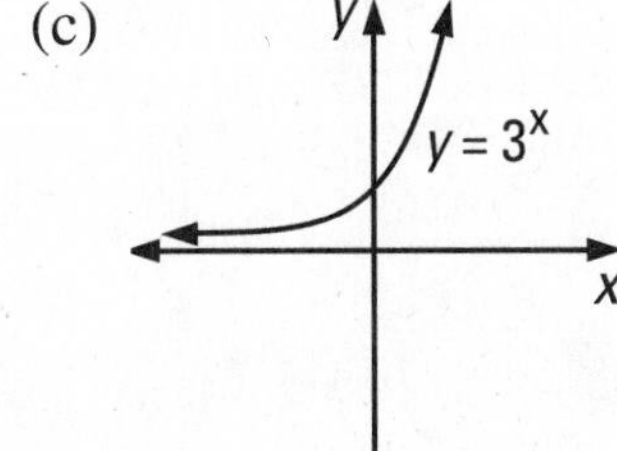

(d)

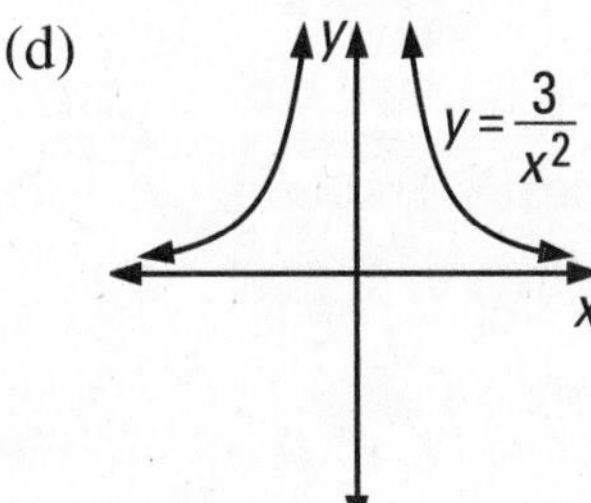

b. On the coordinate axes at the right, graph the inverse of the function that you identified in Part **a**. **b.**

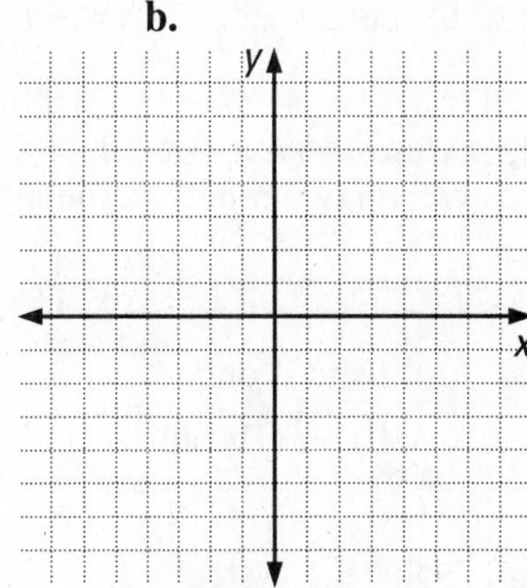

Name

6. Factor $75x^3 - 85x^2 - 210x$ completely over the set of polynomials with integer coefficients. **6.** ______

7. *True or false.* A circle is an ellipse in which the length of the major axis equals the length of the minor axis. **7.** ______

8. Consider these test scores:

83, 69, 87, 88, 88, 93, 88, 86, 93, 95

a. Find the mean. **8. a.** ______

b. Find the median. **b.** ______

c. Find the mode. **c.** ______

In 9 and 10, use the following information. The employees of a local school district commute a mean distance of 8.3 miles a day, with a standard deviation of 3.1 miles. Assume these distances are normally distributed.

9. About what percent of the employees commute between 5.2 and 11.4 miles a day? **9.** ______

10. About what percent of the employees commute at least 14.5 miles a day? **10.** ______

11. The following is row 8 of Pascal's Triangle.

1 8 28 56 70 56 28 8 1

Write row 9 below.

______

12. Calculate $\binom{20}{0} + \binom{20}{1} + \binom{20}{2} + \ldots + \binom{20}{20}$. **12.** ______

13. *Multiple choice.* Of the following quadratic relations, which two represent the same type of conic section? **13.** ______

I. $y = x^2$ II. $y = \frac{1}{x}$ III. $x^2 + y^2 = 1$ IV. $x^2 - y^2 = 1$

(a) I and II only (b) II and IV only

(c) III and IV only (d) none of these

14. Solve the system $\begin{cases} y = 2x - 7 \\ y = 1 - x^2 \end{cases}$. **14.** ______

Name

15. Name the focus, vertex, and directrix of the parabola with equation $y = \frac{1}{8}x^2$.

15. ______________

16. On the conic graph paper at the right, draw the set of points P such that $PF_1 + PF_2 = 16$.

16.

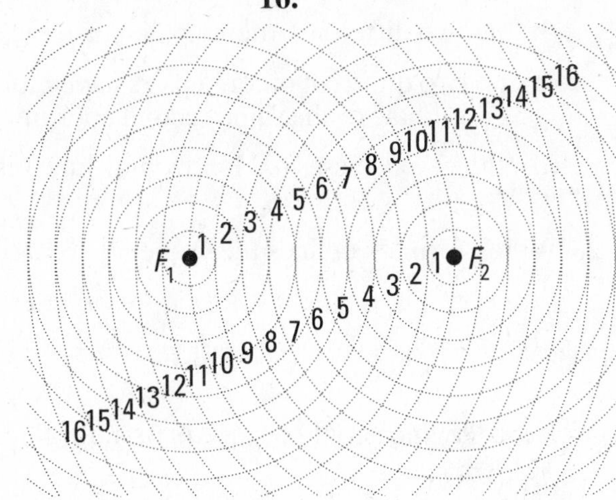

17. Let $P(n) = \frac{\binom{7}{n}}{2^7}$. On the coordinate axes at the right, graph P for integer values of n from 0 through 7.

17.

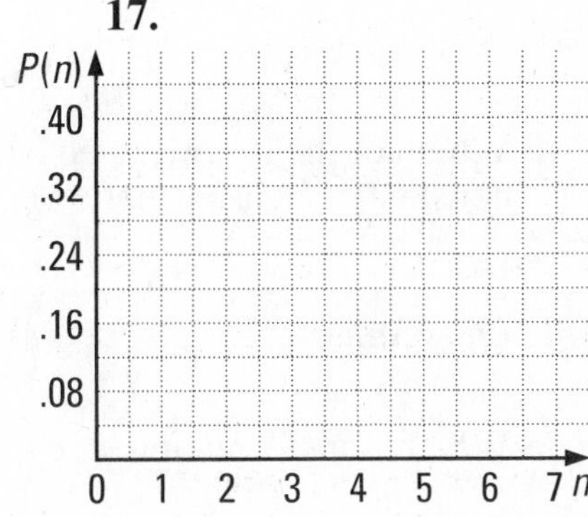

18. Give the slope and y-intercept of the line with equation $13x - 52y = 104$.

18. ______________

19. *True or false.* If n is an odd integer, then the graph of $f(x) = x^n$ can be mapped onto itself by R_{180}.

19. ______________

20. Suppose a new lottery is being played in your state. In this lottery, a player chooses seven numbers from 1 to 15. To win the jackpot, a player must match all seven winning numbers. What is the probability of this occurring?

20. ______________

Check all your work carefully.

Name

COMPREHENSIVE TEST, CHAPTERS 1-13

Multiple choice. **Give the letter of the correct answer.**

1. A function is a relation in which ___?___. **1.** ________

(a) no two different ordered pairs have the same second coordinate

(b) no two different ordered pairs have the same first coordinate

(c) no two different ordered pairs have either the same first coordinate or the same second coordinate

(d) the graph passes the Horizontal-line Test

2. Which formula defines the sequence -65, -58, -51, -44, ... ? **2.** ________

(a) $a_n = -5n + 80$ (b) $a_n = 5n - 80$

(c) $a_n = -7n + 72$ (d) $a_n = 7n - 72$

3. If $k < 0$, which could be an equation for this graph? **3.** ________

(a) $y = kx$ (b) $y = kx^2$

(c) $y = \frac{k}{x}$ (d) $y = \frac{k}{x^2}$

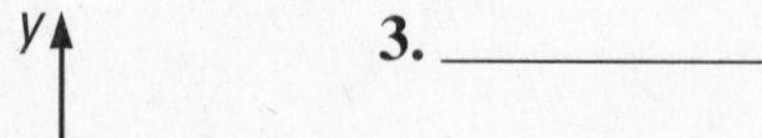

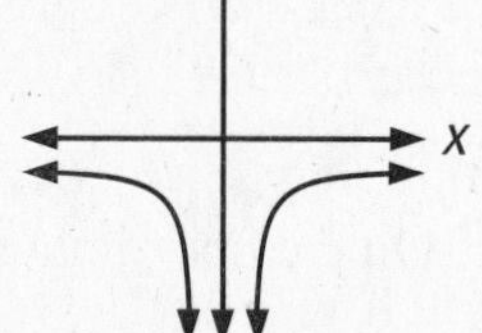

4. Which of the following equations models a constant-increase situation? **4.** ________

(a) $y = 2x^2$ (b) $y = -4x - 5$

(c) $y = \pi x + 4$ (d) $y = 2^x$

5. Which transformation is represented by the matrix $\begin{bmatrix} 0 & 1 \\ 1 & 0 \end{bmatrix}$? **5.** ________

(a) R_{90} (b) r_y (c) $r_{y=x}$ (d) R_{180}

6. Let $\begin{bmatrix} 6 & 7 & 1 \\ -3 & 0 & 2 \end{bmatrix} - \begin{bmatrix} -2 & a & 0 \\ 2 & -4 & b \end{bmatrix} = \begin{bmatrix} c & -4 & 1 \\ -5 & 4 & 7 \end{bmatrix}$. **6.** ________

Then $a + b - c =$ ___?___.

(a) 2 (b) 14 (c) -2 (d) 10

7. Which of the following is equivalent to $1.2^{2.5} \approx 1.58$? **7.** ________

(a) $\log_{1.2} 1.58 \approx 2.5$ (b) $\log_{2.5} 1.58 \approx 1.2$

(c) $\log_{1.58} 2.5 \approx 1.2$ (d) $\log_{2.5} 1.2 \approx 1.58$

8. What is the number of x-intercepts of the parabola with equation $y = 7x^2 + 4x + 12$? **8.** ________

(a) 0 (b) 1 (c) 2 (d) 3

Name

9. Which of the following is equivalent to $\frac{3 - 2i}{4 + 3i}$? 9. ________

(a) $\frac{6}{25} - \frac{7}{25}i$ (b) $\frac{6}{25} - \frac{17}{25}i$

(c) $\frac{18}{5} - \frac{17}{5}i$ (d) $\frac{18}{25} - \frac{17}{25}i$

10. Doyle got x dollars from his grandparents on his 14th birthday. He spent $\frac{1}{3}$ of the money on CD's, $\frac{1}{4}$ of the money on sports equipment, and $\frac{1}{6}$ of the money on movies. He had $42 left. Which of the following equations represents this situation? 10. ________

(a) $\frac{1}{3}x + \frac{1}{4}x + \frac{1}{6}x = 42$ (b) $\frac{1}{3}x + \frac{1}{4}x = \frac{1}{6}x + 42$

(c) $x = \left(\frac{1}{3} + \frac{1}{4} + \frac{1}{6}\right) \cdot 42$ (d) $\frac{1}{3}x + \frac{1}{4}x + \frac{1}{6}x + 42 = x$

11. Suppose z varies directly as x^2 and inversely as y^3. How does the value of z change if both x and y are doubled? 11. ________

(a) z remains the same. (b) z is doubled.

(c) z is tripled. (d) z is halved.

12. Which of the following systems describes the shaded region of the graph at the right? 12. ________

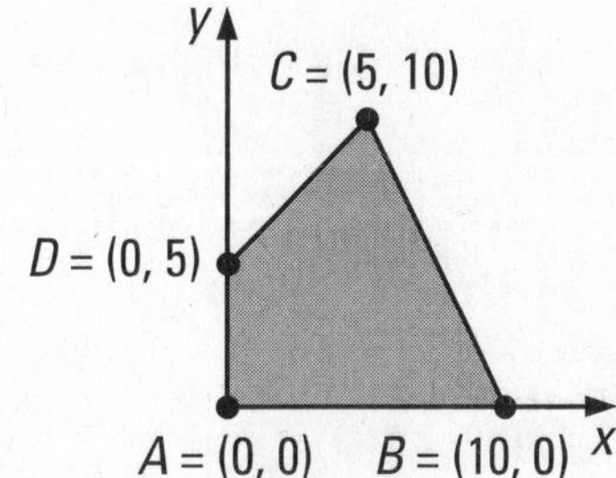

(a) $\begin{cases} 2x + y - 20 \geq 0 \\ x - y + 5 \geq 0 \\ x \geq 0 \\ y \geq 0 \end{cases}$ (b) $\begin{cases} 2x + y - 20 \geq 0 \\ x - y + 5 \leq 0 \\ x \geq 0 \\ y \geq 0 \end{cases}$

(c) $\begin{cases} 2x + y - 20 \leq 0 \\ x - y + 5 \leq 0 \\ x \geq 0 \\ y \geq 0 \end{cases}$ (d) $\begin{cases} 2x + y - 20 \leq 0 \\ x - y + 5 \geq 0 \\ x \geq 0 \\ y \geq 0 \end{cases}$

13. In the solution (x, y) to the system $\begin{cases} 3x - 2y = 7 \\ x + 4y = 7 \end{cases}$, what is the value of $x + y$? 13. ________

(a) 5 (b) 4 (c) 7 (d) 6

14. Which of the following is a true statement? **14.** ________

(a) $\cos 237° = \cos 123°$ (b) $\cos 237° = \cos 57°$

(c) $\cos 237° > 0$ (d) $\cos 237° = \cos 507°$

15. $\left(\frac{16}{25}\right)^{-\frac{5}{2}} =$ __?__ **15.** ________

(a) $\frac{3125}{256}$ (b) $\frac{1024}{3125}$ (c) $\frac{3125}{1024}$ (d) $\frac{256}{3125}$

16. Suppose that, three years ago, \$3250 was deposited at an annual interest rate of 4.8% compounded quarterly. Assume that there were no other deposits or withdrawals in this account. Which of the following describes the amount in the account now? **16.** ________

(a) $3250\,(1 + .048)^{12}$ (b) $3250\left(1 + \frac{.048}{4}\right)^{12}$

(c) $3250\,(1 + .048)^{3}$ (d) $3250\left(1 + \frac{.048}{4}\right)^{3}$

17. Which of the following is *not* true in all triangles *ABC*? **17.** ________

(a) $\frac{\sin A}{b} = \frac{\sin B}{c} = \frac{\sin C}{a}$ (b) $c \sin B = b \sin C$

(c) $b \sin A = a \sin B$ (d) $2ab \cos C = a^2 + b^2 - c^2$

18. Which of the following is an equation for the image of $x^2 + y^2 = 1$ under the transformation $T_{-1,2}$? **18.** ________

(a) $(x + 2)^2 + (y - 1)^2 = 1$ (b) $(x - 2)^2 + (y + 1)^2 = 1$

(c) $(x - 1)^2 + (y + 2)^2 = 1$ (d) $(x + 1)^2 + (y - 2)^2 = 1$

19. Which of the following *cannot* be the graph of the inverse of a function? **19.** ________

(a)

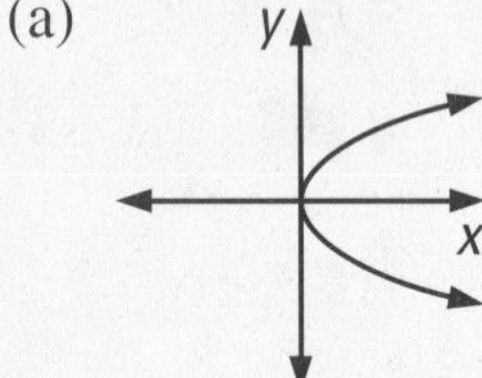

(b)

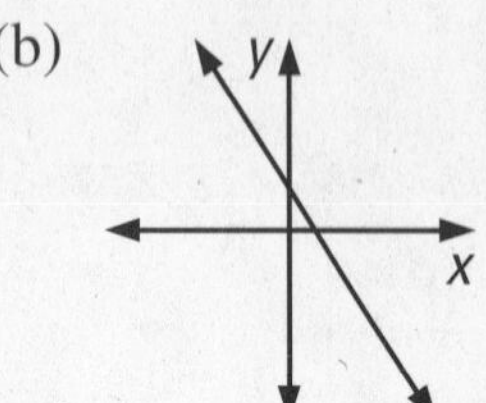

(c)

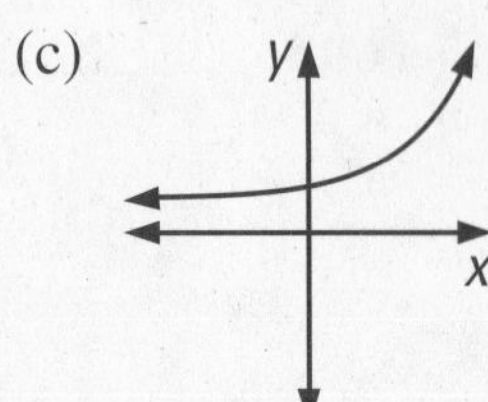

(d)

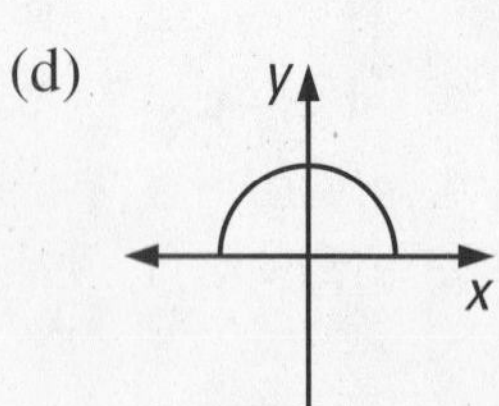

Name

20. Which of the following is an equation for the ellipse with foci (0, 4) and (0, -4) and focal constant 10? **20.** ________

(a) $\frac{x^2}{25} + \frac{y^2}{9} = 1$ (b) $\frac{x^2}{84} + \frac{y^2}{100} = 1$

(c) $\frac{x^2}{9} + \frac{y^2}{25} = 1$ (d) $\frac{x^2}{100} + \frac{y^2}{84} = 1$

21. Let $P(x) = 3x^3 - 2x^2 + 1$. Then $P(3) =$ __?__. **21.** ________

(a) 66 (b) 64 (c) 55 (d) 10

22. $(a + 2b)^5 =$ __?__ **22.** ________

(a) $a^5 + 10a^4b + 40a^3b^2 + 80a^2b^3 + 80ab^4 + 32b^5$

(b) $a^5 + 5a^4b + 10a^3b^2 + 10a^2b^3 + 5ab^4 + 2b^5$

(c) $a^5 + 10a^4b + 40a^3b^2 + 40a^2b^3 + 10ab^4 + b^5$

(d) $a^5 + 10a^4b + 80a^3b^2 + 80a^2b^3 + 10ab^4 + 32b^5$

23. $x^4 - 2x^3 - 3x^2 =$ __?__ **23.** ________

(a) $x^2(x - 3)(x + 1)$ (b) $x^2(x + 3)(x - 1)$

(c) $x^2(x + 3)(x + 1)$ (d) $x^2(x - 3)(x - 1)$

24. A fair coin is tossed three times. What is the probability of getting exactly three heads? **24.** ________

(a) $\frac{1}{2}$ (b) $\frac{1}{4}$ (c) $\frac{1}{8}$ (d) 1

25. Let $f(x) = 3x^2 - 1$ and $g(x) = \frac{2}{x}$. What is the value of $f \circ g(4)$? **25.** ________

(a) $\frac{2}{47}$ (b) 11 (c) $-\frac{1}{4}$ (d) $\frac{1}{2}$

26. $\frac{\log_6 18 + \log_6 12}{\log_6 72 - \log_6 2} =$ __?__ **26.** ________

(a) 1 (b) $\log_6 \frac{3}{2}$ (c) 2 (d) $\frac{3}{2}$

Check all your work carefully.

Answers and Evaluation Guides*

Quiz — Lessons 1-1 Through 1-3

1. the division ($24 \div 6 = 4$)
2. *cs* students
3. 48
4. No. Explanations may vary. Sample: When $V = 2$, $n = -2$, or $n = 2$.
5. a. {-3, -2, -1, 1, 2, 3}
   b. {1, 2, 3}
6. 7 and -7
   Explanations will vary. Sample: Each of these values would make the denominator ($x^2 - 49$) have a value of zero.
7. 75
8. 30
9. $22,480

Quiz — Lessons 1-4 Through 1-7

1. $\{y: y \geq 1\}$
2. $f(4) = 2$
3. No. Explanations may vary. Sample: A vertical line can intersect the graph in more than one point.
4. $x = 25$
5. $t = 4$
6. 1400 students
7. $2000 in the savings account, $3000 in the CD
8. a. 85 cm^3
   b. $h = \frac{3V}{\pi r^2}$

Chapter 1 Test, Form A

1. 13, 25, 45, 73
2. 6, 14, 38, 110
3. Answers will vary. Sample: It would be easier to find the 80th term of A, since you only need to replace *n* with 80 in the formula. With sequence B, you need to find the first 79 terms.
4. $\begin{cases} t_1 = 8 \\ t_n = t_{n-1} + 5, \\ \text{for integers } n \geq 2 \end{cases}$
5. 405
6. 220
7. $b_1 = \frac{2A - hb_2}{h}$, or $b_1 = \frac{2A}{h} - b_2$
8. $\frac{c}{32}$ cents per ounce
9. 3054 cm^3
10. $\{h: h > 0\}$
11. $h = \frac{V}{\pi r^2}$
12. a. {-256, -81, -16, -1, 1, 16, 81, 256}
    b. {1, 2, 3, 4}
13. Yes. Explanations may vary. Sample: Each value of *x* corresponds to exactly one value of *y*.
14. $x = 3$
15. $z = -4$
16. 8 seconds
17. a. $\begin{cases} h_1 = 144 \\ h_n = h_{n-1} + 1, \\ \text{for integers } n \geq 2 \end{cases}$
    b. 147 (inches)
18. 195 bags
19. Estimates may vary. Sample: $\approx$ 570,000
20. Answers may vary. Sample: $\approx$ -210,000; from 1980 to 1993, the number of Army personnel decreased by about 210,000.
21. Answers will vary. Check students' graphs.

Chapter 1 Test, Form B

1. -6, 9, 34, 69
2. 7, 31, 127, 511
3. Answers will vary; Sample: It would be easier to find the 80th term of A, since you only need to replace *n* with 80 in the formula. With sequence B, you need to find the first 79 terms.
4. $\begin{cases} t_1 = 11 \\ t_n = t_{n-1} + 6, \\ \text{for integers } n \geq 2 \end{cases}$
5. -810
6. 286
7. $V = \frac{4\pi r^3}{3}$
8. $\frac{d}{20}$ cents per bag
9. 377 cm^3
10. $\{h: h > 0\}$
11. $h = \frac{3V}{\pi r^2}$
12. a. {-4, -3, -2, -1, 1, 2, 3, 4}
    b. {1, 16, 81, 256}
13. No. Explanations may vary. Sample: There are two values of *y* that correspond to $x = 4$.
14. $x = 4$
15. $y = 5$
16. 27 miles
17. a. $\begin{cases} S_1 = 500 \\ S_n = S_{n-1} + 100, \\ \text{for integers } n \geq 2 \end{cases}$
    b. 1500 (dollars)
18. 43 magazines
19. Estimates may vary. Sample: $\approx$ 13,000,000
20. Answers may vary. Sample: $\approx$ 1,700,000; from 1980 to 1992, the number of motor vehicles produced in the United States increased by about 1,700,000.
21. Answers may vary. Sample: Apply the Vertical-Line Test.

*Evaluation Guides for Chapter Tests, Forms C and D, are on pages 219–244.

Quiz — Lessons 2-1 Through 2-3

1. (b)
2. (a), (c)
3. (d)
4. Answers will vary. Sample: $y = 2x^2$
5. It is doubled.
6. It is divided by 4.
7. $w = .0007\ell^3$
8. about 5.5 pounds
9. about 27.7 ft^3

Quiz — Lessons 2-4 Through 2-6

1. Answers may vary. Sample: It is the part of the coordinate plane that shows on the screen as set by the manufacturer.
2. $\frac{2}{3}$
3.

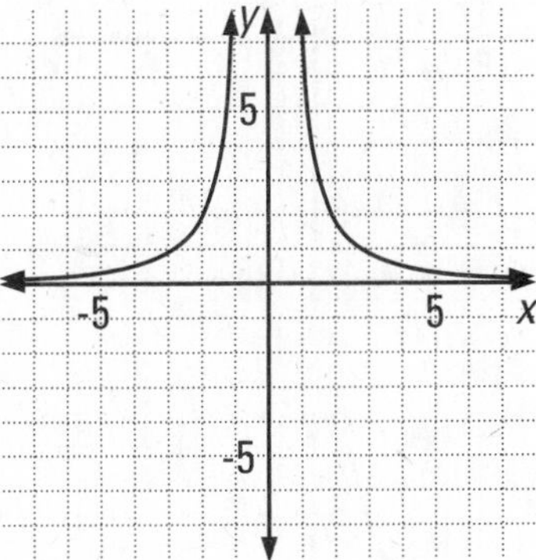

4. 6
5. 10
6. Answers may vary. Sample: The graph of $y = x^2$ is a parabola, so the rate of change between different pairs of points is not constant.
7. quadrants II and IV
8.

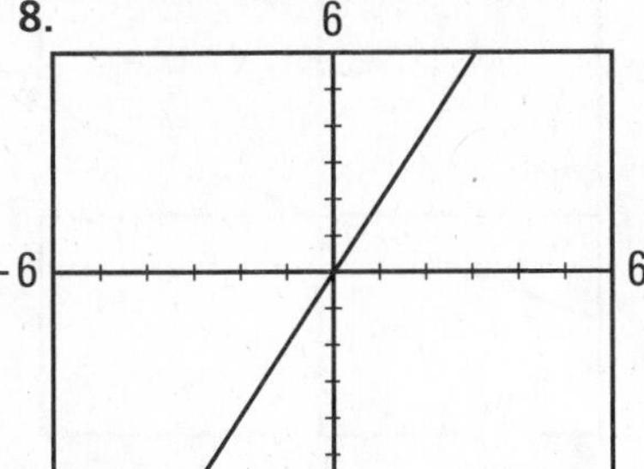

Chapter 2 Test, Form A

1. L varies directly as the square of d.
2. 400
3. $\frac{25}{9}$, or $2.\overline{7}$
4. 228.6
5. $V = \frac{228.6t}{p}$, where V is volume in cm^3, t is temperature in °K, and p is pressure in cm of mercury
6. 931 cm^3
7. It is multiplied by 4.
8. It is divided by 9.
9. inversely
10. directly
11. -2
12. $-\frac{2}{3}$
13. Answers will vary. Sample: The graph of $y = \frac{4}{x}$ is a hyperbola, not a line, and so the rate of change between different pairs of points is not constant.
14. $y = \frac{1}{4}$
15. (b)
16. Answers will vary. Sample:

x	-2	-1	0	1	2
y	6	3	0	-3	-6

17.

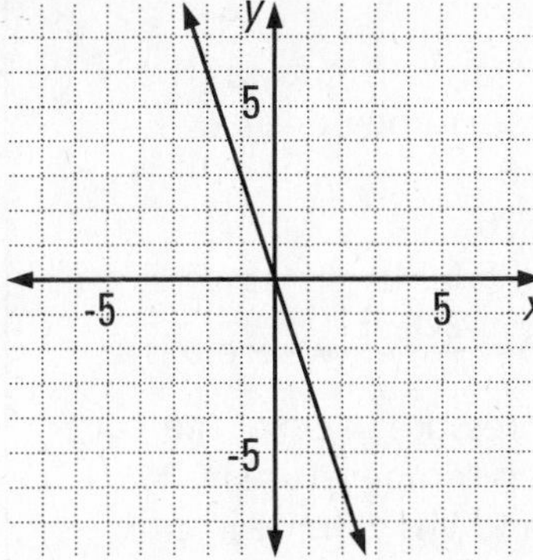

18. -3
19. a. Answers may vary. Sample: $-10 \le x \le 10$, $-10 \le y \le 10$
    b. the x-axis and the y-axis
20. $w = knR^2L$
21.

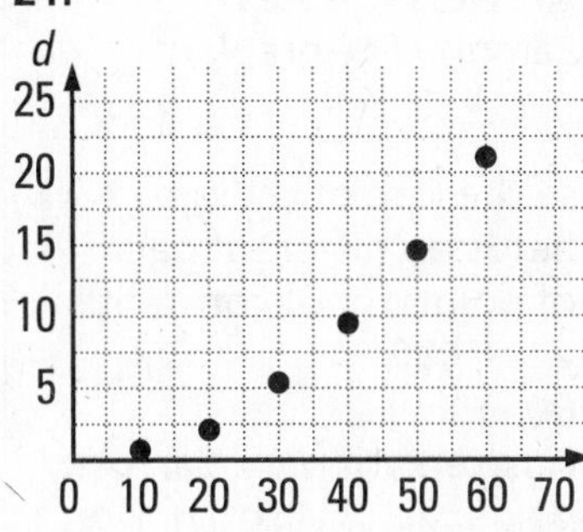

22. (c)

ANSWERS

Chapter 2 Test, Form B

1. y varies directly as the fourth power of x.
2. 16
3. 576
4. 228.6
5. $p = \frac{228.6t}{V}$, where p is pressure in cm of mercury, t is temperature in °K, and V is volume in cm^3
6. 62.9 cm of mercury
7. It is divided by 16.
8. It is multiplied by 9.
9. inversely
10. directly
11. -6
12. $-\frac{10}{9}$
13. Answers will vary. Sample: The graph of $y = \frac{8}{x^2}$ is not a line, and so the rate of change between different pairs of points is not constant.
14. $y = -1080$
15. (a)
16. Answers will vary. Sample:

x	-2	-1	0	1	2
y	-10	-5	0	5	10

17.

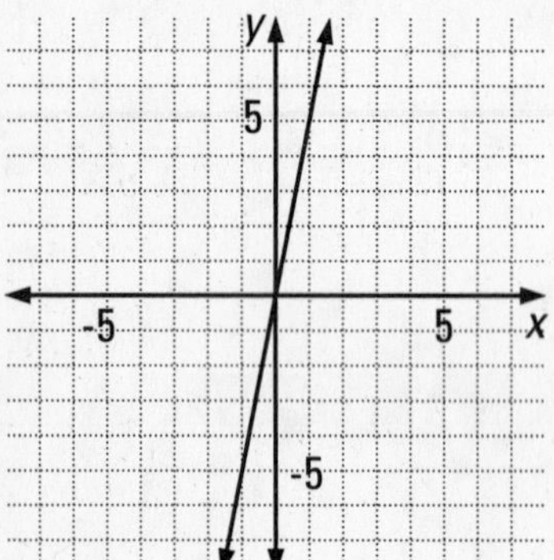

18. 5
19. a. Answers may vary. Sample: $-10 \le x \le 10$, $0 \le y \le 10$
    b. the x-axis and the y-axis
20. $L = kxm^2d^2$
21.

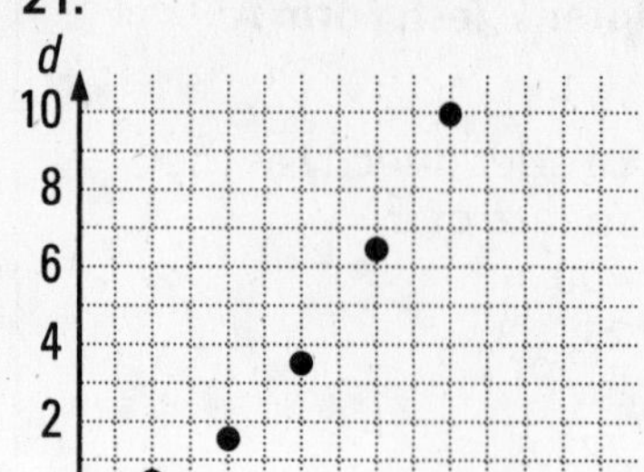

22. (b)

Chapter 2 Test, Cumulative Form

1. (e)
2. (b)
3. -3, -1, 1, 3
4. (f)
5. (e)
6. It is multiplied by 36.
7. 144
8. 53
9. $m = \frac{10l}{3r^2}$
10. $c = 4n + 2$
11. No. Explanations may vary. Sample: If you replace n with 6 in the equation from Question 10, you would arrive at a cost of $26, which is more than you have.
12. $y = -\frac{4}{9}$
13.

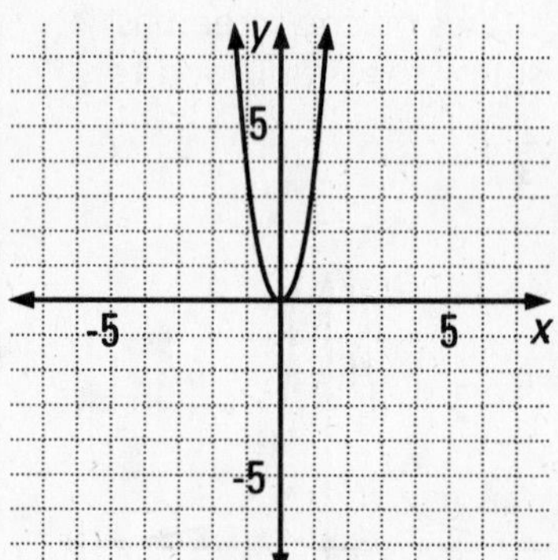

14.

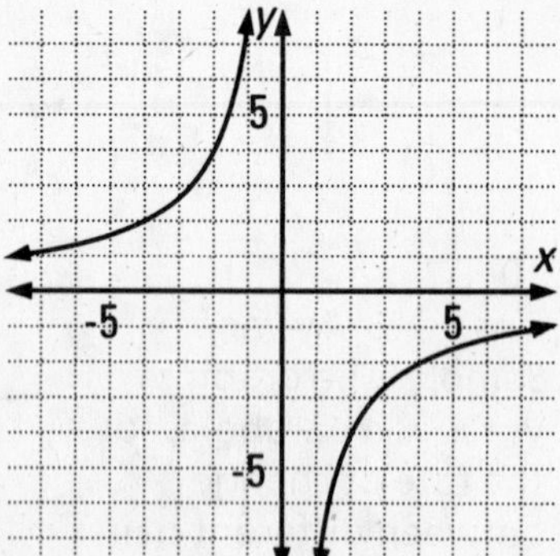

15.

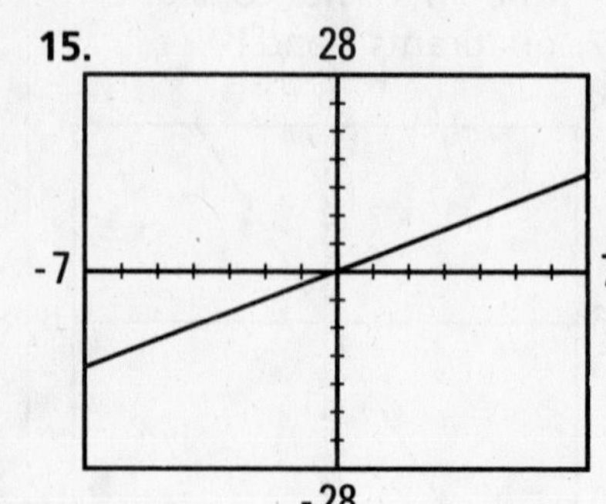

16. 54 feet

17.

18. $s = \frac{k}{n}$

19. 20; $s = \frac{20}{n}$

20. $1\frac{2}{3}$ ft^2

21. a. Answers may vary. Sample: The first term is π. Each term after that is derived by multiplying the preceding term by -3.

b. $\begin{cases} t_1 = \pi \\ t_n = -3t_{n-1}, \\ \text{for integers } n \geq 2 \end{cases}$

22. No; Sample: It fails the Vertical-line Test.

23. $y \leq 0$

24. Yes; Sample: Each value of x corresponds to exactly one value of y.

25. (c)

Quiz — Lessons 3-1 Through 3-3

1.

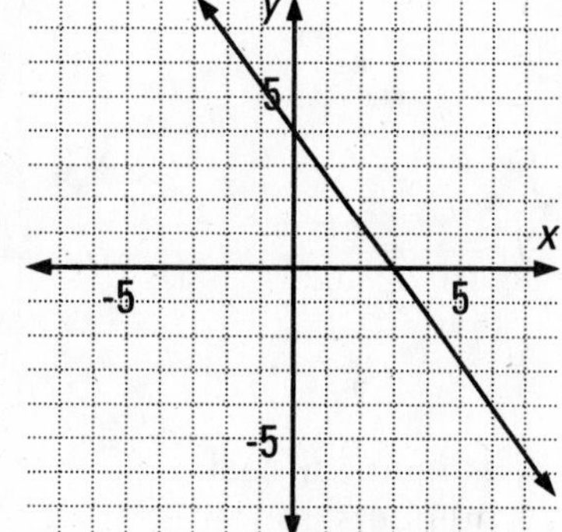

2. Answers will vary. Sample: (1, -3) and (2, -3)
3. slope: 0; y-intercept: -3
4. {-3}
5. (d)
6. $d = 288 - 45h$
7. 3.4 hours
8. $.3x + .1y = 45$
9. 225 pounds

Quiz — Lessons 3-4 Through 3-6

1. false
2. 10
3. $y = -\frac{15}{13}x + \frac{102}{13}$
4. $y = -\frac{8}{3}x + \frac{50}{3}$
5. 3
6. $108.75
7. See graph below.
8. $y = -.02x + 12.49$, where x represents the year after 1900
9. -.55
10. No. Explanations may vary. Sample: The correlation coefficient, -.55, is not very close to 1. This indicates only a moderate linear relationship between the quantities.

7.

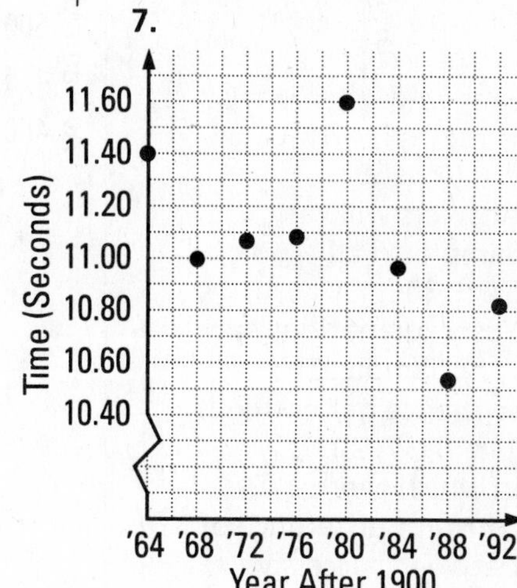

ANSWERS

Chapter 3 Test, Form A

1. $a_n = 8n + 3$
2. $\begin{cases} a_1 = 11 \\ a_n = a_{n-1} + 8, \\ \text{for integers } n \geq 2 \end{cases}$
3. a. $A = 5500 - 75m$
   b. $4150
4. -5
5. $-\frac{2}{3}$
6. 2
7. 3
8. 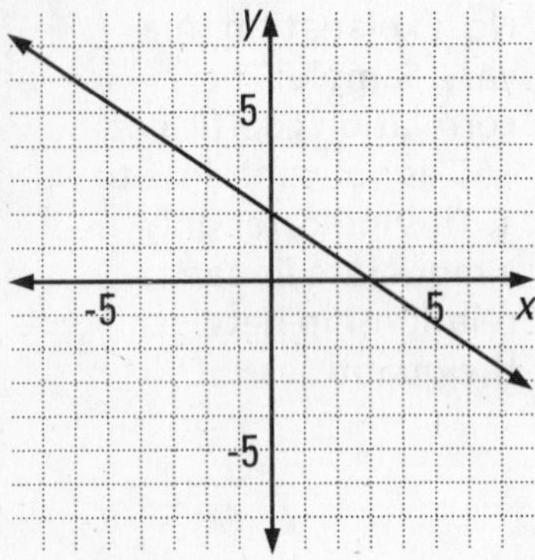

9. $y = 6x + 58$
10. Answers will vary. Sample: $x = 1$
11. $5A + 30C$
12. Yes. Explanations may vary. Sample: The sequence generated is 11, 14, 17, 20, . . . , in which there is a constant difference of 3 between successive terms.
13. $y = -\frac{5}{2}x + 5$
14. (c)
15. (a)
16. (c)
17. (b)
18. $5.88
19. a. 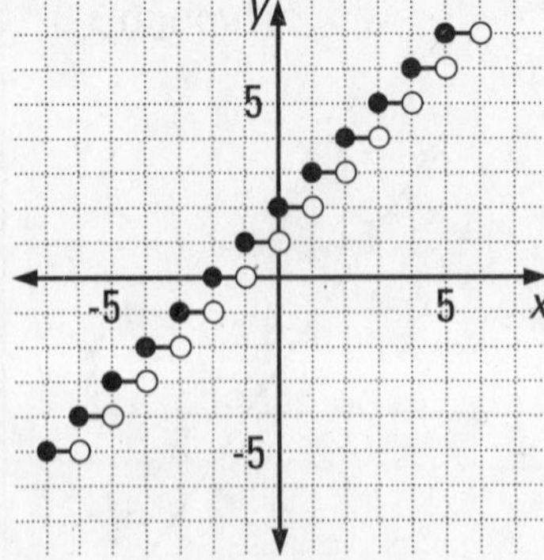

   b. domain: all real numbers; range: the set of integers
20. a. 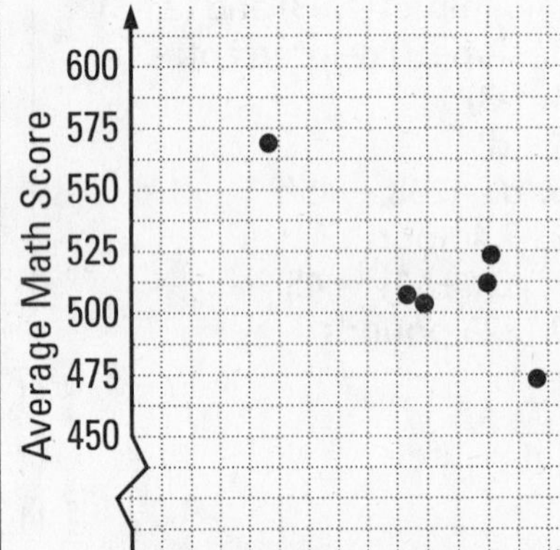

   b. $y = -1.64x + 599.21$, where x represents the percent who say they're good at math
   c. -.85
   d. ≈ 545.1

Chapter 3 Test, Form B

1. $a_n = 2n - 9$
2. $\begin{cases} a_1 = -7 \\ a_n = a_{n-1} + 2, \\ \text{for integers } n \geq 2 \end{cases}$
3. a. $F = 2800 + 100m$
   b. $6400
4. -3
5. $-\frac{3}{2}$
6. 3
7. 2
8. 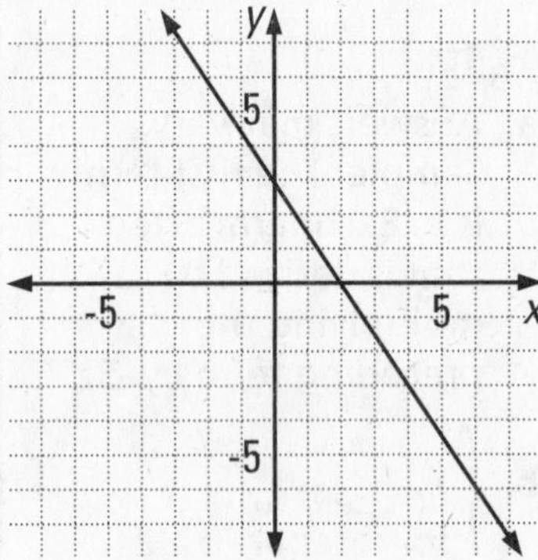

9. $y = 3x + 14$
10. Answers will vary. Sample: $y = 1$
11. $1.5A + .75C$
12. No. Explanations may vary. Sample: The sequence generated is -3, 0, 5, 12, . . . , in which there is not a constant difference between successive terms.
13. $y = \frac{3}{2}x + \frac{1}{2}$
14. (c)
15. (a)
16. (c)
17. (b)
18. $12.15

ANSWERS

19. a.

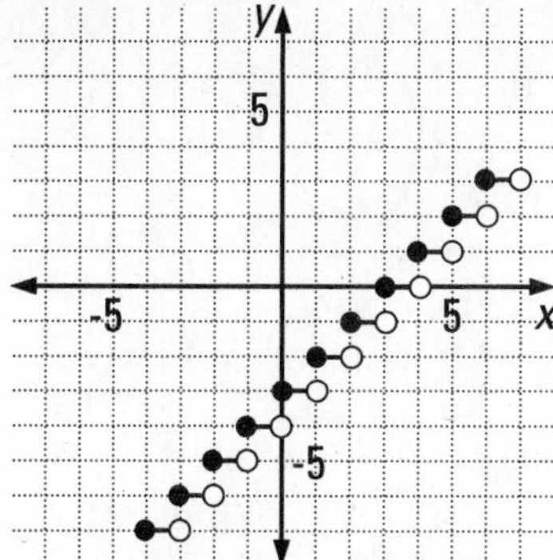

b. domain: all real numbers; range: all integers

20. a.

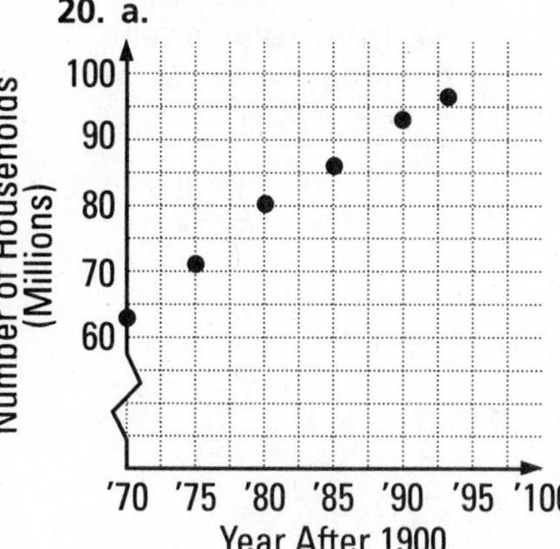

b. $y = 1.45x - 36.84$, where x represents the year after 1900

c. .996

d. $\approx$ 108.2 million

Chapter 3 Test, Cumulative Form

1. $x = 6000$
2. Answers will vary. Sample: A person has \$10,000 to invest. Some will be placed in a savings account paying 4% interest and some in a CD paying 6% interest. How much should be placed in each account to earn a total of \$480 interest in one year?
3. $a_n = 2n - 5$
4. **a.** $h = 60 + 2t$
   b. 108 inches
5. domain: $\{x: x \geq 0\}$; range: $\{y: y \geq 3\}$
6. 1042
7. $y = \frac{5}{4}x + \frac{41}{4}$
8. 27.6 hours
9. See graph below.
10. **a.** 7 **b.** 9
    c. false
11. **a.** No. Explanations may vary. Sample: There is not a constant difference between successive terms.
    b. $\begin{cases} a_1 = 5 \\ a_n = 2a_{n-1}, \\ \text{for integers } n \geq 2 \end{cases}$
12. It is multiplied by 16.
13. **a.** {1, 4, 9, 16}
    b. {1, 2, 3, 4}
14. $\frac{2}{3}$
15. x-intercept: 6; y-intercept: -4

9.

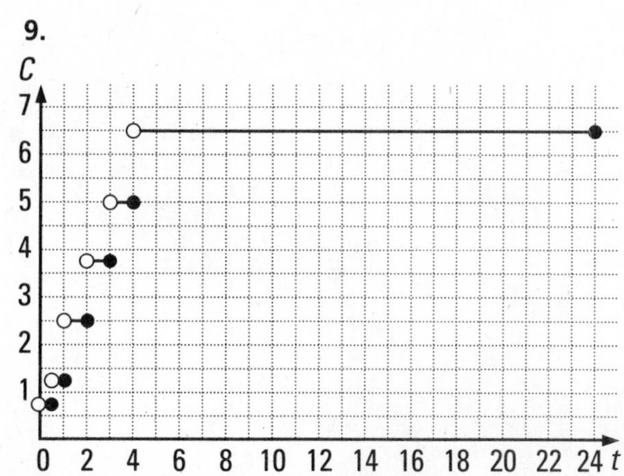

16.

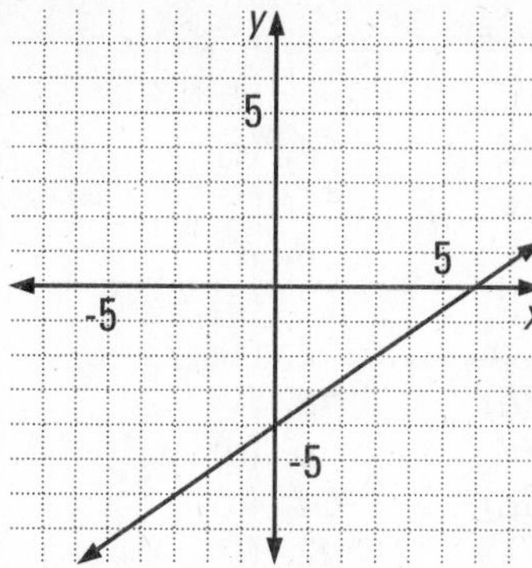

17. (c)

18. a. Answers will vary. Sample:

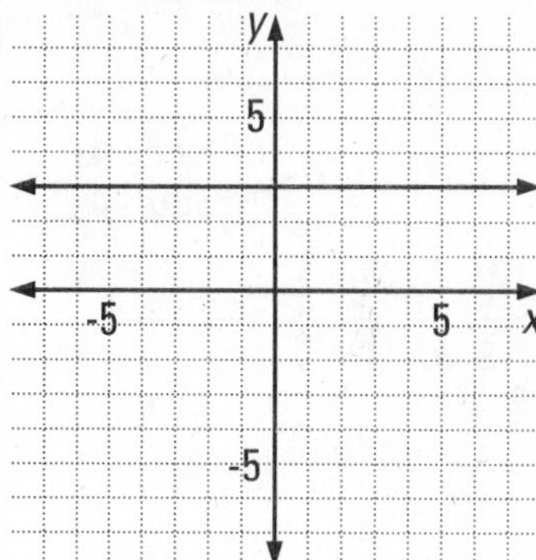

b. Answers will vary. Sample: $y = 3$

19. a. $12l + 20G = 120$

b.

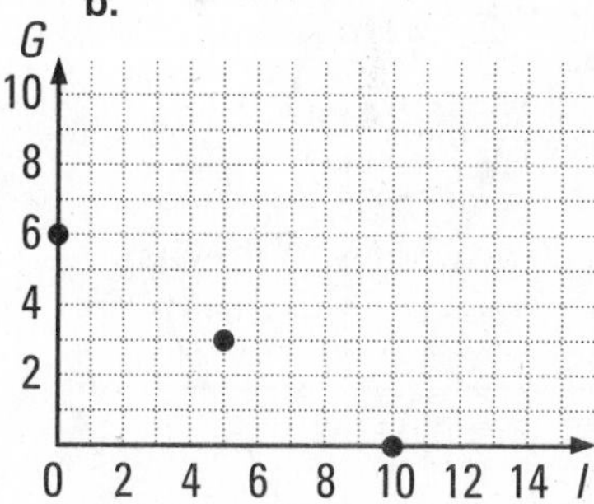

20.

21. $y = .33x - 19.29$, where x is the year after 1900

22. $\approx$ \$13.71

23. 6859

ANSWERS

Comprehensive Test, Chapters 1–3

1. (c)	14. (a)
2. (b)	15. (c)
3. (a)	16. (c)
4. (b)	17. (d)
5. (c)	18. (c)
6. (d)	19. (b)
7. (c)	20. (d)
8. (d)	21. (d)
9. (a)	22. (c)
10. (b)	23. (d)
11. (c)	24. (a)
12. (c)	25. (a)
13. (d)	

Quiz Lessons 4-1 Through 4-3

1. $\begin{bmatrix} -5 & -1 & 6 & 4 & -2 \\ -3 & -7 & -2 & 5 & 3 \end{bmatrix}$
2. $\begin{bmatrix} -35 & 16 \\ -12 & 41 \end{bmatrix}$
3. a. 6 b. 3
4. $\begin{bmatrix} 6 & -46 \\ -2 & -23 \end{bmatrix}$
5. false
6.

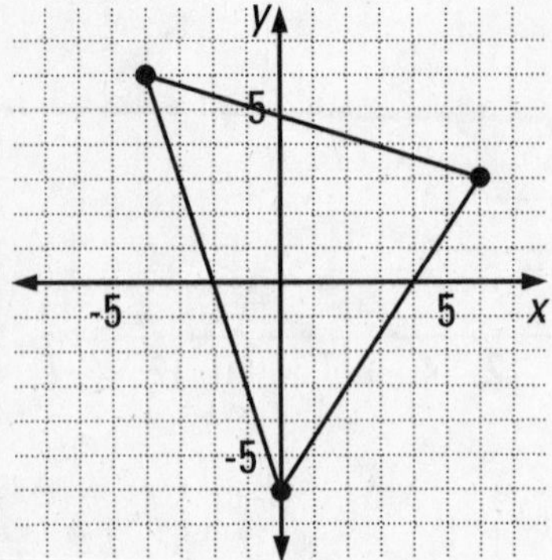

7. outlet 1: $109,450; outlet 2: $132,600

Quiz Lessons 4-4 Through 4-7

1. Answers will vary. Sample: For any 2×2 matrix A,
$A \bullet \begin{bmatrix} 1 & 0 \\ 0 & 1 \end{bmatrix} = \begin{bmatrix} 1 & 0 \\ 0 & 1 \end{bmatrix} \bullet A = A.$
2. a. $S_{3,4}$ b. $\begin{bmatrix} 3 & 0 \\ 0 & 4 \end{bmatrix}$
3. $\begin{bmatrix} -1 & 0 \\ 0 & 1 \end{bmatrix}$ 4. $\begin{bmatrix} 5 & 0 \\ 0 & 5 \end{bmatrix}$
5. false 6. false
7.

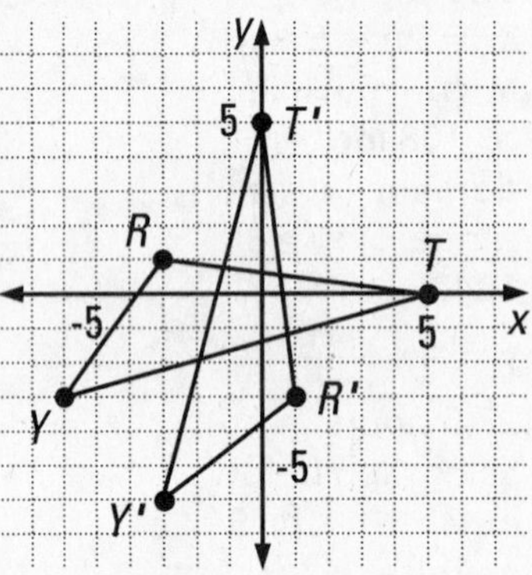

8. $\begin{bmatrix} 0 & -1 \\ 1 & 0 \end{bmatrix}$

Chapter 4 Test, Form A

1. a. $\begin{bmatrix} 1 & -3 & -5 & 1 & 2 \\ -5 & -5 & -1 & 4 & 1 \end{bmatrix}$
   b. 2×5
2. a. 73
   b. the normal temperature for New York in April
3. a. *BA* does not exist. Explanations may vary. Sample: The product *BA* can exist only if the number of columns of *B* equals the number of rows of *A*; since *B* has three columns and A has two rows, *BA* does not exist.
   b. $AB = \begin{bmatrix} 0 & -6 & 0 \\ -6 & 36 & 24 \end{bmatrix}$
4. $a = 2$
5. Answers will vary.
   Sample: $A = \begin{bmatrix} 1 & 2 \\ 3 & 4 \end{bmatrix}$,
   $B = \begin{bmatrix} 1 & 0 \\ 0 & 1 \end{bmatrix}$
6. $\begin{bmatrix} 2 & -14 & 0 & -17 \\ 9 & -1 & 9 & -1 \end{bmatrix}$
7. (f)
8. (c)
9. (a)
10. (e)
11. (b)
12. (g)
13. $y = -\frac{1}{2}x + 10$
14. a. $\begin{bmatrix} 1 & 0 \\ 0 & 2 \end{bmatrix}$
    b. $\begin{bmatrix} -4 & 2 & 2 & -4 \\ 4 & 4 & -2 & -2 \end{bmatrix}$

ANSWERS

15. a. $\begin{bmatrix} 2 & -1 & -3 \\ 4 & 6 & -5 \end{bmatrix}$

b.

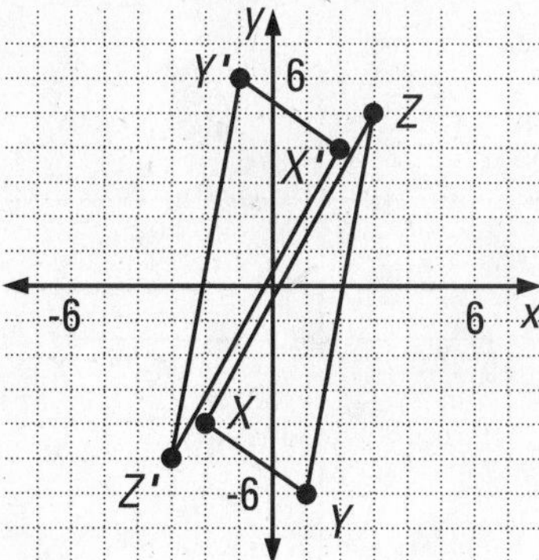

16. $T_{3,-2}$, or

$\begin{bmatrix} 3 & 3 & 3 & 3 & 3 \\ -2 & -2 & -2 & -2 & -2 \end{bmatrix}$

17. a. $\begin{bmatrix} -1 & 0 \\ 0 & -1 \end{bmatrix}$

b. R_{180}

18. a. true

b. true

b. false

19. Opal: $2745; Alfonso's: $2912.50; Natural Foods: $1647.50

20. $\begin{bmatrix} 175 & 264.5 & 37.5 \\ 226.5 & 1.5 & 9.5 \end{bmatrix}$

Chapter 4 Test, Form B

1. a. $\begin{bmatrix} 2 & 5 & -5 & -3 \\ 5 & -4 & -2 & 3 \end{bmatrix}$

b. 2×4

2. a. 1,572,000 people

b. the number of persons over five years of age in American households who spoke Italian in 1980

3. a. *AB* does not exist. Explanations may vary. Sample: The product *AB* can exist only if the number of columns of *A* equals the number of rows of *B*; since *A* has three columns and *B* has two rows, *AB* does not exist.

b. $BA = \begin{bmatrix} -20 & 20 & 6 \\ -2 & -53 & -33 \end{bmatrix}$

4. $x = 3$

5. Answers will vary.

Sample: $A = \begin{bmatrix} 1 & 2 \\ 3 & 4 \end{bmatrix}$,

$B = \begin{bmatrix} 1 & 1 \\ 1 & 1 \end{bmatrix}$

6. $\begin{bmatrix} 17 & -2 \\ -3 & 4 \\ -3 & -5 \end{bmatrix}$

7. (b)
8. (g)
9. (a)
10. (e)
11. (c)
12. (f)
13. $y = x + 4$

14. a. $\begin{bmatrix} 2 & 0 \\ 0 & 2 \end{bmatrix}$

b. $\begin{bmatrix} -4 & 2 & 2 & -4 \\ 2 & 2 & -4 & -4 \end{bmatrix}$

15. a. $\begin{bmatrix} -3 & -6 & -1 \\ 1 & 3 & 6 \end{bmatrix}$

b.

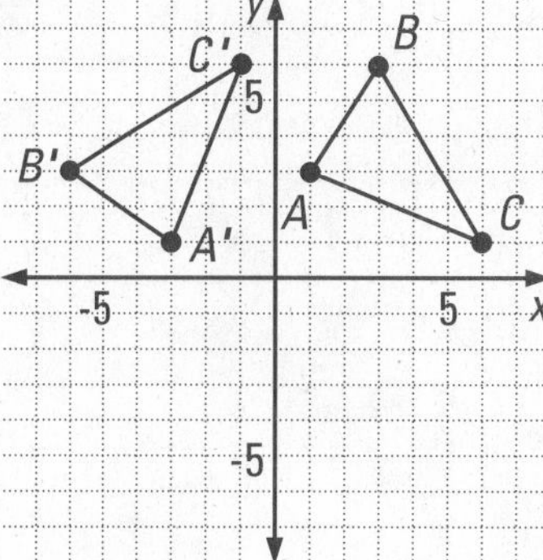

16. $T_{2,3}$, or

$\begin{bmatrix} 2 & 2 & 2 & 2 \\ 3 & 3 & 3 & 3 \end{bmatrix}$

17. a. $\begin{bmatrix} 0 & 1 \\ 1 & 0 \end{bmatrix}$

b. $r_{y=x}$

18. (b)

19. Eddie's: $1470.75; Hilltop: $1436.75

20. $\begin{bmatrix} 846 & 914 \\ 1812 & 1646 \\ 1204 & 1194 \end{bmatrix}$

ANSWERS

Chapter 4 Test, Cumulative Form

1. $y = -2x + 10$

2. a. $\begin{bmatrix} 5 & 3 & -1 & -3 \\ 0 & 4 & 6 & -1 \end{bmatrix}$

   b. 2×4

3. $\begin{bmatrix} 20 & 12 & -4 & -12 \\ 0 & 8 & 12 & -2 \end{bmatrix}$

4. false

5. a. $\begin{bmatrix} 0 & -4 & -6 & 1 \\ 5 & 3 & -1 & -3 \end{bmatrix}$

   b.

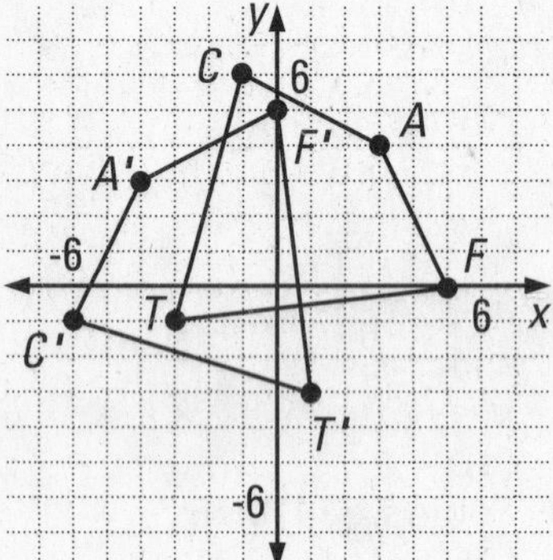

6. $T_{0,-3}$, or

   $\begin{bmatrix} 0 & 0 & 0 & 0 \\ -3 & -3 & -3 & -3 \end{bmatrix}$

7. a. $\begin{bmatrix} 1 & 0 \\ 0 & -1 \end{bmatrix}$

   b. r_x

8.

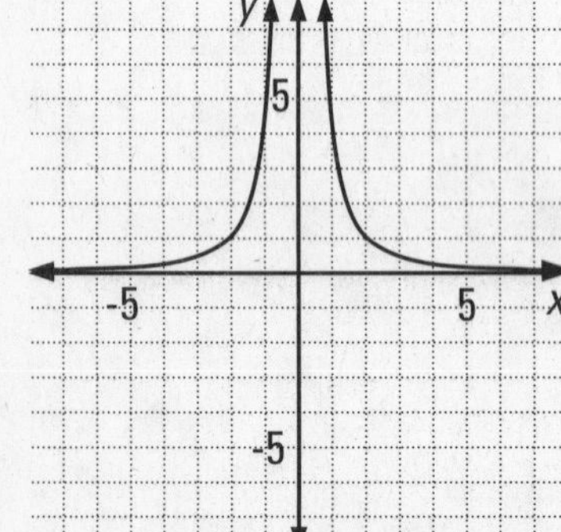

9.

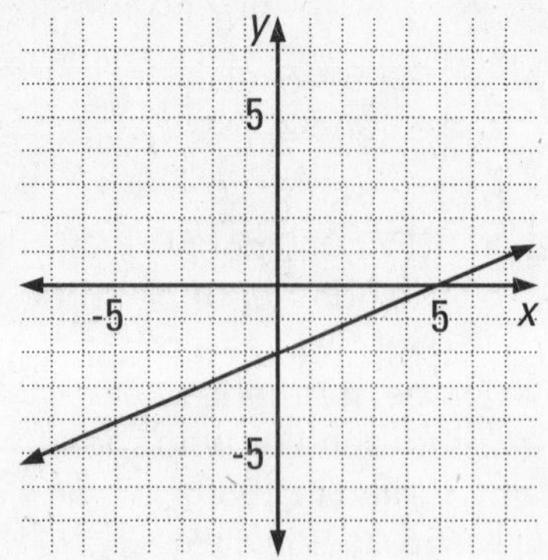

10. a. \$100, \$175, \$250, \$325, \$400

    b. $\begin{cases} A_1 = 100 \\ A_n = A_{n-1} + 75, \\ \text{for integers } n \geq 2 \end{cases}$

11. inversely

12. 28

13. a.

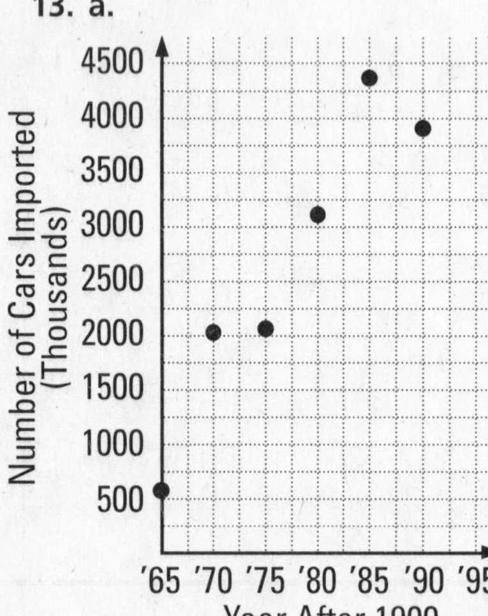

    b. $y = 143.42x - 8430.23$, where x represents the year after 1900

    c. .95

    d. Yes. Explanations may vary. Sample: The correlation coefficient, .95, is fairly close to 1. This indicates a fairly strong linear relationship between the quantities.

14. a. 2,042,000

    b. Answers may vary. Sample: In 1985, the population of the northeast region was 2,042,000 greater than the population of the west region.

15. $y = -\frac{2}{3}x + \frac{41}{3}$

16. location 1: \$930; location 2: \$1000

17. a.

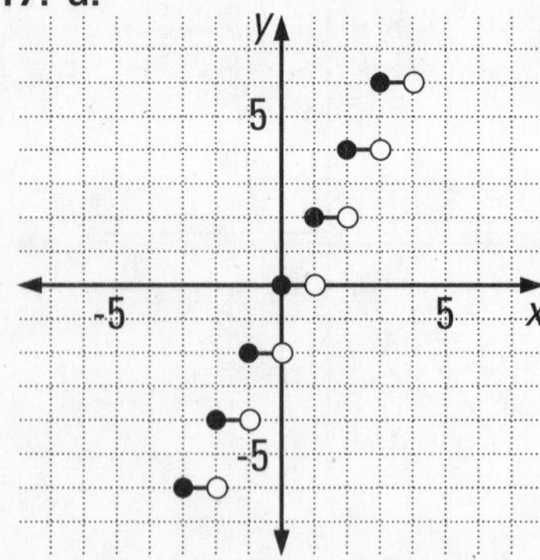

    b. domain: all real numbers; range: all integers

18. $\begin{bmatrix} 11 & 13 \\ -47 & 26 \\ -13 & 3 \\ 10 & 2 \end{bmatrix}$

19. $a = -3$, $b = 3$

20. $v = \frac{ft}{m} + v_0$

21. $w = -1$

ANSWERS

Quiz — Lessons 5-1 Through 5-4

1. a. $17 \le a < 22$, where a represents the age of the candidate
   b.

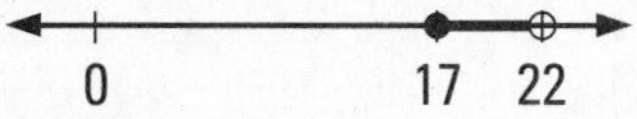

2. (2, -4)
3. (-1, 3)
4. a. consistent
   b. two
5. The system has no solution when $k = 9$. Explanations may vary. Sample: The two equations in the system are linear. When $k = 9$, the lines have the same slope, $-\frac{9}{2}$, but different y-intercepts. This means that the lines are parallel, and the system has no solution.
6. $\begin{cases} y = 45 + .27x \\ y = 27 + .36x \end{cases}$
7. a. 200 miles
   b. $99

Quiz — Lessons 5-5 Through 5-7

1. No. Explanations may vary. Sample: If two matrices are inverses, their product must be the identity matrix, $\begin{bmatrix} 1 & 0 \\ 0 & 1 \end{bmatrix}$. But $\begin{bmatrix} 7 & -5 \\ 11 & 8 \end{bmatrix}\begin{bmatrix} 8 & 5 \\ 11 & 7 \end{bmatrix} = \begin{bmatrix} 1 & 0 \\ 176 & 111 \end{bmatrix}$, and $\begin{bmatrix} 8 & 5 \\ 11 & 7 \end{bmatrix}\begin{bmatrix} 7 & -5 \\ 11 & 8 \end{bmatrix} = \begin{bmatrix} 111 & 0 \\ 154 & 1 \end{bmatrix}$.
2. a. -2
   b. $\begin{bmatrix} -1 & 2 \\ \frac{5}{2} & -\frac{9}{2} \end{bmatrix}$
3. (5, -3, 4)
4. a. $y < -\frac{2}{3}x + 2$
   b. Answers will vary. Sample: (0,0) and (2,0)
5. a. $25x + 15y \le 150$
   b.

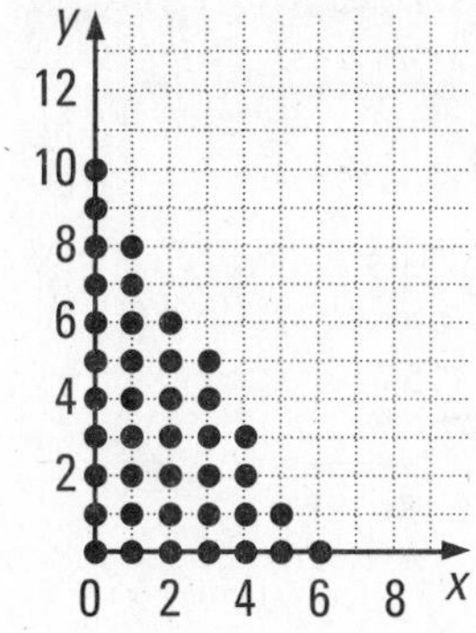

Chapter 5 Test, Form A

1. a. $39 \le w \le 46$
   b.

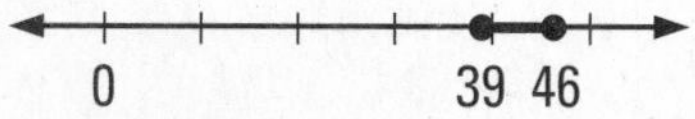

2. Estimates may vary. Sample: $\approx$ (2.3, 2.6), $\approx$ (-1.3, -4.5)
3. (a)
4. (-2, 6)
5. (1, 1, 2)
6. a. $x < -\frac{17}{3}$
   b.

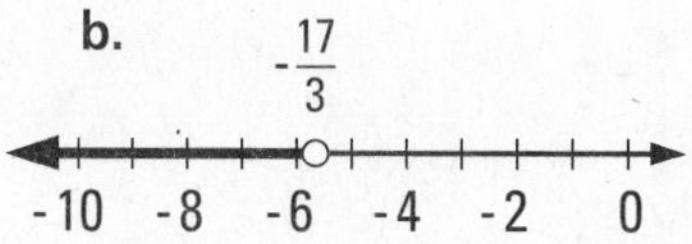

7. when you make less than 200 minutes of calls in the home territory per month
8. a. 41
   b. $\begin{bmatrix} \frac{3}{41} & \frac{4}{41} \\ -\frac{5}{41} & \frac{7}{41} \end{bmatrix}$
9.

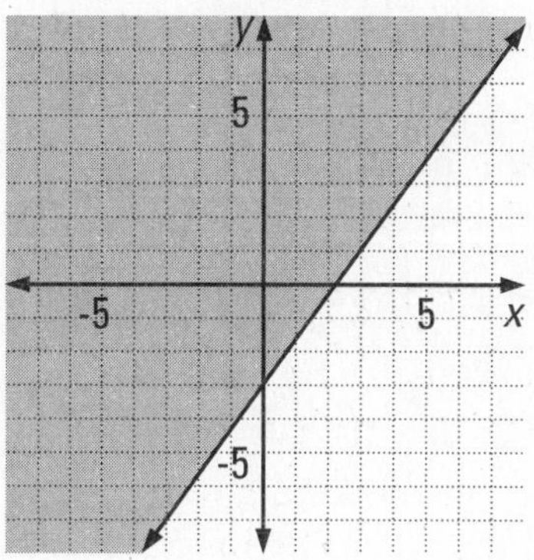

ANSWERS

ADVANCED ALGEBRA © Scott, Foresman and Company

10. Answers will vary.
Sample: (0, 0) and (1, 0)

11. $t = -12$

12. (5, -4)

13. $\begin{cases} y < 1.5x + 4 \\ y \geq -2 \end{cases}$

14. (-4, -2)

15. $25 + 27.50h$

16. a. $\begin{cases} 36x + 27y \leq 324 \\ 8x + 12y \leq 96 \\ x \geq 0 \\ y \geq 0 \end{cases}$

b.

8x + 12y = 96

36x + 27y = 324

c. 6 small quilts, 4 large quilts

Chapter 5 Test, Form B

1. a. $0 < d < 0.02$

b.

0 0.02 0.1

2. Estimates may vary.
Sample: ≈ (1.8, .9),
≈ (-2.3, -1.1)

3. (b)

4. (-7, -2)

5. (3, -2, 4)

6. a. $x \leq -\frac{3}{4}$

b.

$-\frac{3}{4}$

-1 0 1

7. when you swim more than 50 times in a year

8. a. 4

b. $\begin{bmatrix} \frac{3}{4} & -2 \\ -1 & 3 \end{bmatrix}$

9.

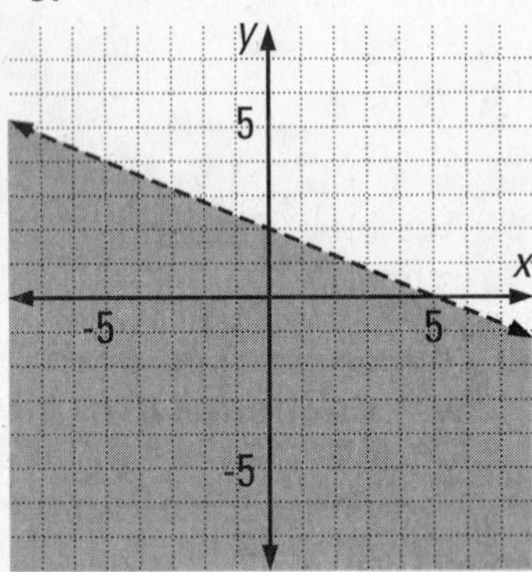

10. Answers will vary.
Sample: (4, 1) and (3, 2)

11. $t = -15$

12. (-2, 7)

13. $\begin{cases} y \leq -.5x + .5 \\ x > -3 \end{cases}$

14. (-3, 2)

15. $45 + 22.50h$

16. a. $\begin{cases} 3x + 6y \leq 48 \\ 6x + 6y \leq 60 \\ x \geq 0 \\ y \geq 0 \end{cases}$

b.

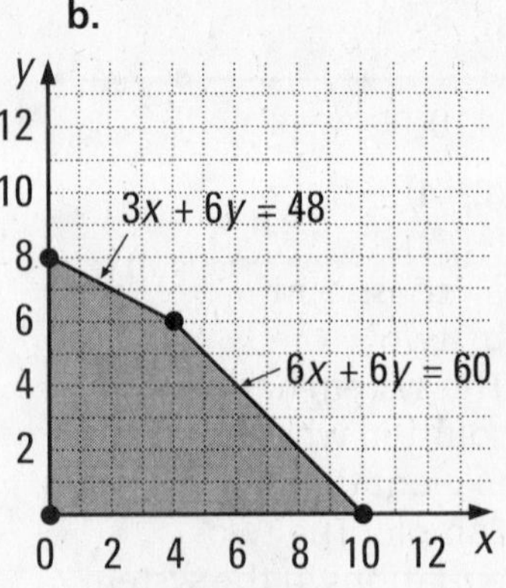

c. 4 holiday arrangements, 6 "get-well" arrangements

ANSWERS

Chapter 5 Test, Cumulative Form

1. a. $2800 + 400t$
   b. 18 months
2. (a)
3. a. AB exists. Explanations may vary. Sample: If the number of columns of A equals the number of rows of B; since A has three columns and B has three rows, the product AB exists.
   b. $AB = \begin{bmatrix} 86 & 0 & 53 \\ 41 & -1 & 47 \end{bmatrix}$
4. $\begin{bmatrix} -2 & 1 \\ 1.5 & -.5 \end{bmatrix}$
5. all t such that $t \neq 20$
6. $y = 7x + 46$
7. $L = \frac{k}{R}$, where k is a constant
8. a.

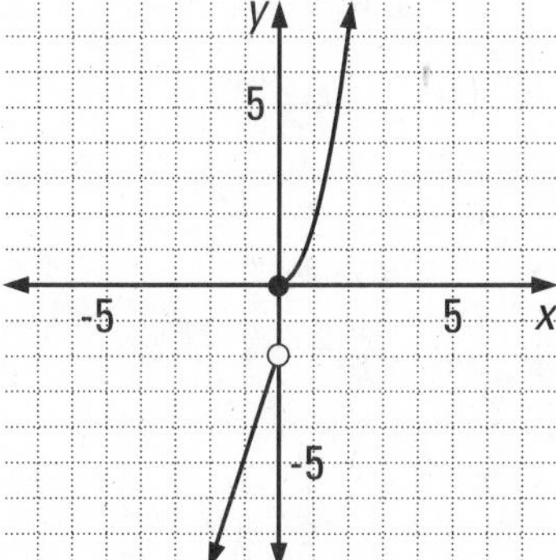

   b. true
9. a. $\begin{cases} x = y + 10 \\ 5x + 8y = 570 \end{cases}$
   b. 50 student tickets, 40 adult tickets
10. a.

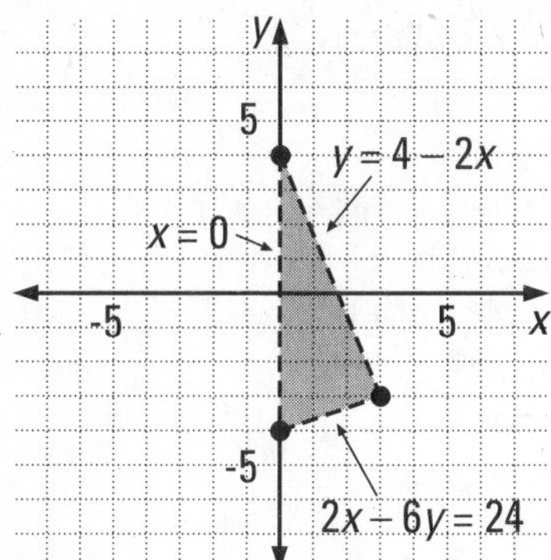

   b. (0, 4), (0, -4), $\left(\frac{24}{7}, -\frac{20}{7}\right)$
11. a. -4, 5, 20, 41, 68, 101
    b. No. Explanations may vary. Sample: The difference between successive terms is not constant. For example, $t_2 - t_1 = 5 - (-4) = 9$, but $t_3 - t_2 = 20 - 5 = 15$.
12. (b)
13. a. the number of deaths other than battle deaths among navy personnel in World War I
    b. the total number of battle deaths among army, navy, and marine personnel in World War II
14. a. $\begin{bmatrix} 184{,}364 & 27{,}532 \\ 36{,}519 & 18{,}808 \\ 17{,}272 & 4{,}388 \end{bmatrix}$

    This matrix represents the increase in each type of death among army, navy, and marine personnel from World War I to World War II.
15. a. $x \le -14$
    b.

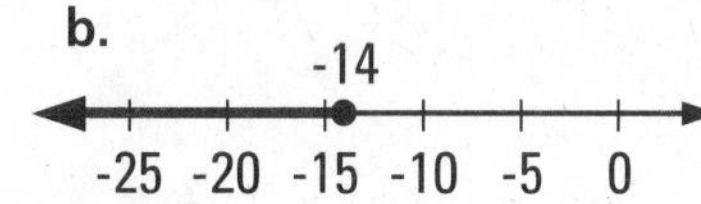

16. Estimates may vary. Sample: $\approx (1.8, 2.8)$, $\approx (-2.8, -1.8)$
17. (-5, 6)
18. (-1, -1, 2)
19. $250 + 7p$
20.

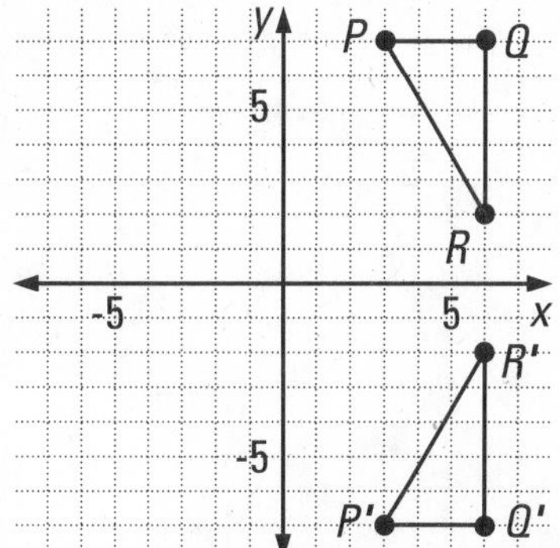

Quiz — Lessons 6-1 Through 6-4

1. $9r^2 + 48r + 64$
2. for all $x \le 0$
3. $m = 6$ or $m = -6$
4. $4w^2 + 300w + 5400$ square inches
5. a. $T_{-5,5}$
   b. $y - 5 = -2(x + 5)^2$
   c. $y = -2x^2 - 20x - 45$
6. $h = -16t^2 + 65t + 4$
7. 53 feet
8. ≈ 4.1 seconds

Quiz — Lessons 6-5 Through 6-7

1. 225
2. a. $y + 2 = 4(x - 1.5)^2$
   b. (1.5, -2)
3. a. $r(n) = .5n^2 + .5n + 1$
   b. 211 regions
4. No. Explanations may vary. Sample: Since $h(390) = 1.16$, the height of the ball is 1.16 feet when it is 390 feet from home plate; this height is not great enough to take the ball over a fence that is 8 feet high.
5. $c = -10$ or $c = 12$
6. $r = \frac{16 \pm 2\sqrt{69}}{2}$ so $r \approx 16.31$ or $r \approx -.31$.

Chapter 6 Test, Form A

1. no real solutions Explanations may vary. Sample: The discriminant is -103; when the discriminant is negative, there are no real solutions.
2. $2 + 0i$
3. $8 - 6i$
4. $-15 + 41i$
5. $2 \pm i$
6. a. 8
   b. There are two real, irrational roots.
7. $y + 1 = 2(x - 2)^2$
8. Descriptions may vary. Sample: The graph is a parabola that opens upward. There are two x-intercepts. The y-intercept is 7. The vertex is (2, -1), which represents the minimum value of -1. The equation of the axis of symmetry is $x = 2$.
9. a. $y - 5 = 2(x + 4)^2$
   b. (-2, 13)
   c. true
10. $y = 2x^2 + 16x + 37$
11. a. (-4, -3)
    b. -3 and -5
12.

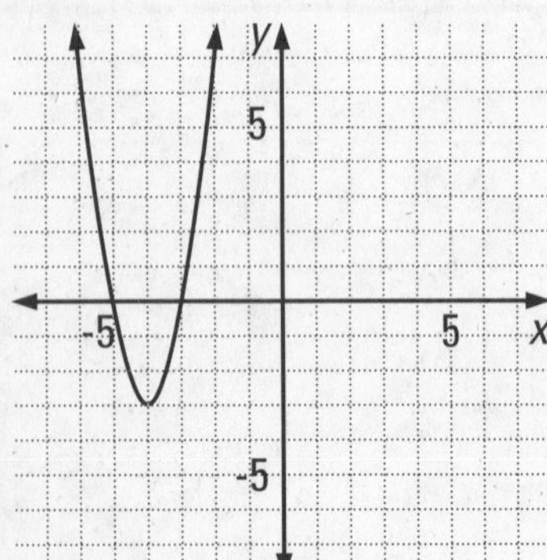

13. none
14. a. 2 m
    b. about 10.2 seconds after launch
    c. at about .5 seconds after launch and again at about 19.9 seconds after launch

15. a.

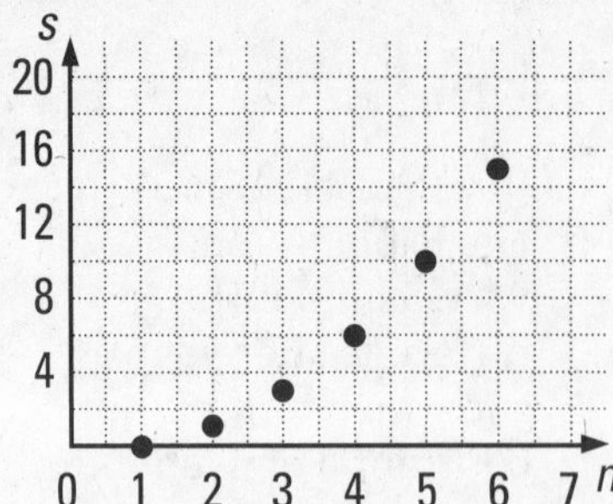

   b. $s(n) = .5n^2 - .5n$
   c. 2415
16. 6 inches
17. 40c
18. $-11 + 8i$
19. $p = \frac{1 \pm \sqrt{13}}{3}$
20. $m = .5 \pm 2i$

Chapter 6 Test, Form B

1. two real solutions Explanations may vary. Sample: The discriminant is 29; when the discriminant is positive, there are two real solutions.
2. $-90 + 0i$
3. $-8 + 13i$
4. $47 - 14i$
5. $-1 \pm i$
6. a. -24
   b. There are two complex conjugate roots.
7. $y + 2 = -3(x - 1)^2$
8. Descriptions may vary. Sample: The graph is a parabola that opens downward. There are no x-intercepts. The y-intercept is -5. The vertex is (1, -2), which represents the maximum value of -2. The equation of the axis of symmetry is $x = 1$.
9. a. $y + 6 = 5(x - 3)^2$
   b. (-2, 119)
   c. false
10. $y = 5x^2 - 30x + 39$
11. a. (5, -2)
    b. 4 and 6
12.

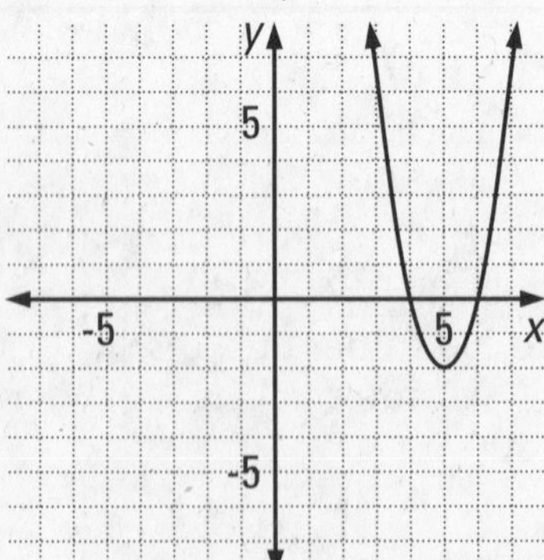

13. 10
14. a. $h = -16t^2 + 30t + 8$
    b. about 22.1 feet
    c. after about 2.1 seconds

ANSWERS

15. a.

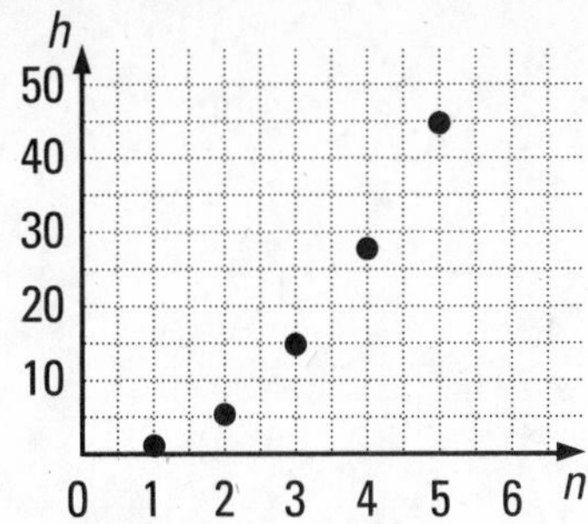

b. $h(n) = 2n^2 - n$

c. 7140

16. $\sqrt{\frac{96}{\pi}}$ cm or $\approx$ 5.6 cm

17. $-84m$

18. $31 - 18i$

19. $q = \frac{8 \pm \sqrt{304}}{10}$

20. $y = -1.25 \pm 1.25i$

Chapter 6 Test, Cumulative Form

1. $45k^2 - 210k + 245$

2. a. $h = -16t^2 + 26$

b. after about 1.3 seconds

c.

3. $j = \pm i$

4. $m = \pm 6i$

5. (4, 3, -5)

6. $r = 9$

7. $0 + 36i$

8. $-4 + 0i$

9.

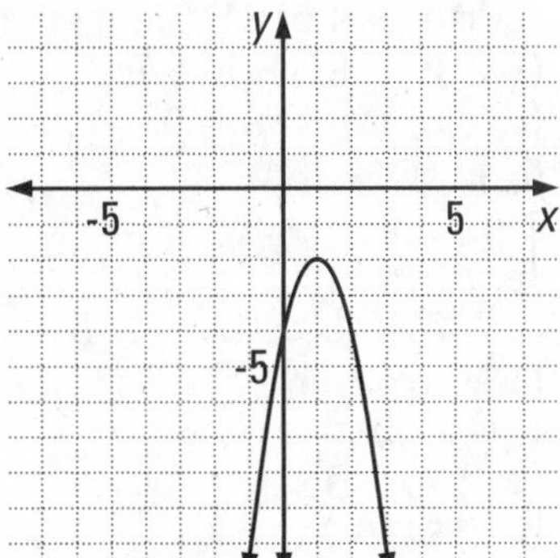

10. The discriminant is 49, so there are two x-intercepts.

11. $a = \frac{y - bx - c}{x^2}$

12. $\begin{bmatrix} 3 & 0 \\ 0 & 2 \end{bmatrix}$

13.

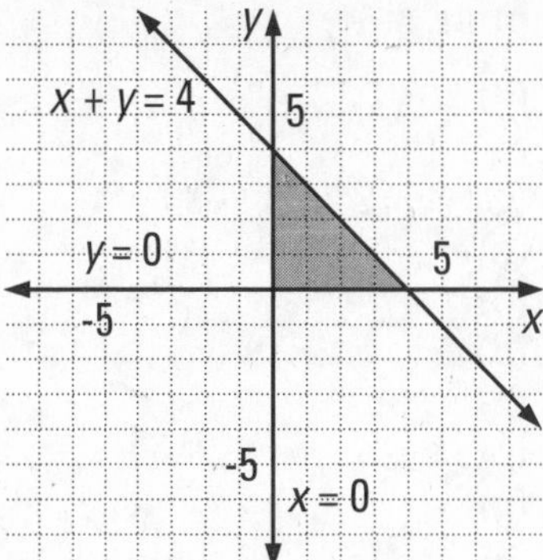

14. 10 large animals, 15 small animals

15. $C = 6s + 3.5$

16. -3.7, 2.3, 8.3, 14.3, 20.3

17. $m = 2$

18. $\ell w + 4\ell + 4w + 16$ square inches

19. a.

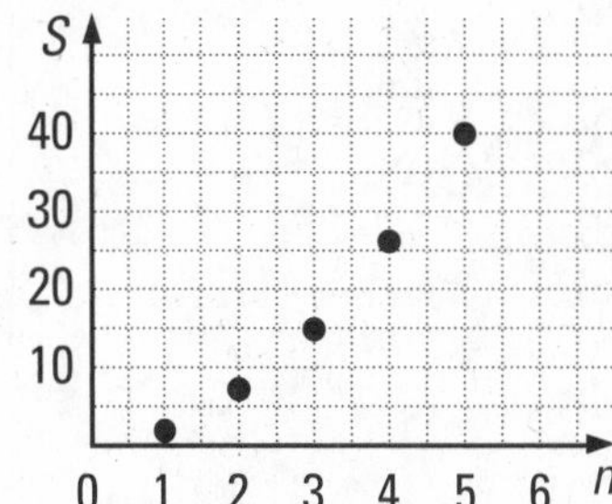

b. $S(n) = 1.5n^2 + .5n$

c. 15,050

20. a.

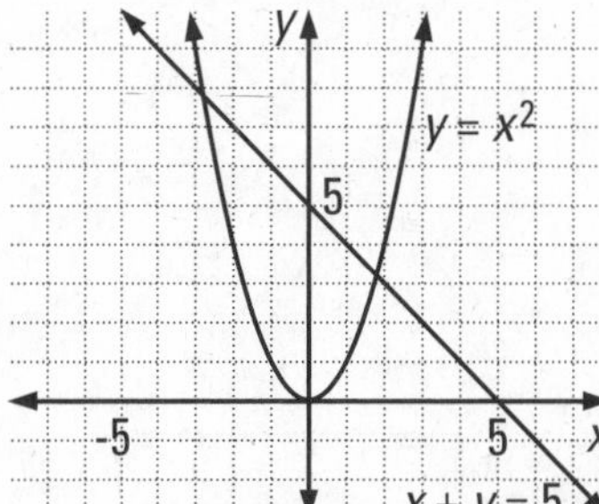

b. Estimates may vary. Sample: $\approx$ (-2.8, 7.8), $\approx$ (1.8, 3.2)

ANSWERS

Comprehensive Test, Chapters 1–6

1. (d)
2. (c)
3. (c)
4. (b)
5. (d)
6. (d)
7. (d)
8. (a)
9. (b)
10. (a)
11. (b)
12. (a)
13. (c)
14. (d)
15. (a)
16. (a)
17. (c)
18. (d)
19. (d)
20. (a)
21. (a)
22. (b)
23. (a)
24. (b)
25. (b)
26. (d)
27. (c)
28. (c)
29. (d)
30. (b)

Quiz Lessons 7-1 Through 7-3

1. $\frac{1}{343}$
2. 4,194,304
3. $\frac{25}{4}$
4. $\frac{3b^6}{4a^5}$
5. $x^{11}y^{39}$
6. (b)
7. $\{y: y \geq 0\}$
8. It has rotation symmetry. The graph can be mapped onto itself under a 180° rotation around the origin.
9. $\approx$1566 pounds

Quiz Lessons 7-4 Through 7-6

1. 2
2. -5
3. No. Explanations may vary. Sample: If $-i\sqrt{3}$ is a fourth root of 81, then $(-i\sqrt{3})^4 = 81$. However, $(-i)^4(\sqrt{3})^4 = 1 \cdot 9 = 9$.
4. 6, 3, 1.5
5. Yes. Explanations may vary. Sample: The ratio between successive terms (.5) is constant.
6. $t_n = 6(.5)^{n-1}$
7. a. \$2927.15
   b. \$5470.26

Chapter 7 Test, Form A

1. $\frac{1}{16}$ 2. 10,000
3. $\frac{243}{32}$ 4. 1
5. $\frac{3}{4}$
6. $\begin{cases} g_1 = \frac{3}{2} \\ g_n = \frac{3}{4}g_{n-1}, \\ \text{for integers } n \geq 2 \end{cases}$
7. $g_n = \frac{3}{2}\left(\frac{3}{4}\right)^{n-1}$ for integers $n: n \geq 1$
8. a. domain: all reals
   range: $\{y: y \geq 0\}$
   b. I and II
9. (a)
10. No. Explanations may vary. Sample: If $3i$ is a sixth root of 729, then $(3i)^6 = 729$. However, $(3i)^6 = 3^6 i^6 = 729(-1) = -729$.
11. \$867.31
12. $405a^{26}b^{11}$
13. $\frac{4m^7}{n^8}$
14. Graph $y = x^6$ and $y = 18$ on the same set of coordinate axes. Estimate the x-coordinates of the two points where the graphs intersect. There are two real roots of $x^6 = 18$.
15. $\approx 3.23 \times 10^8$ Btu
16. 15.02
17. ≈ 418.83 in^2
18. a. $h_n = 2(.5)^{n-1}$ for integers $n: n \geq 1$
    b. .5 ft
19. $w = \pm 2$ 20. $m = \frac{1}{25}$
21. $x^2, x^{\frac{3}{2}}, x, x^{-4}$
22. $p = \pm 3^{-\frac{9}{4}}$
23. $q = \frac{4}{7}$
24. a. $y = x^8$
    b. Answers will vary. Sample: (1, 1), (0, 0), (-1, 1), (-2, 256)
25. \$6588.90

ANSWERS

Chapter 7 Test, Form B

1. $\frac{1}{49}$
2. 100,000
3. $\frac{81}{16}$
4. 1
5. $\frac{3}{5}$
6. $\begin{cases} g_1 = \frac{1}{2} \\ g_n = \frac{3}{5}g_{n-1}, \\ \text{for integers } n \geq 2 \end{cases}$
7. $g_n = \frac{1}{2}\left(\frac{3}{5}\right)^{n-1}$
   for integers n: $n \geq 1$
8. a. domain: all real numbers; range: all real numbers
   b. I and III
9. (c)
10. Yes. Answers may vary. Sample: If $5i$ is a 4th root of 625, then $(5i)^4 = 625$; but $(5i)^4 = 5^4 i^4 = 625(1) = 625$.
11. $940.22
12. $48m^{11}n^6$
13. $7a^4b^5$
14. Graph $y = x^5$ and $y = -15$ on the same set of coordinate axes. Estimate the x-coordinate of the only point where the graphs intersect. There is one real root of $x^5 = -15$.
15. ≈ 565 pounds
16. 172.74
17. ≈ 141.70 million miles
18. a. $h_n = 2.4(.6)^{n-1}$
    for integers n: $n \geq 1$
    b. .5184 m
19. $w = \pm 3$
20. $m = \frac{1}{125}$
21. $x^{-2}, x^{\frac{1}{2}}, x, x^{\frac{5}{4}}$
22. $p = 16^{\frac{1}{3}}$
23. $q = \frac{3}{5}$
24. a. $y = x^5$
    b. Answers will vary. Sample: (1, 1), (0, 0), (-1, -1), (-2, -32)
25. $3438.42

Chapter 7 Test, Cumulative Form

1. $\frac{64}{125}$
2. $\frac{1}{27}$
3. 6
4. a. $35.4d$
   b. 17th day
5. Explanations may vary. Sample: The discriminant is 925. Since $925 > 0$, by the Discriminant Theorem, the equation has two real roots.
6. domain: the set of all real numbers; range: $\{y: y \geq 0\}$
7. (b)
8.

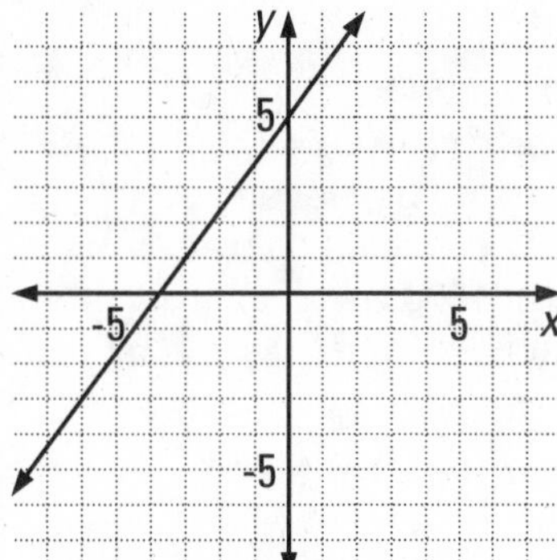

9. $w = 128$
10. $t = \pm 3.5$
11. a. $h = -16t^2 + 15t + 50$
    b. at about 1.92 seconds
12. $26 - 18i$
13. $y = \frac{2}{9}x - \frac{50}{9}$
14. (c)
15. ≈ 472 acres
16. $\begin{cases} g_1 = 3 \\ g_n = \frac{3}{4}g_{n-1}, \\ \text{for integers } n \geq 2 \end{cases}$
17. $g_n = 3\left(\frac{3}{4}\right)^{n-1}$
    for integers n: $n \geq 1$
18. (d)
19. 29 cans
20. x and n are integers: $x \geq 1$ and $|n| \geq 1$
21. $\frac{15}{8a^3b^5}$
22. $k = \frac{4}{9}$
23. fixed amount: $28.20; hourly fee: $43.40
24.

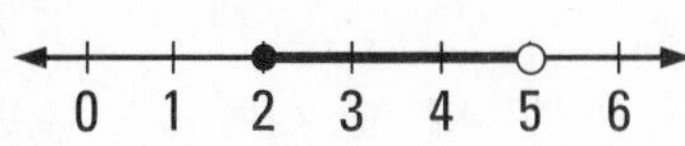

25. ≈ 119 square inches
26.

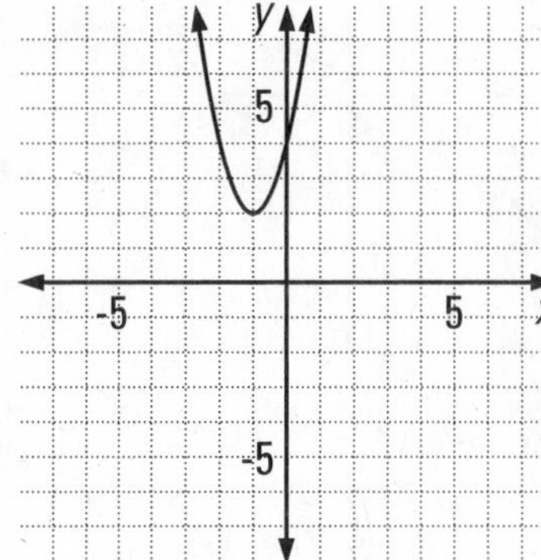

27. $1158.72

ANSWERS

Quiz — Lessons 8-1 Through 8-3

1. -7
2. 5
3. 21
4. $f(f(x)) = 16x - 35$
5. a.

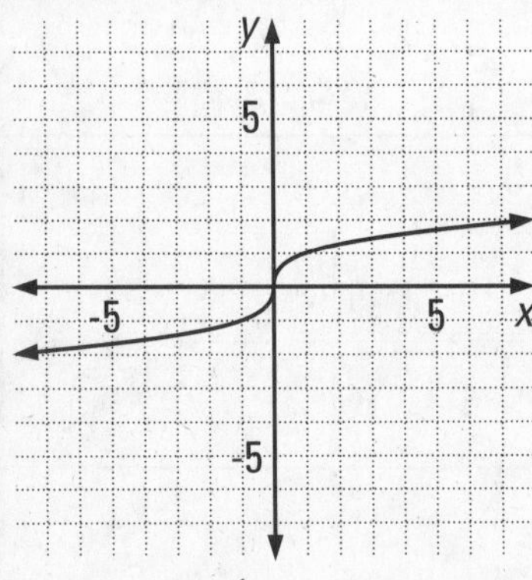

b. $y = x^{\frac{1}{3}}$

c. Yes. Explanations may vary. Sample: The graph of the inverse passes the Vertical-Line Test for a function.

6. $y = \frac{1}{5}x + \frac{3}{5}$
7. domain: $\{x: x = -2\}$; range: the set of all real numbers
8. (d)
9. false

Quiz — Lessons 8-4 Through 8-6

1. 3
2. 4
3. $\frac{5}{3}$
4. 2.32
5. $3n^3$
6. $2m\sqrt[4]{8m^3}$
7. $\frac{\sqrt{2t}}{2t}$
8. false
9. $\sqrt{5} + 2$
10. $\approx$ 39,900 km

Chapter 8 Test, Form A

1. 960
2. $f \circ g(x) = 4x^2 - 1$
3. Yes. Explanations may vary. Sample: Apply the Inverse Function Theorem: $p \circ q\,(x) = (x + 1) - 1 = x$; $q \circ p\,(x) = (x - 1) + 1 = x$
4. -2
5. 5
6. $y = \frac{13}{8}$
7. 3.02
8. $x = y^2$
9. No. Explanations may vary. Sample: The graph of $y = x^2$ does not pass the Horizontal-Line Test.
10. $\frac{3\sqrt{2m}}{m}$
11. a. $d(w) = 25w$

    b. $d^{-1}(1500) = 60$; it takes the glacier about 60 weeks to travel 1500 cm.
12. (c)
13.

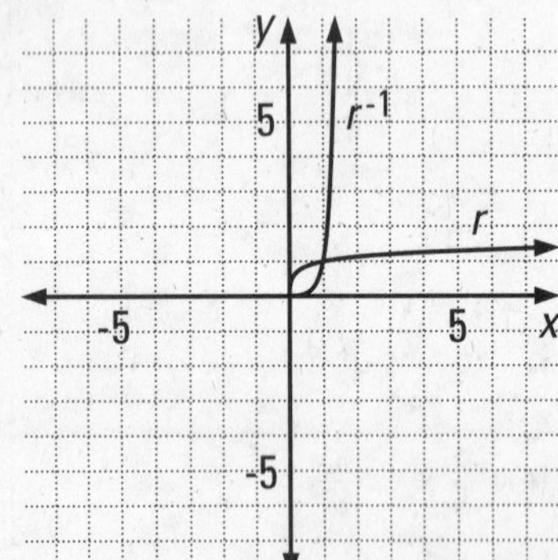

14. domain: $\{x: x \geq 0\}$; range: $\{y: y \geq 0\}$
15. domain: $\{x: x \geq 0\}$; range: $\{y: y \geq 0\}$
16. Answers will vary. Sample: $\sqrt[4]{(-1)^4} = 1 \neq -1$
17. $a = -26$
18. $m = 128$
19. $\approx$ 5.76 cm
20. $\approx$ 151.25 feet
21. $2r^2\sqrt[4]{2}$
22. $-7s\sqrt[3]{s}$
23. $4t\sqrt[6]{t}$
24. true

Chapter 8 Test, Form B

1. 186
2. $r \circ t\,(x) = 63x^2 - 252x + 253$
3. No. Explanations may vary. Sample: An equation for f is $y = x + 3$; an equation for its inverse is $x = y + 3$, or $y = x - 3$.
4. -8
5. 3
6. $x = \frac{11}{6}$
7. 3.95
8. $x = y^5$
9. Yes. Explanations may vary. Sample: Graph of $y = x^5$ passes the Horizontal-Line Test.
10. $\frac{\sqrt{6y}}{3y}$
11. a. $d(h) = 2h$

    b. $d^{-1}(18) = 9$; it takes the stick about 9 hours to travel 18 mi.
12. (b)
13.

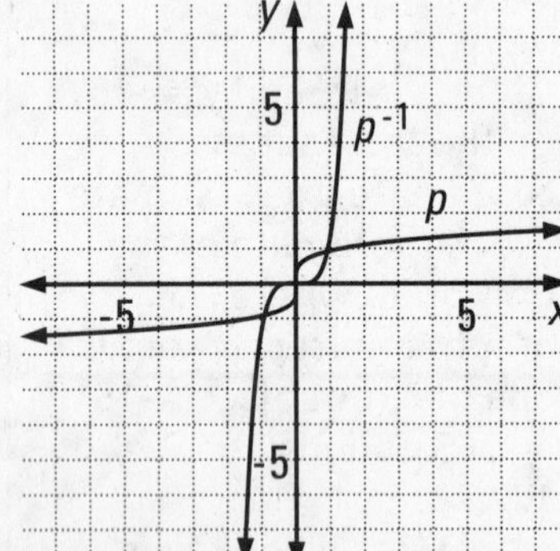

14. domain: all real numbers; range: all real numbers
15. domain: all real numbers; range: all real numbers
16. Answers will vary. Sample: $\sqrt[8]{(-1)^8} = 1 \neq -1$
17. no real solutions
18. $n = 16$
19. $\approx$ 5.37 cm
20. $\approx$ 211.25 feet
21. $2b^2\sqrt[5]{2}$
22. $-5c\sqrt[3]{c}$
23. $6d\sqrt[4]{d}$
24. false

Chapter 8 Test, Cumulative Form

1. all $x \geq 0$
2. a. -3, 6, -12, 24, -48, 96

   b. $\begin{cases} g_1 = -3 \\ g_n = -2g_{n-1}, \\ \text{for integers } n \geq 2 \end{cases}$
3. No. Explanations may vary. Sample: After ten years, the amount will be only \$162.89.
4. a.

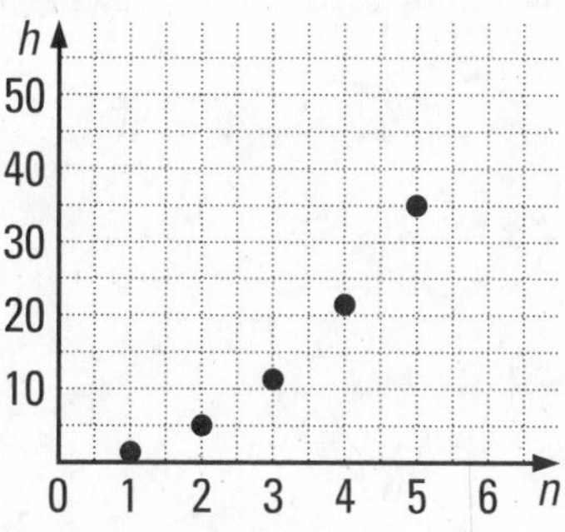

   b. $h(n) = 1.5n^2 - .5n$

   c. 3725
5. ≈ 417 m
6. (c)
7. a. 344

   b. 19
8. (c)
9. $m = \frac{1}{32}$
10. $d = 129$
11. Explanations may vary. Sample: Graph $y = x^4$ and $y = -16$ on the same set of coordinate axes. The graph of $y = x^4$ will be in quadrants I and II. The graph of $y = -16$ will be in quadrants III and IV. Since the two graphs will not intersect, there are no real solutions to $x^4 = -16$.
12. (1.5, 2.5)
13.

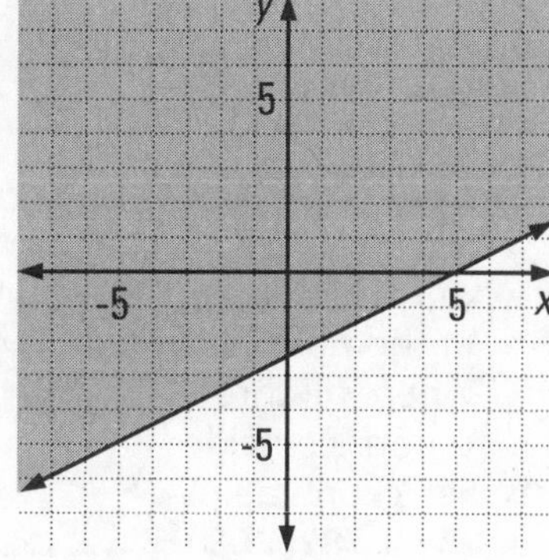

14. $-2x^2y^4\sqrt[5]{3x}$
15. $\frac{1}{8}$
16. $C(p) = 3.5p + 450$
17. -6
18. $\frac{2}{3}$
19. $\frac{1}{343}$
20. $k < 0$
21. false

Quiz — Lessons 9-1 Through 9-3

1. false
2. \$402.60
3. (c)
4. a.

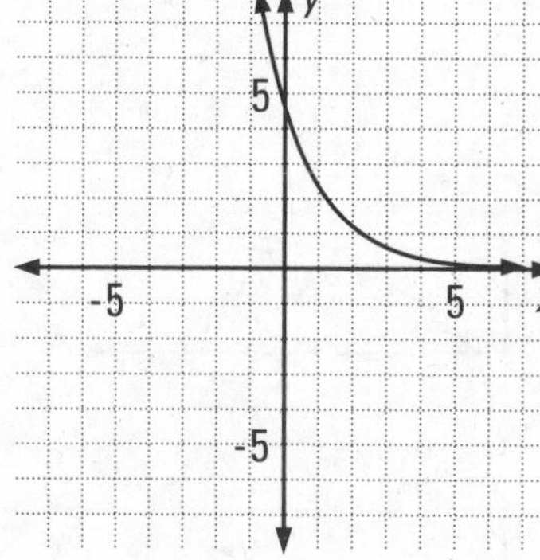

   b. $\frac{1}{2}$

   c. exponential-decay function
5. \$57,395.63
6. $\approx 549{,}524$

Quiz — Lessons 9-4 Through 9-7

1. -2
2. 5
3. 1.75
4. $\log_{25}\left(\frac{1}{125}\right) = -\frac{3}{2}$
5. $x = 100{,}000$
6. $x = 216$
7. Choice of labeled points may vary.

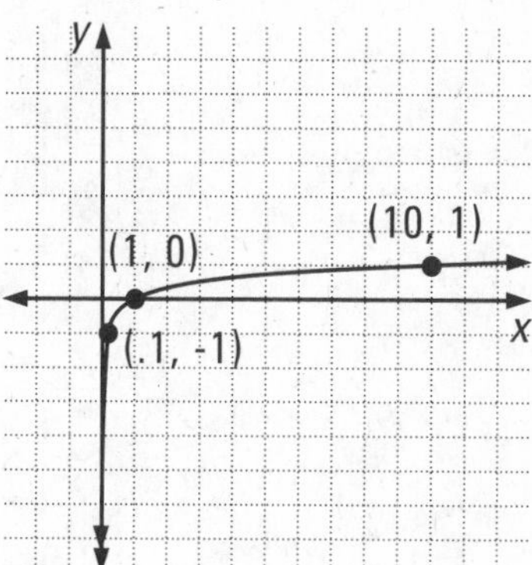

8. false
9. 100 times
10. a. $P = 7.585(1.004)^t$

    b. ≈ 7.967 million

ANSWERS

Chapter 9 Test, Form A

1. (c)
2. ln 1024
3. log 180
4. $\frac{1}{2}$
5. 4
6.

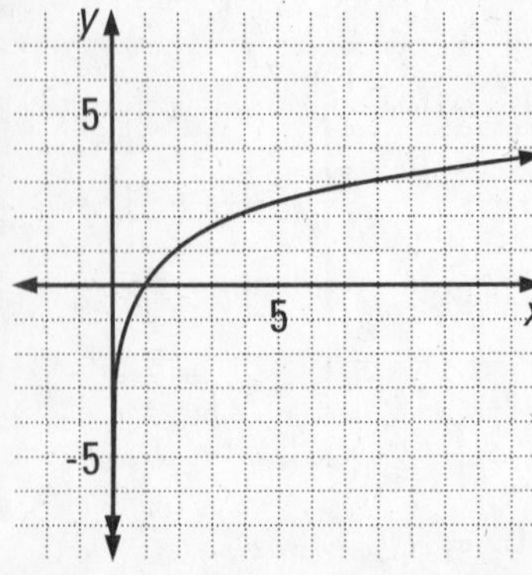

7. $\{x: x > 0\}$
8. $y = 2^x$
9. Yes. Explanations may vary. Sample: The graph of $y = \log_2 x$ passes the Horizontal-Line Test for inverses.
10. all real numbers
11. $\approx$ 8.7 mm
12. $s = -2$
13. $t \approx .63$
14. $p \approx 10{,}938.02$
15. $q \approx -2.69$
16. 4 choices
17. true
18. 10,000 times as acidic
19. a. $y = 3^x$
    b. Answers will vary. Sample: Since $2.5 < e < 3$, the graph of $y = e^x$ will be between the graphs of f and g except at the point (0, 1), where all three graphs coincide.
20. a. See graph below.
    b. $P = 1.782(1.034)^t$
    c. $\approx$ 50.7 million
21. false
22. $4803.26
23. $\approx$ 22.7 years

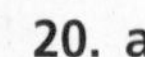
20. a.

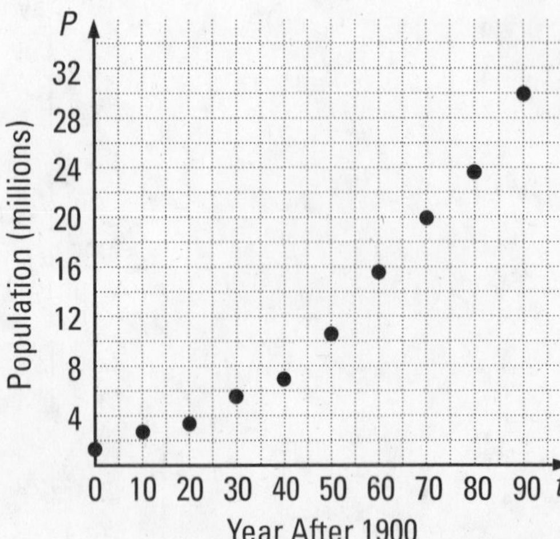

Chapter 9 Test, Form B

1. (b)
2. ln 256
3. log 7
4. $\frac{1}{5}$
5. 3
6.

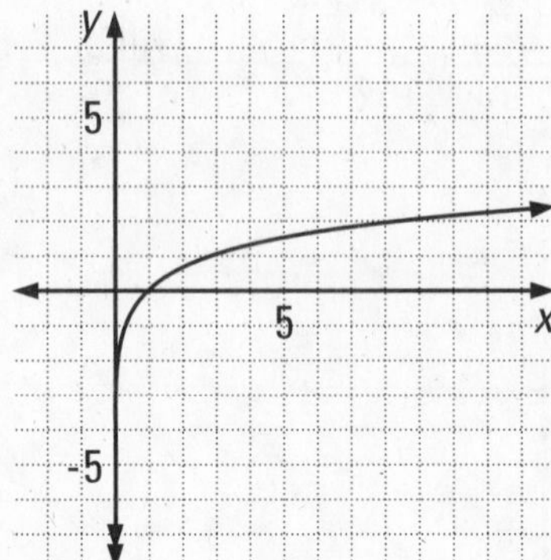

7. $\{x: x > 0\}$
8. $y = 3^x$
9. Yes. Explanations may vary. Sample: The graph of $y = \log_3 x$ passes the Horizontal-Line Test for inverses.
10. all real numbers
11. $\approx$ 499.2 cm
12. $t = -2$
13. $s \approx 40.32$
14. $x \approx .33$
15. $r \approx 5.72$
16. 8 choices
17. true
18. about 316.2 times as acidic
19. a. $y = 4^x$
    b. Answers will vary. Sample: When $x = 0$, all three graphs intersect. When $x > 0$, the graph of $y = e^x$ is below the graphs of f and g; when $x < 0$, it is above them.

20. a. See graph below.
b. $P = 1.058(1.864)^h$
c. ≈ 2.88 million

21. false
22. $6466.35
23. ≈ 22.9 years

20. a.

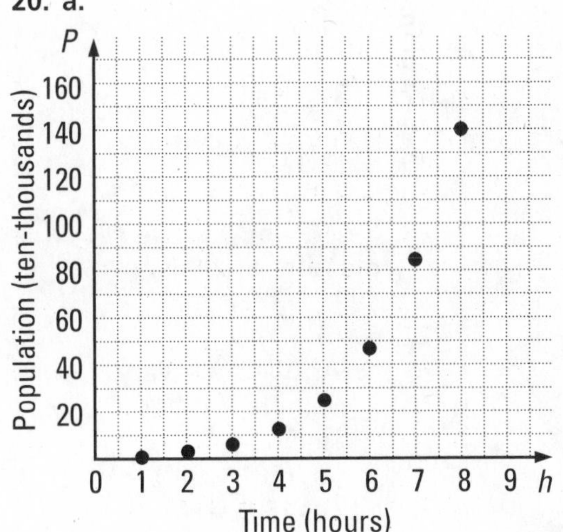

Chapter 9 Test, Cumulative Form

1. 3
2. $\frac{3}{2}$
3. $-\frac{2}{3}$
4. a. 8, 24, 72, 216
   b. $t_n = 8 \cdot 3^{n-1}$ for integers $n: n \geq 1$
   c. Yes. Explanations may vary. Sample: There is a common ratio (3) between successive terms.
5. false
6. $x \approx 29.37$
7. $w \approx .94$
8. a. $y = \frac{1}{9}x - \frac{2}{9}$
   b. Yes. Explanations may vary. Sample: The graph of $y = 9x + 2$ is a line with slope 9; this graph passes the Horizontal-Line Test for inverses.
9. 64
10. $w = \frac{5}{6} \pm \frac{\sqrt{23}}{6}i$
11. ≈ 7.5 million
12. about 316 times as loud
13. $2c^2d^4\sqrt[4]{3d}$
14.

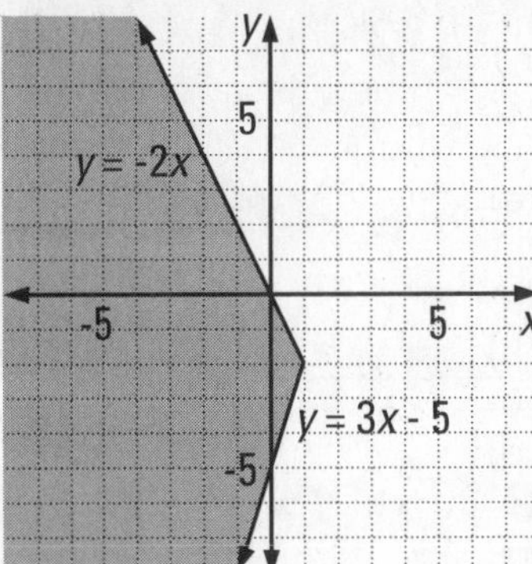

15. a. 3
    b. 33
16. log 875
17. (c)
18. a. 13×3
    b. Alcedo
    c. the height of the Lascar volcano in Chile
19. a. $y = 2^x$
    b. Answers will vary. Sample: Since $2 < e < 4$, the graph of $y = e^x$ will be between the graphs of f and g except at the point (0, 1), where all three graphs intersect.
20. a. 21 feet
    b. at about 2.6 seconds
21. (d)
22. a. all real numbers
    b. all positive real numbers
23. ≈ 2.36 m
24. $1347.35
25. $1349.86

ANSWERS

Comprehensive Test, Chapters 1–9

1. (c)
2. (c)
3. (a)
4. (c)
5. (a)
6. (b)
7. (d)
8. (d)
9. (d)
10. (b)
11. (b)
12. (b)
13. (b)
14. (d)
15. (c)
16. (a)
17. (a)
18. (a)
19. (c)
20. (b)
21. (a)
22. (d)
23. (b)
24. (d)
25. (a)

Quiz Lessons 10-1 Through 10-3

1. .583
2. cos
3. 1
4. $\frac{1}{2}$
5. 1
6. true
7. ≈ 3.3
8. $\approx 74.5°$
9. $\approx$ 143,007 feet, or $\approx$ 27.1 miles

Quiz Lessons 10-4 Through 10-7

1. (d)
2. $-\frac{\sqrt{3}}{3}$
3. $\frac{\sqrt{2}}{2}$
4. 0
5. $\frac{1}{2}$
6. 240°, 300°
7.

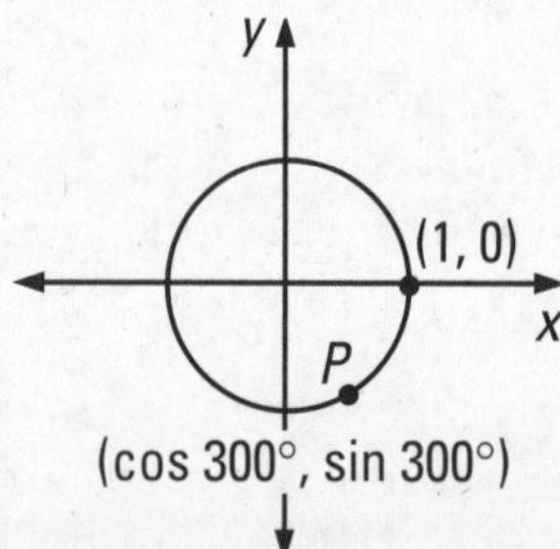

8. negative
9. ≈ 2.6
10. ≈ 8.3

Chapter 10 Test, Form A

1. .811
2. .740
3. $\approx 12°$
4. 360°
5. $\{f(\theta): -1 \leq f(\theta) \leq 1\}$
6. 30°, 150°
7.

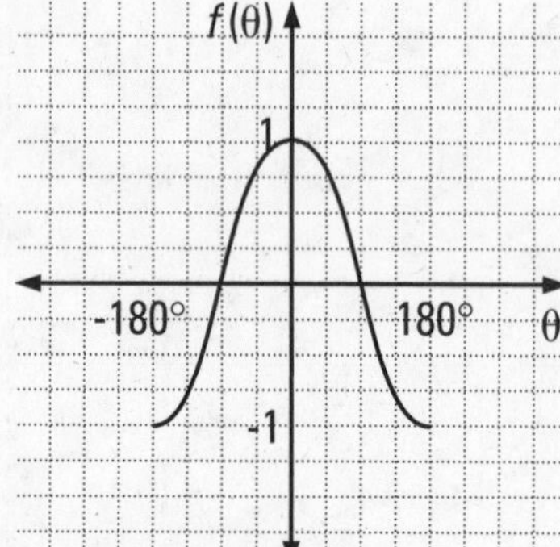

8. Explanations will vary. Sample: Since $\tan \theta = \frac{\sin \theta}{\cos \theta}$, $\tan 270° = \frac{\sin 270°}{\cos 270°} = \frac{-1}{0}$, which is undefined.
9. *a*
10. *f*
11. $\pm \frac{\sqrt{3}}{2}$
12. -120°
13. $\frac{7\pi}{4}$ radians
14. $\approx 45°$
15. ≈ 11.2
16. -1
17. $\sqrt{3}$
18. $\approx$ 4.7 miles
19. ≈ 17.9
20. $\approx 37°$
21. Yes. Other possible measure of $\angle O$ is $180° - 37° = 143°$.
22. a. (i)
    b. Answers will vary. Sample: Let $\theta = 90°$; $\sin 90° = 1$; $\cos(90° + 90°) = \cos 180° = -1$

ANSWERS

Chapter 10 Test, Form B

1. 1.607
2. .849
3. $\approx 4°$
4. 360°
5. $\{g(\theta): -1 \le g(\theta) \le 1\}$
6. 135°
7.

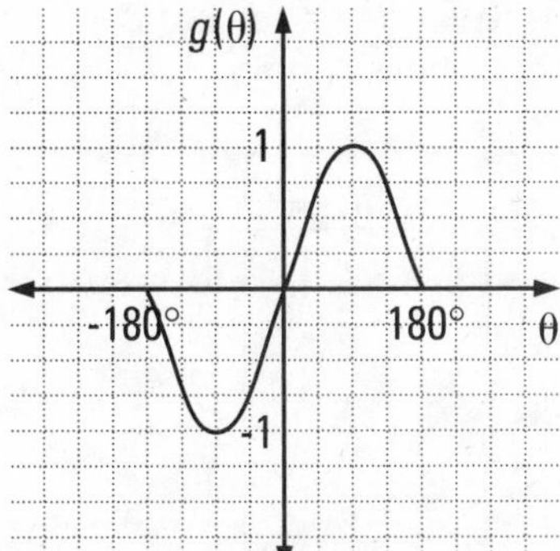

8. Explanations will vary. Sample: Since $\tan \theta = \frac{\sin \theta}{\cos \theta}$, $\tan(-90°) = \frac{\sin(-90°)}{\cos(-90°)} = \frac{-1}{0}$, which is undefined.
9. *b*
10. *e*
11. $\pm .8$
12. 225°
13. $\frac{9\pi}{2}$ radians
14. $\approx 77.4°$
15. ≈ 19.3
16. -1
17. $\frac{\sqrt{2}}{2}$
18. ≈ 226.8 feet
19. ≈ 10.6
20. $\approx 22°$
21. No. Explanations may vary. Sample: The only other possible measure is 158°. But 25° + 158° > 180°, so a 25° angle and a 158° angle cannot be in the same triangle.
22. a. (ii)
    b. Answers will vary. Sample: Let $\theta = 45°$; $\cos\theta + \sin\theta = \frac{\sqrt{2}}{2} + \frac{\sqrt{2}}{2} = \sqrt{2}$, which is not equal to 1.

Chapter 10 Test, Cumulative Form

1. .643 **2.** 1
3. -3
4. $e^{3.97} \approx 53$
5. ≈ 3.3 feet
6. ≈ 10.3
7. $\approx 83.1°$
8. $r \approx 2.71$
9. $m \approx .35$
10. $j = 64$
11. $x = \frac{15}{4}y + 15$
12. $y + 4 = 2(x - 2)^2$
13. ≈ 37.4 feet
14. a.

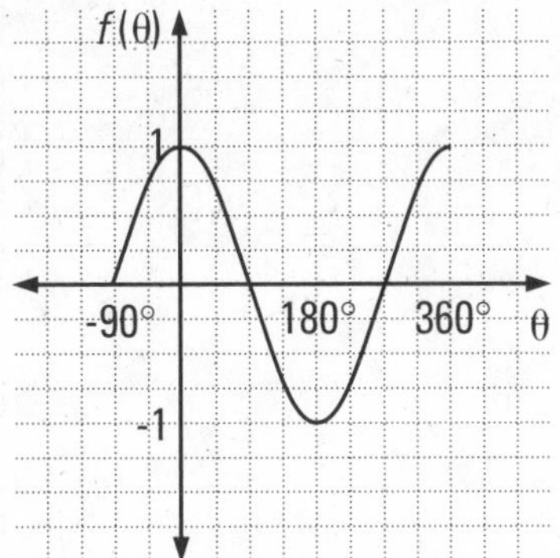

    b. -90°, 90°, 270°
15. ≈ 39.9 miles
16. (c) **17.** $\approx 250°$
18. $\approx 242°$, $\approx 298°$
19. a. $\frac{2\pi}{15}$ radians
    b. $-\frac{133\pi}{36}$ radians
20. a. -99 **b.** 73
21. $\begin{bmatrix} 825 & 900 \\ 480 & 600 \\ 900 & 525 \end{bmatrix}$
22. $2449.08
23. $2451.37
24. a. See graph below.
    b. $P = .272(1.014)^t$
    c. ≈ 10.10 million

24. a.

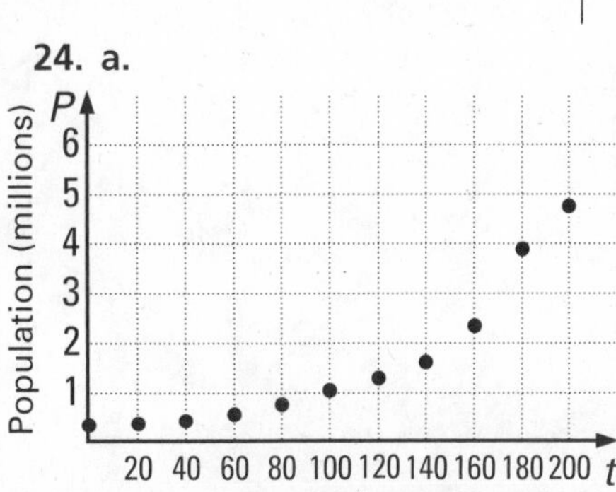

Quiz — Lessons 11-1 Through 11-3

1. 7 **2.** 13
3.

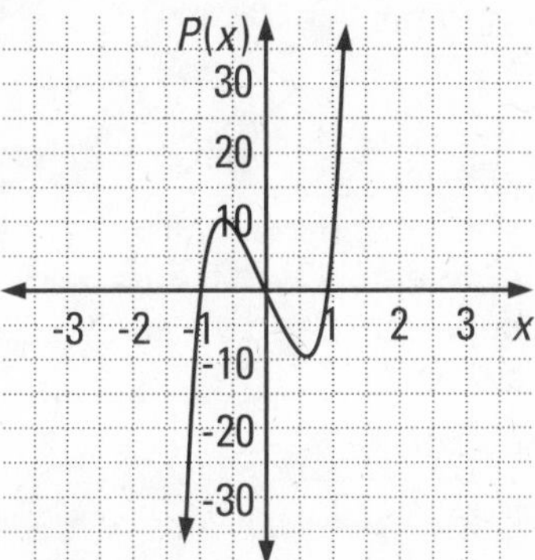

4. $12m^3 - 10m^2 - 8m - 6$
5. $36w^3 - 96w^2 + 15w$
6. $3x^2y(2x^2 - 3xy - 6y^2)$
7. $(4m^2 + 17)(4m^2 - 17)$
8. Yes. Explanations may vary. Sample: The discriminant is 96. Since 96 is not a perfect square, $12n^2 + 12n + 1$ is prime over the set of rational numbers.
9. $V(x) = x^3 + 6x^2 + 12x + 8$
10. $30x^2 + 50x + 75$

Quiz — Lessons 11-4 Through 11-7

1. -3 and -2; -1 and 0; 1 and 2
2. (-.3, -4.8)
3. Answers may vary. Sample: $P(x) = (x - 2)(2x + 3)(x + 1)$
4. a. $f(x) = x(5x + 1)(2x - 1)$
   b. $0, -\frac{1}{5}, \frac{1}{2}$
5. $(4x + 3)(2x + 7)$
6. $(m - 23)(m + 25)$
7. $-2z(2z - 1)(4z + 3)$
8. $\pm 1, \pm 2, \pm 4, \pm 8$
9. $\pm 1, \pm 2, \pm 4, \pm\frac{1}{3}, \pm\frac{2}{3}, \pm\frac{4}{3}$
10. $-\frac{4}{3}, -1, \frac{7}{2}$

ANSWERS

Chapter 11 Test, Form A

1. $100x^3 + 125x^2 + 150x + 200$
2. $612.94
3. 3
4. $\pm 1, \pm 2, \pm 4, \pm 8$
5. integer zero: -4; noninteger zeros are between -1 and 0 and between 2 and 3
6. a.

20 cm
x x
x x
28 cm
x x
x x

b. $S(x) = (28 - 2x)(20 - 2x) + 2x(28 - 2x) + 2x(20 - 2x)$

7. $2x^2(x + 1)(x - 5)$
8. 0, -1, 5
9.

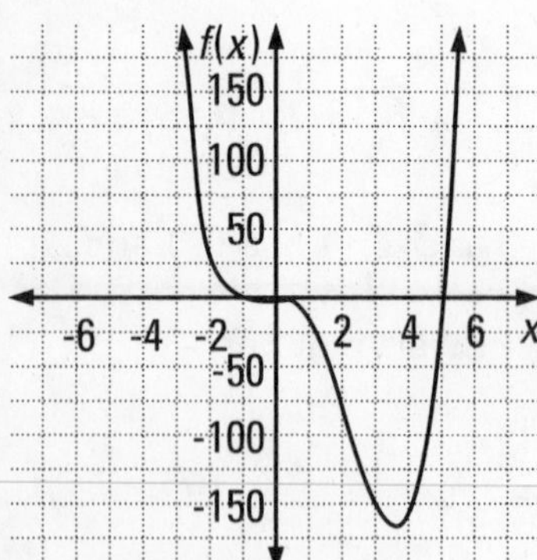

10. Answers may vary. Sample: $g(x) = 2x(x + 1)(x - 5)$
11. 0
12. $P(x) = x(x - 2)(x + 5)$
13. $P(x) = x^3 + 3x^2 - 10x$
14. 2
15. $f(n) = n^2 + 2n$
16. 168
17. No. Explanations may vary. Sample: None of the first five differences is constant.
18. $2r^3s^2(3s + 8r)(3s - 8r)$
19. $3\left(q - \frac{6 + 2\sqrt{6}}{3}\right) \cdot \left(q - \frac{6 - 2\sqrt{6}}{3}\right)$
20. $125x^3 + 75x^2 + 15x + 1$
21. $c^3 + 3c^2 - c - 3$
22. a. 3
    b. trinomial
    c. 8
23. (c)

Chapter 11 Test, Form B

1. $1000x^4 + 2500x^3 + 1750x^2 + 1500x + 3000$
2. $10,568.86
3. 3
4. $\pm 1, \pm 3, \pm 5, \pm 15$
5. integer zero: 3; noninteger zeros are between -2 and -1 and between 4 and 5
6. a.

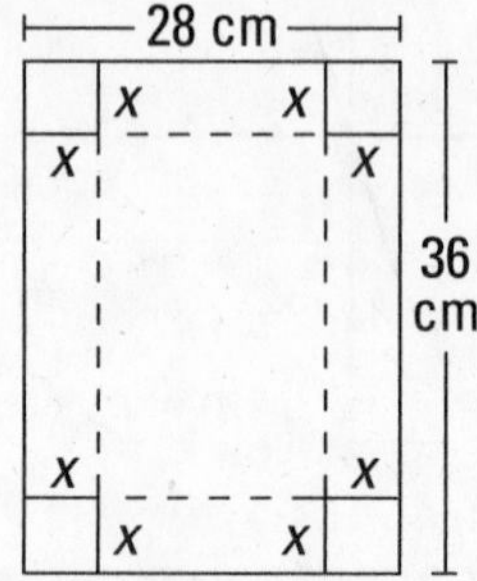

b. $S(x) = (36 - 2x)(28 - 2x) + 2x(36 - 2x) + 2x(28 - 2x)$

7. $3x^2(x - 3)(x + 4)$
8. 0, -4, 3
9.

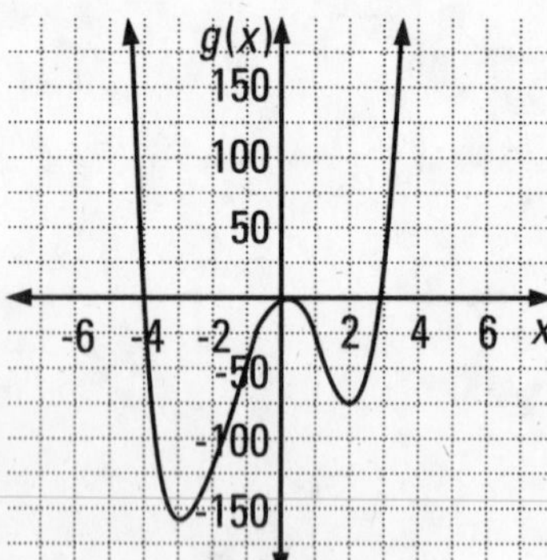

10. Answers will vary. Sample: $g(x) = 3x^3(x - 3)(x + 4)$
11. 0
12. $P(x) = x(x + 5)(x + 3)(x - 3)$
13. $P(x) = x^4 + 5x^3 - 9x^2 - 45x$
14. 2
15. $f(n) = n^2 + n - 1$
16. 155

17. Yes. Explanations may vary. Sample: The third differences are 18, which means that these data can be modeled by a polynomial of degree 3.
18. $4mn(m + n)^2$
19. $8\left(p - \frac{7 + \sqrt{145}}{16}\right) \cdot \left(p - \frac{7 - \sqrt{145}}{16}\right)$
20. $27x^3 - 54x^2 + 36x - 8$
21. $c^3 - 8$
22. a. 4
    b. trinomial
    c. -7
23. Answers may vary. Sample: Karl Friedrich Gauss is the person who first proved the Fundamental Theorem of Algebra.

Chapter 11 Test, Cumulative Form

1. (c)
2. Answers will vary. Sample: $3x^2 - x + 5$
3. $-\frac{1}{2}$
4. 150°, 210°
5. Choice of labeled points may vary.

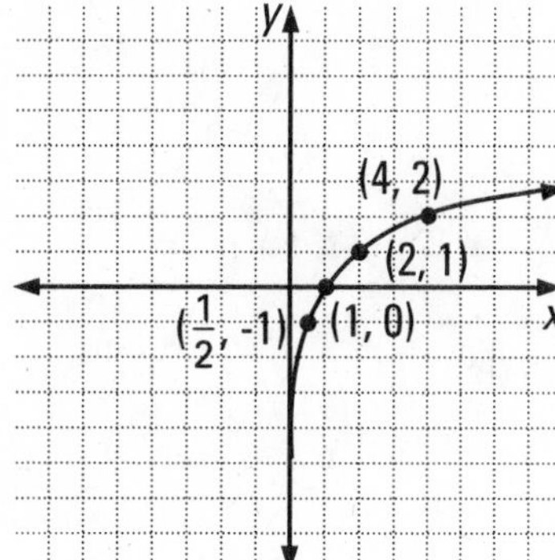

6. 32 strokes
7. $8a^4 + 20a^3 - 18a^2 - 15a + 9$
8. $(x + 9y)(x - 9y)$
9. $4(p + 3)(p - 10)$
10. $-\frac{17}{3}, 0, \frac{17}{3}$
11. 2π radians
12. -1 and 0, 2 and 3, 3 and 4
13. a. 2
    b. $f(t) = 3.6t^2$
    c. 360 cm
14. -.3, 1.6
15. ≈ 13.9
16. ≈ 74 miles
17. a. $x = y^4$
    b. No. Explanations may vary. Sample: The graph of $y = x^4$ does not pass the Horizontal-Line Test for inverses.
18. No. Explanations may vary. Sample: -1 is paired with both 1 and 4.
19. $(x + 15)(x + y + 7) = x^2 + 22x + 15y + xy + 105$
20. a.

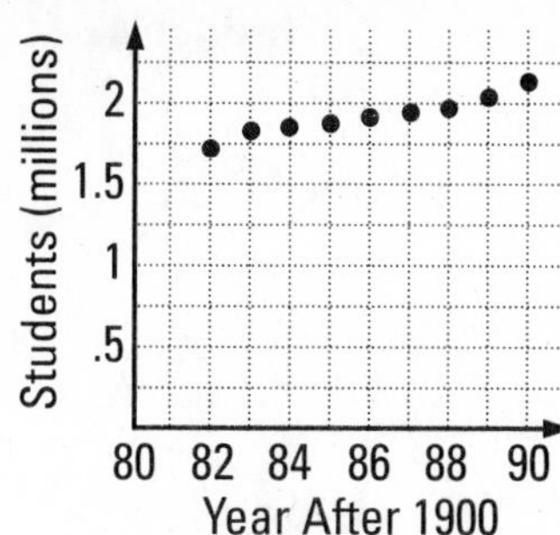

    b. $y = .045x - 1.91$, where x represents the number of years after 1900
    c. ≈ 2.5 million students

ANSWERS

Quiz **Lessons 12-1 Through 12-3**

1. (3, 3)
2. $y - 3 = \frac{1}{4}(x - 3)^2$
3. $y = 2$
4. (5, 2)
5. 3.25
6. (-1, 3)
7. 4
8.

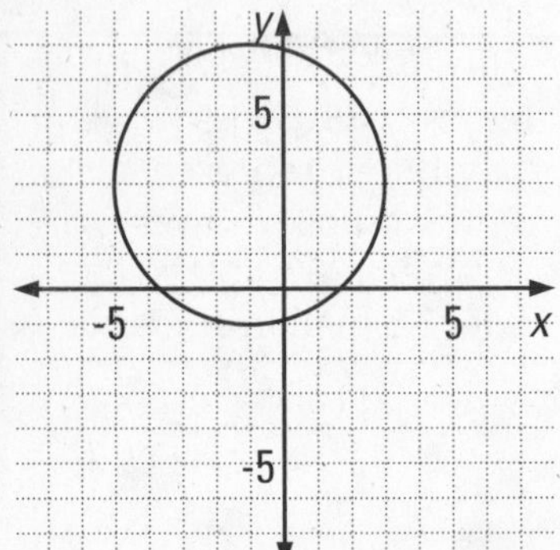

9. $(x + 1)^2 + (y - 3)^2 > 16$
10. $\approx .75$ m

Quiz **Lessons 12-4 Through 12-7**

1. 48π square units
2. $(4\sqrt{2}, 4\sqrt{2})$, $(-4\sqrt{2}, -4\sqrt{2})$
3.

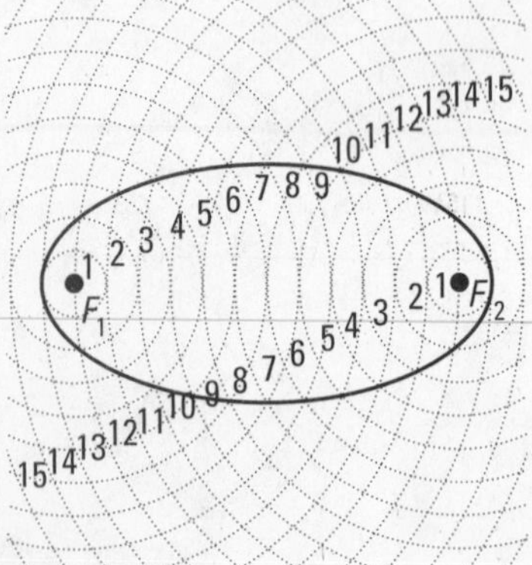

4. $\frac{x^2}{25} + \frac{y^2}{4} = 1$
5. $\frac{x^2}{156.25} + \frac{y^2}{56.25} = 1$
6. $y = \pm\frac{3}{4}x$

7.

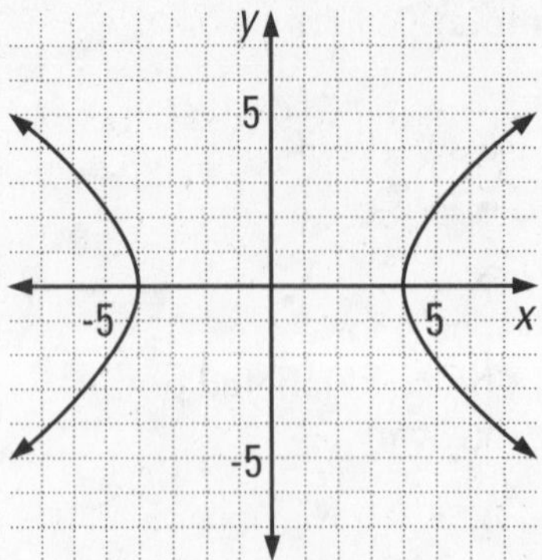

Chapter 12 Test, Form A

1. true
2. $y = \pm\frac{10}{3}x$
3. $\frac{x^2}{49} + \frac{y^2}{36} = 1$
4. $S_{7,6}$
5. (7, 0), (-7, 0), (0, 6), (0, -6)
6. 14 units
7. 42π sq units
8. true
9. (2, 1)
10. $\frac{x^2}{9} + \frac{y^2}{16} = 1$
11. $(x - 1)^2 + (y + 2)^2 = 4$
12. $\frac{x^2}{25} - \frac{y^2}{11} = 1$
13. $(x + 1)^2 + (y - 6)^2 < 25$
14. a.

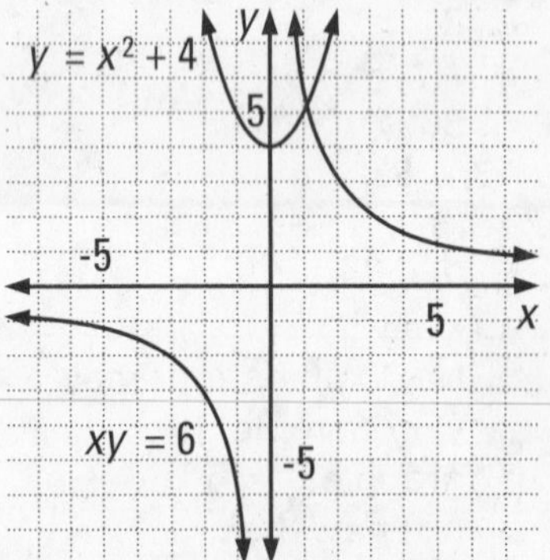

b. Estimates may vary. Sample: $\approx$ (1.1, 5.3)

15. (-2, -4), (2, -4)
16. See graph below.
17. Yes. Explanations will vary. Sample: Set up a coordinate system with the center of the semicircle at the origin. An equation of the circle determined by the tunnel opening is $x^2 + y^2 = 100$. For the truck to go through the tunnel, the point (5.5, 8) must be in the interior of this circle. That is, it must satisfy the inequality $x^2 + y^2 < 100$. Check: $5.5^2 + 8^2 = 30.25 + 64 = 94.25 < 100$. So, the truck will fit through the tunnel.
18.

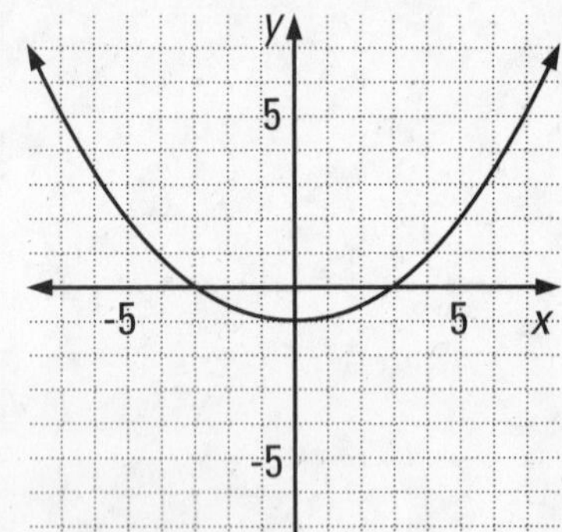

19. (0, 1)

16.

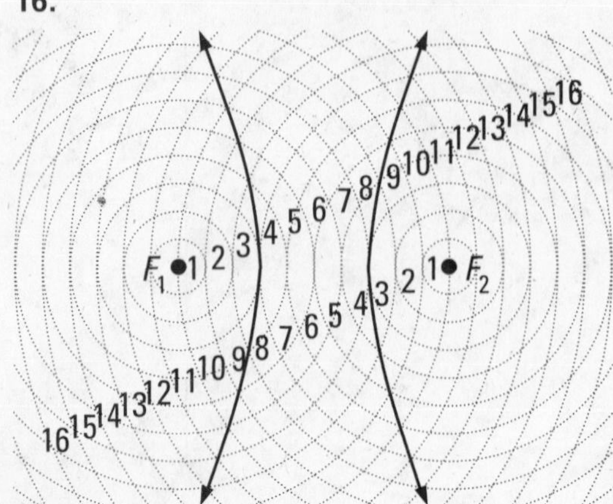

ANSWERS

Chapter 12 Test, Form B

1. false
2. $y = \pm 2x$
3. $\frac{x^2}{16} + \frac{y^2}{25} = 1$
4. $S_{4,5}$
5. (4, 0), (-4, 0), (0, 5), (0, -5)
6. 10 units
7. 20π square units
8. false
9. (1, 3), $\left(-\frac{1}{3}, \frac{1}{3}\right)$
10. $\frac{x^2}{25} + \frac{y^2}{9} = 1$
11. $(x + 1)^2 + (y - 1)^2 = 16$
12. $\frac{x^2}{100} - \frac{y^2}{125} = 1$
13. $(x + 1)^2 + (y - 2)^2 < 49$
14. a.

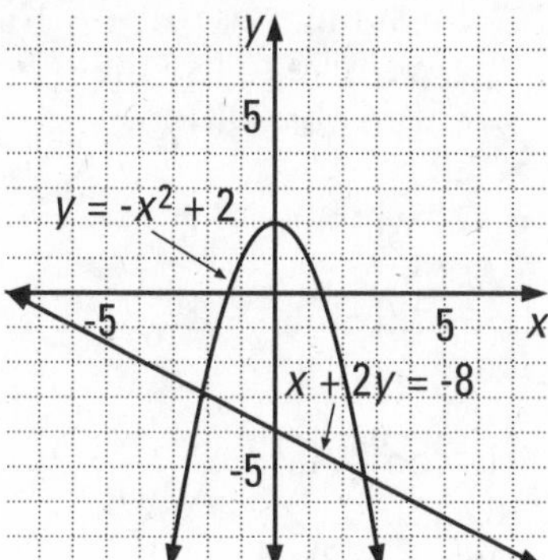

b. Estimates will vary. Sample: $\approx$ (-2.2, -2.9), $\approx$ (2.7, -5.4)

15. (5, 3)
16.

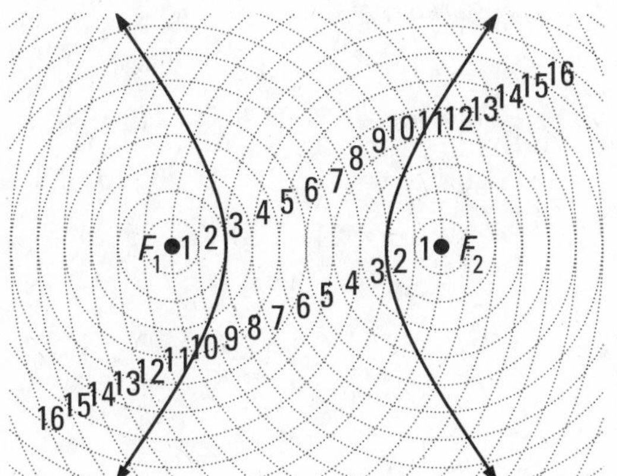

17. Yes. Explanations will vary. Sample: The portion of the truck that must fit through the semicircular arch is 2 feet high and 6 feet wide. Set up a coordinate system with the center of the semicircle at the origin. An equation of the circle determined by the arch is $x^2 + y^2 = 36$. For the truck to go through the tunnel, the point (3, 2) must be in the interior of this circle. That is, it must satisfy the inequality $x^2 + y^2 < 36$. Check: $3^2 + 2^2 = 9 + 4 = 13 < 36$. So, the truck will fit through the tunnel.
18.

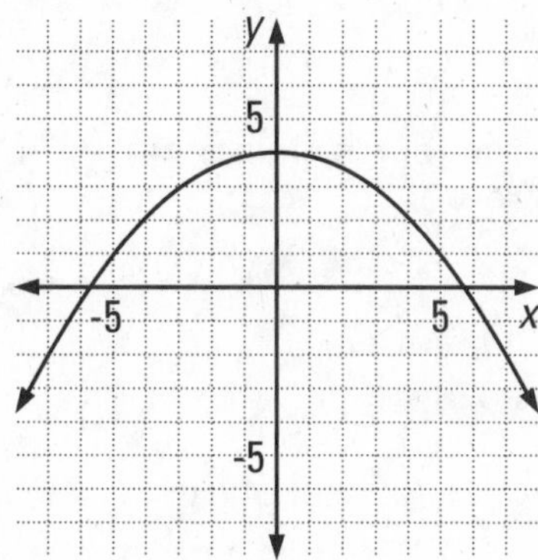

19. (0, 2)

Chapter 12 Test, Cumulative Form

1. $y = -2x^2 + 5x + 4$
2. a. d b. g
3. $25x^2 + 16y^2 - 400 = 0$
4. $\frac{x^2}{16} - \frac{y^2}{20} = 1$
5. $\approx$ .6 foot
   Explanations will vary. Sample: Set up a coordinate system with the center of the half-ellipse at the origin. An equation of the ellipse determined by the walls is $\frac{x^2}{324} + \frac{y^2}{144} = 1$. The head of each bed touches the wall at the point $(x, 3)$. So, solve $\frac{x^2}{324} + \frac{3^2}{144} = 1$; $x \approx \pm 17.4$. This means that the bottom of the headboard is about 17.4 feet from the center of the ellipse; this places the bottom of the headboard about (18 − 17.4) feet, or about .6 foot, from the bottom of the wall it touches.
6. $\approx$ 339.3 square feet
7. $y - 1 = \frac{1}{16}x^2$
8. length: 175 meters; width: 53 meters
9. $(x - 3)^2 + (y + 3)^2 = 9$
10. Answers may vary. The graph given below is the graph of $P(x) = (x + 1)(x - 1)(x - 3)$.

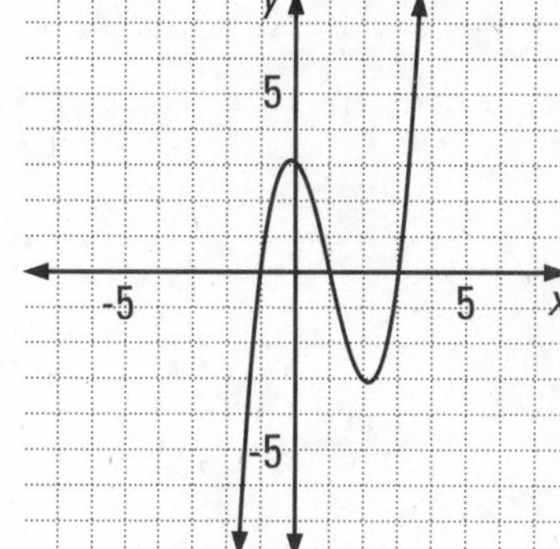

ANSWERS

11. a. $\pm 1, \pm 2, \pm \frac{1}{2}, \pm \frac{1}{3}, \pm \frac{1}{6}, \pm \frac{2}{3}$

b. $-\frac{1}{2}, \frac{2}{3}, 1$

12. Explanations may vary. Sample: To solve an equation by applying the Zero-Product Theorem, one side of the equation must be 0.

13. {-10, 0, 2, 6}

14. $x = 1$

15. $\frac{x^2}{49} + \frac{y^2}{100} = 1$

16. a.

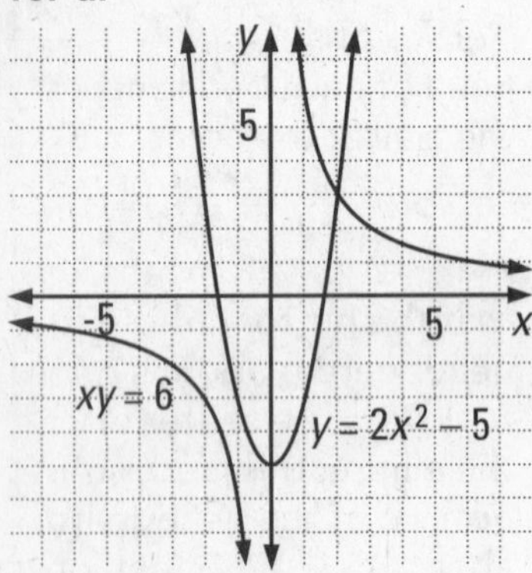

b. (2, 3)

17. $7t^3(2t + 3)(2t - 3)$

18. $2265.08

Quiz — Lessons 13-1 Through 13-3

1. (c)
2. $\sum_{i=1}^{6}(4i - 2)$
3. 1275
4. 24 arrangements
5. 40,440
6. 336
7. a. 118
   b. 2380
8. 14
9. 765
10. $\approx$ $714.20

Quiz — Lessons 13-4 Through 13-7

1. $22,000
2. $17,000
3. 5
4. $\approx .72$
5. the fourth element in row 5
6. (b)
7. 1
8. 1
9. 1820
10. 23
11. $x^4 + 8x^3y + 24x^2y^2 + 32xy^3 + 16y^4$
12. $27m^6 - 108m^4n + 144m^2n^2 - 64n^3$
13. 324,632 ways
14. false

Chapter 13 Test, Form A

1. a. arithmetic
   b. $\sum_{i=1}^{101}(3i - 1)$
   c. 15,352
2. a. geometric
   b. $\sum_{i=1}^{31} 7\left(\frac{1}{2}\right)^{i-1}$
   c. ≈ 14
3. See below.
4. 8192
5. third element in row 7
6. 2,598,960
7. 2925
8. a. the set of all television sets bought last year
   b. It may be too time-consuming or too expensive to use the entire population.
9. a. 82 wins
   b. 71 wins
10. 28 points
11. 256 outcomes
12. $\frac{28}{256} \approx .11$
13. 210 combinations
14. $16x^4 - 96x^3z + 216x^2z^2 - 216xz^3 + 81z^4$
15. $\approx 68.2\%$
16. $\approx 2.3\%$

3.

row 3 ⟶ 1 3 3 1

row 4 ⟶ 1 4 6 4 1

row 5 ⟶ 1 5 10 10 5 1

row 6 ⟶ 1 6 15 20 15 6 1

row 7 ⟶ 1 7 21 35 35 21 7 1

ANSWERS

17. a. See table below.

b.

$P(n)$: .40, .32, .24, .16, .08; n: 0 1 2 3 4 5 6

c. false

18. job B

Explanations may vary.

Sample:

Total pay for job A is:

$\sum_{i=1}^{10} (130 + (i - 1)15)$

$= \$1975.$

Total pay for job B is:

$\sum_{i=1}^{10} 200(1.5)^{i-1}$

$= \$2637.50.$

19. $\frac{1}{\binom{50}{5}} = \frac{1}{2,118,760}$

20. $\frac{\binom{4}{3}\binom{36}{1}}{\binom{40}{4}} = \frac{144}{91,390}$

$= \frac{72}{45,695}$

$\approx .0016$

Chapter 13 Test, Form B

1. a. arithmetic

b. $\sum_{i=1}^{63} (5i - 2)$

c. 9954

2. a. geometric

b. $\sum_{i=1}^{20} 5(3)^{i-1}$

c. $\approx$ 8,716,961,000

3. See below.

4. 1,048,576

5. sixth element in row 8

6. 190 **7.** 455

8. a. the set of all registered voters

b. It may be too time-consuming or too expensive to poll the entire population.

9. a. 85 wins

b. 85 wins

10. 93

11. 512 outcomes

12. $\frac{84}{512} \approx .16$

13. 56 combinations

14. $625m^4 - 4000m^3n + 9600m^2n^2 - 10,240mn^3 + 4096n^4$

15. $\approx$ 68.2% **16.** $\approx$ 2.3%

3.

row 3 ⟶ 1 3 3 1

row 4 ⟶ 1 4 6 4 1

row 5 ⟶ 1 5 10 10 5 1

row 6 ⟶ 1 6 15 20 15 6 1

row 7 ⟶ 1 7 21 35 35 21 7 1

row 8 ⟶ 1 8 28 56 70 56 28 8 1

17. a. See table below.

b.

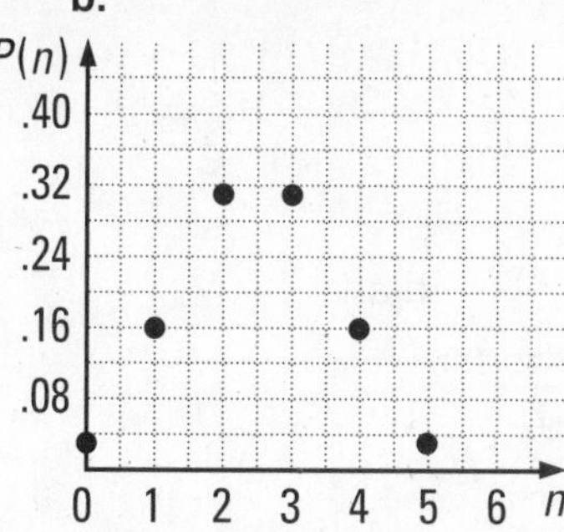

c. true

18. job B

Explanations may vary.

Sample:

Total pay for job A is:

$\sum_{i=1}^{10} (115 + (i-1)10)$

$= \$1600.$

Total pay for job B is:

$\sum_{i=1}^{5} 200(1.25)^{i-1}$

$\approx \$1641.41.$

19. $\frac{1}{\binom{25}{6}} = \frac{1}{177,100}$

20. $\frac{\binom{7}{6}\binom{28}{1}}{\binom{35}{7}} = \frac{196}{6,724,520}$

$= \frac{49}{1,681,130}$

$\approx .00003$

17. a. Form A

n	0	1	2	3	4	5	6
$P(n)$	$\frac{1}{64} \approx .02$	$\frac{6}{64} \approx .09$	$\frac{15}{64} \approx .23$	$\frac{20}{64} \approx .31$	$\frac{15}{64} \approx .23$	$\frac{6}{64} \approx .09$	$\frac{1}{64} \approx .02$

17. a. Form B

n	0	1	2	3	4	5
$P(n)$	$\frac{1}{32} \approx .03$	$\frac{5}{32} \approx .16$	$\frac{10}{32} \approx .31$	$\frac{10}{32} \approx .31$	$\frac{5}{32} \approx .16$	$\frac{1}{32} \approx .03$

Chapter 13 Test, Cumulative Form

1. 1824
2. $243 + 810x + 1080x^2 + 720x^3 + 240x^4 + 32x^5$
3. 138,415
4. $\frac{16\pi}{9}$ radians
5. a. (c)
   b.

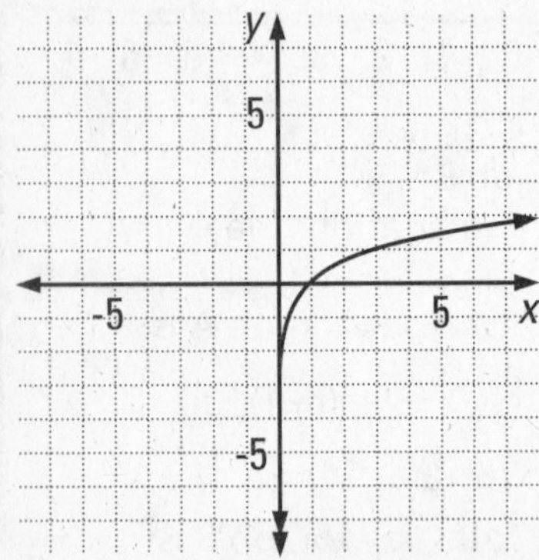

6. $5x(5x + 6)(3x - 7)$
7. true
8. a. 87 b. 88
   c. 88
9. $\approx$ 68.2%
10. $\approx$ 2.3%
11. 1 9 36 84 126 126 84 36 9 1
12. 1,048,576
13. (b)
14. (2, -3) and (-4, -15)
15. (0, 2); (0, 0); $y = -2$
16.–17. See graphs below.
18. $\frac{1}{4}$; -2
19. true
20. $\frac{1}{6435}$

Comprehensive Test, Chapters 1–13

1. (b)
2. (d)
3. (d)
4. (c)
5. (c)
6. (c)
7. (a)
8. (a)
9. (b)
10. (d)
11. (d)
12. (d)
13. (b)
14. (a)
15. (c)
16. (b)
17. (a)
18. (d)
19. (d)
20. (c)
21. (b)
22. (a)
23. (a)
24. (c)
25. (c)
26. (d)

16.

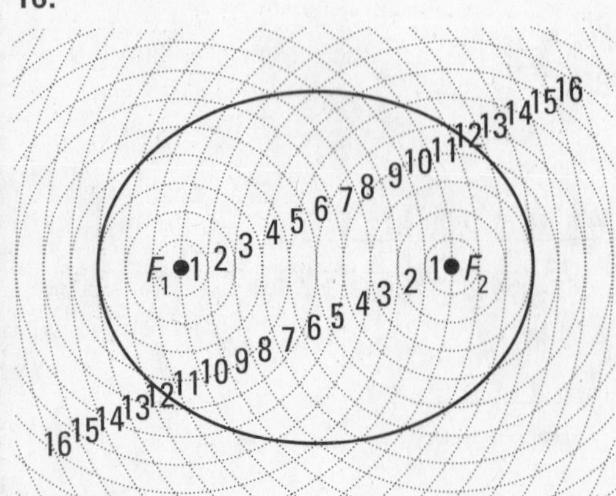

17.

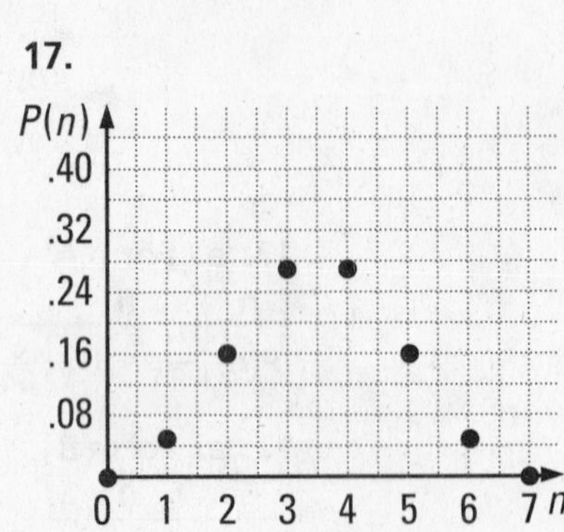

1. a. Describe a real-world situation that might be modeled by the expression $80 + 5n$.

b. Evaluate the expression when $n = 3$, when $n = -3$, and when $n = 3.25$.

c. Indicate the real-world meaning of the values of the expression for at least one value of n.

Objectives A, I

- ☐ Is able to evaluate expressions.
- ☐ Is able to use expressions to model real-world situations.
- ☐ Gives an appropriate situation, such as: If you start with $80 and save $5 a week, the total saved in dollars after *n* weeks is $80 + 5n$.
- ☐ Gives the correct value of the expression for the given values of *n* (95, 65, and 96.25).
- ☐ Identifies whether the values have meaning in the situation chosen.

2. Given $I = prt$, the following are equivalent.

$$p = \frac{I}{rt} \qquad r = \frac{I}{pt} \qquad t = \frac{I}{pr}$$

Leah thinks she sees a pattern in these formulas. So, given $A = p(1 + rt)$, she says that the following are all equivalent.

$$p = \frac{A}{1 + rt} \qquad r = \frac{A}{1 + pt} \qquad t = \frac{A}{1 + pr}$$

Do you agree or disagree with Leah? Explain why or why not.

Objective D

- ☐ Demonstrates an ability to rewrite formulas.
- ☐ Recognizes that only $p = \frac{A}{1 + rt}$ is correct.
- ☐ Gives an appropriate explanation.

3. If $f(x) = \frac{1}{2}x - \frac{2}{3}x$, how is $f(-24)$ different from $f(x) = -24$?

Objectives A, B, C

- ☐ Understands function notation.
- ☐ Is able to evaluate expressions.
- ☐ Is able to solve and check linear equations.
- ☐ Gives a logical explanation of the difference between $f(-24)$ and $f(x) = -24$.

4. Explain the difference between an explicit formula and a recursive formula for a sequence. Give an example of each.

Objectives E, F

- ☐ Is able to evaluate sequences.
- ☐ Is able to write a recursive definition for a sequence.
- ☐ Gives a logical explanation of the difference, such as: Explicit formula – you find the *n*th term directly by substituting the number of the term for *n*; recursive formula – you find the *n*th term by identifying the first term and using the rule that generates terms from the previous ones.
- ☐ Gives an appropriate example of each.

5. Explain how you know from the graph that the relation at the right is a function. Then tell as many facts as you can about the function, its domain, and its range.

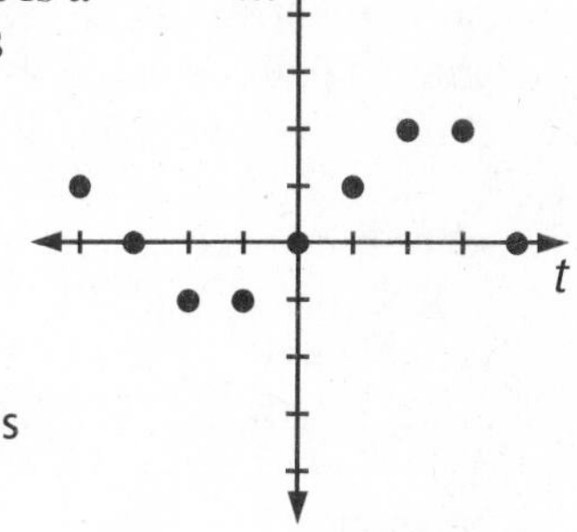

Objectives L, M

- ☐ Demonstrates an understanding of functions and their characteristics.
- ☐ Demonstrates an understanding of the Vertical-Line Test.
- ☐ Gives a logical explanation of the Vertical-Line Test in relation to this function.
- ☐ States several facts about the function, such as:
  The function consists of nine ordered pairs.
  The independent variable is *t*; the dependent variable is *M*.
  There are exactly 9 values in the domain and 4 values in the range.

Teacher Notes

Objectives B, G, H, I, J

Concepts and Skills This activity requires students to:

- read information from text, tables, and a graph.
- recognize whether a relation is a function.
- give multiple representations of a function.
- identify the domain and the range of a function.
- identify independent and dependent variables.
- use functions to represent real-world situations.
- choose appropriate forms to display information.
- organize information into an informative article.

Guiding Questions

- How do you recognize a function?
- Can you represent every function using a graph? function notations? sets of ordered pairs? a table? How do you know if one or more of these representations is not possible?

Answers

a. Answers will vary. Samples: In a multi-story home, the recommended number of smoke detectors is a function of the number of levels; the amount of U.S. fire losses is a function of the year.

b. Answers will vary. The following is a sample response for the first underwriter's formula.
function notations:
$F(q) = 2q^2 + q$;
$F: q \to 2q^2 + q$
It is not possible to list the entire function as a set of ordered pairs or in a table.

F
40
20
0 2 4 q

c. Answers will vary. For the first underwriter's formula: both the domain and range are the set of nonnegative real numbers; the independent variable is q and the dependent variable is F.

d. Articles will vary. Check students' work.

Extensions

Have students use reference books, magazines, and newspapers to find several other facts, tables, and graphs that convey information about fires and fire fighting. (You might suggest that they search for data specific to your city or town.) Then have them identify examples of functions in the data they have collected.

Evaluation

Level	Standard to be achieved for performance at specified level
5	The student demonstrates an in-depth understanding of functions and their applications. The student readily names several functions and correctly identifies their properties (domain and range, independent and dependent variables) and appropriate representations. The article is thoughtful and well-organized, and it may contain significant insights.
4	The student demonstrates a clear understanding of functions and their applications. The student is able to identify several functions, but may make minor errors in identifying their properties or in giving appropriate representations. The article is well-organized and easy to read, but it may lack in some detail.
3	The student demonstrates a fundamental understanding of functions and their applications. The student correctly names some functions, but may make errors in identifying their properties. There may be one or more major errors or omissions in the student's representations of the functions. The student writes an appropriate article, but it may be somewhat disorganized and difficult to read.
2	The student demonstrates some understanding of functions, but needs considerable assistance in naming the functions in the given situation. There are several major errors or omissions in the student's attempts to identify properties of the functions, and the representations of the functions contain several inaccuracies. The student attempts to write an article, but it is jumbled and incomplete.
1	The student demonstrates little if any understanding of functions. Even with prompting, the student cannot identify any functions in the given situation. Any attempts to identify properties of the functions are superfluous or irrelevant. Rather than write an original article, the student may simply copy or restate the given information.

1. Suppose that y varies inversely as the cube of x, and $y = 54$ when $x = 2$. Show how to use the constant of variation and an equation to find the value of y when $x = 6$. Explain how your result illustrates the Fundamental Theorem of Variation.

Objectives B, D

- ☐ Is able to solve variation problems.
- ☐ Demonstrates an understanding of the Fundamental Theorem of Variation.
- ☐ Identifies the variation equation as $y = \frac{432}{x^3}$.
- ☐ Uses the equation to determine that $y = 2$ when $x = 6$.
- ☐ Gives an appropriate explanation of how the Fundamental Theorem of Variation applies to the situation. (Sample: Since $6 = 3 \cdot 2$, the value of x is being multiplied by 3. So, the value of y will be divided by 3^3, or 27. Since $54 \div 27 = 2$, the value of y will be 2.)

2. In the formula $d = rt$, d is distance traveled, r is a constant rate of travel, and t is time spent traveling at that rate. Suppose you must travel exactly 120 miles. What type of variation exists in the relationship between r and t? Write a variation equation that represents the situation and give two examples of how you might use it.

Objectives F, G

- ☐ Recognizes variation situations.
- ☐ Is able to solve real-world variation problems.
- ☐ Recognizes that the relationship between r and t is an inverse variation.
- ☐ Gives an appropriate variation equation, such as $r = \frac{120}{t}$ or $t = \frac{120}{r}$.
- ☐ Gives appropriate examples. (Sample: To travel 120 mi in 20 h, the rate is 6 mi/h; to travel 120 mi in 10 h, the rate is 12 mi/h.)

3. Use rates of change to demonstrate that the graph of $y = \frac{48}{x}$ is not a line.

Objective C

- ☐ Is able to find rates of change.
- ☐ Recognizes that slope of a line is constant.
- ☐ Gives a logical explanation why the graph is not a line. (Sample: The rate of change from $x = 1$ to $x = 2$ is -24, while the rate of change from $x = 2$ to $x = 3$ is -8. Since the rate is not constant between each pair of points, the graph is not a line.)

4. State as many facts as you can about the graph of an equation of the form $y = \frac{k}{x^2}$.

Objectives E, I

- ☐ Identifies properties of variation functions.
- ☐ Is able to graph variation equations.
- ☐ States facts about the graph, such as: If $k > 0$, the branches are in the first and second quadrants. If $k < 0$, the branches are in the third and fourth quadrants. The graph is symmetric to the y-axis. The asymptotes are the x-axis and the y-axis.

5. Len and Mai each graphed $y = \frac{1}{2}x^2$ using an automatic grapher. Their graphs are shown at the right. Which graph do you think gives a better picture of the function? How could you adjust it in any way to improve the picture?

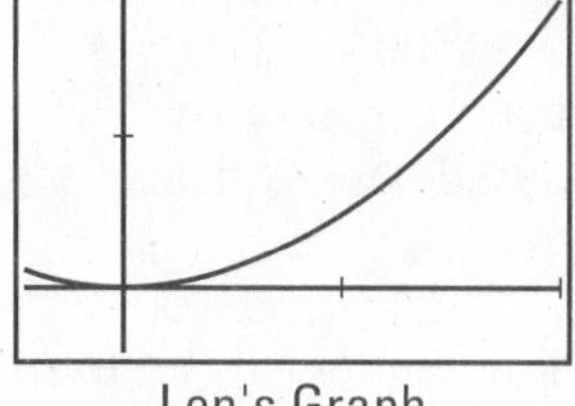
Len's Graph

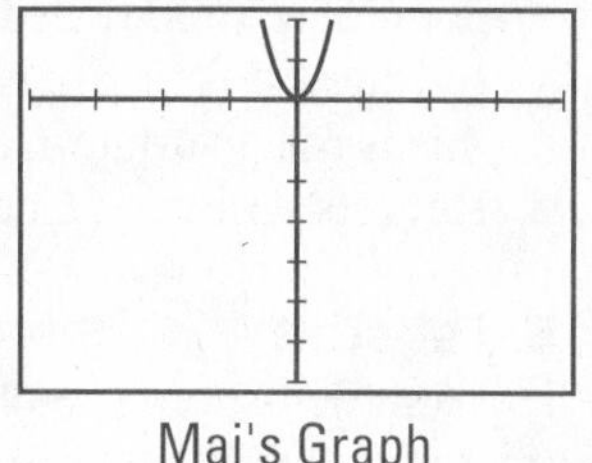
Mai's Graph

Objective K

- ☐ Recognizes the effects of a change in viewing window on the graph of a variation equation.
- ☐ Makes a reasonable choice of picture, and gives a logical explanation for the choice.
- ☐ Gives an appropriate description of how the chosen graph might be adjusted.

Teacher Notes

Objectives D, E, F, G, I

Concepts and Skills This activity requires students to:
- read information from text, a table, and a diagram.
- evaluate formulas.
- decide whether given relations are variations.
- use the Fundamental Theorem of Variation.
- recognize the properties of variation functions.
- graph variation equations.
- solve real-world variation problems.
- make real-world decisions based on given information and mathematical reasoning.
- summarize results in a written report.

Guiding Questions
- What do you substitute for B in the formula $V = Bh$ in order to find the volume of the prism? to find the volume of each cylinder?
- How do you recognize whether a relationship between two quantities is a variation relation?

Answers
a. top layer: 1339 ft^3; middle layer: 1548 ft^3; bottom layer: 2046 ft^3; total: 4933 ft^3

b. Each volume increases as s increases. Each relationship is a variation relation, since it can be represented by $V = ks^2$, where k is a constant. For the top, $k = 1.488$; for the middle, $k = 1.720$; for the bottom, $k = 2.273$; and for the entire fountain, $k = 1.488 + 1.720 + 2.273 = 5.481$.

c. The area decreases as s increases. However, the relationship is not a variation relation. Reasons may vary. Sample: The total area of the plot is 1600 ft^2; a formula for the area outside the fountain is $A = 1600 - 2.273s^2$; this is not a variation equation.

d. Reports will vary. Check students' work.

Extension
Have students explore other measures related to the fountain and determine whether variation relations are involved. (For example, they might examine the surface area and perimeter.) Then have students discuss other quantities related to planning the park and determine whether variation relations are involved. (Sample: If the fountain is lighted, the intensity of the light will vary inversely as the square of the distance of the light source from the fountain.)

Evaluation

Level	Standard to be achieved for performance at specified level
5	The student demonstrates an in-depth understanding of variation and its application to the given situation. All responses and calculations are accurate and complete, and they demonstrate sound mathematical reasoning. The student prepares a thoughtful, well-organized report, and may choose to explore additional questions. (For example, the student may explore the effects of varying s and h simultaneously.)
4	The student demonstrates a clear understanding of variation. The student responds to all questions and performs all required tasks, but may make minor errors in calculation or reasoning. The report is well-organized and articulate, but it may lack in some detail.
3	The student demonstrates a fundamental understanding of variation, but needs some assistance in applying the concept to the given situation. The student responds to all questions and performs all required tasks, but there may be one or more major errors or omissions in the calculations or reasoning. The report is essentially complete, but it may be somewhat disorganized.
2	The student demonstrates some understanding of variation, but has considerable difficulty in applying the concepts to the given situation. Even with assistance, the student may make several major errors in calculation or reasoning, or may omit one or more major steps. The student attempts to prepare a report, but it is jumbled and incomplete.
1	The student demonstrates little if any understanding of variation, and is unable to apply the concept to the given situation. The student may attempt some calculations, but they are superfluous or irrelevant, and they display no evidence of mathematical reasoning. Instead of preparing a report, the student may simply copy or restate the given information.

1. State as many facts as you can about the line graphed at the right and about the function it represents. (*Hint:* Think of the equation of the line and of properties such as its slope and intercepts.)

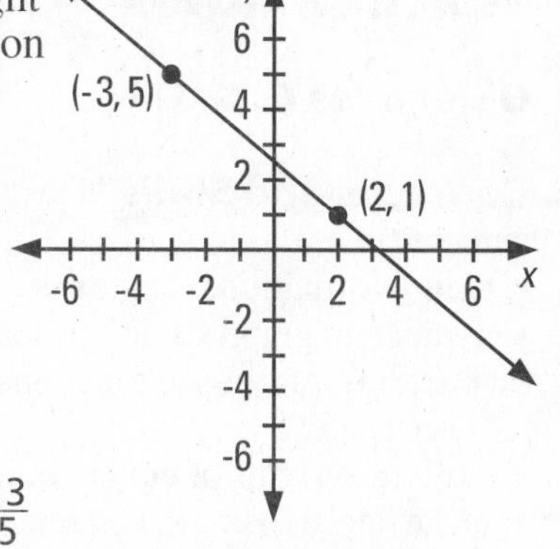

Objectives A, B, E, L

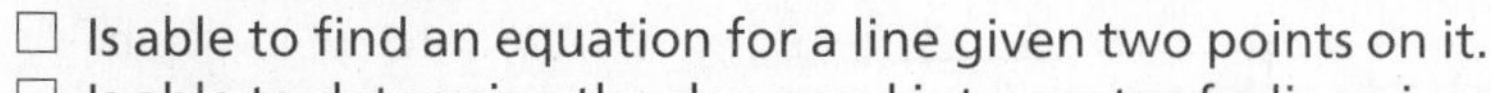

- ☐ Is able to find an equation for a line given two points on it.
- ☐ Is able to determine the slope and intercepts of a line given its equation.

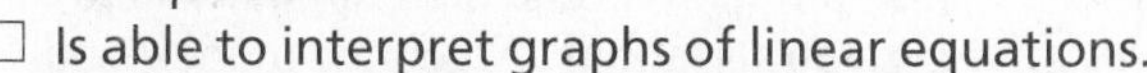

- ☐ Is able to interpret graphs of linear equations.
- ☐ Recognizes properties of linear functions.
- ☐ States several facts about the line and the function, such as: equation: $y = -\frac{4}{5}x + \frac{13}{5}$; slope: $-\frac{4}{5}$; x-intercept: $\frac{13}{4}$; y-intercept: $\frac{13}{5}$

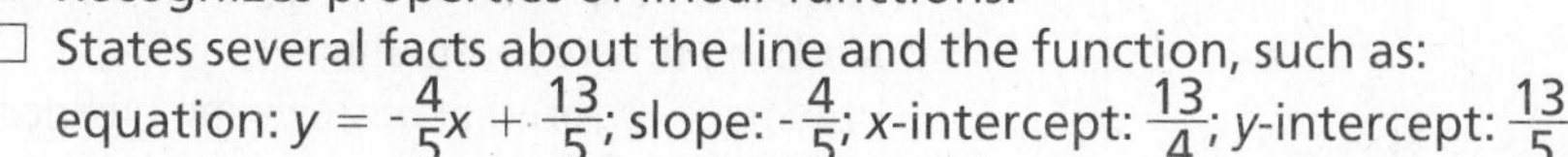

2. Make up two different arithmetic sequences in which the constant difference between terms is -3. Give an explicit formula and a recursive formula for each sequence. How are the formulas for your two sequences alike? How are they different?

Objectives D, F

- ☐ Is able to find explicit and recursive formulas for arithmetic sequences.
- ☐ Recognizes properties of arithmetic sequences.
- ☐ Gives two appropriate sequences.
- ☐ Gives correct recursive formulas for the sequences.
- ☐ Gives correct explicit formulas for the sequences.
- ☐ Gives an appropriate description of similarities and differences between the formulas.

3. A relative of yours saw the unfamiliar symbol $\lfloor\ \rfloor$ in your math book and wondered what it meant. How would you explain it? Write a brief description of what you would say. Include an example of a real-world situation that you can model algebraically with the use of this symbol.

Objectives C, K

- ☐ Is able to evaluate expressions based on step functions.
- ☐ Is able to model situations leading to step functions.
- ☐ Gives a logical explanation of the symbol, such as: $\lfloor x \rfloor$ represents the greatest integer less than or equal to x.
- ☐ Gives an appropriate real-world situation.

4. The following is a popular children's problem.

   There are a total of 20 chickens and cows in a barnyard. The animals have 52 legs in all. How many of each animal are there?

   Explain how to solve this problem.

Objective H

- ☐ Is able to model situations leading to linear combinations.
- ☐ Demonstrates how the problem relates to linear combinations. (*Sample:* If C represents the number of chickens and W represents the number of cows, then an equation that models the situation is $2C + 4W = 52$.)
- ☐ Gives the correct solution to the problem (14 chickens and 6 cows).

5. Jenna entered data about the average basic monthly rate for cable TV service from the years 1970 through 1993 into her calculator. She obtained this display.

   y = ax + b
   a =.655010553
   b = -43.15682144
   r = .9113235732

   Explain the meaning of the numbers in the display. How can Jenna use them to predict the rate in the year 2000?

Objective J

- ☐ Is able to fit lines to data.
- ☐ Gives a logical explanation of the numbers.
- ☐ Describes a method for making a prediction, such as: Let 70, 80, 90, and so on represent the years, substitute 100 for x in $y = .66x - 43.16$.

Teacher Notes

Objectives G, K, L, M

Concepts and Skills This activity requires students to:

- read information from text and a table.
- model and graph situations leading to linear functions, piecewise functions, and step functions.
- explore systems of equations.
- make decisions based on real-life experiences.
- summarize results in a written report.

Guiding Questions

- How can you tell if a function constantly increases or decreases? if a function is a step function? if a function is a piecewise function?
- Why do you think the costs of shipping and packaging are not included in the total expenses?

Answers

a. i. $W = 0.75 + 1.25n$ (for $1 \le n \le 6$)
ii. $R = 3.43 + .12(p - 1)$ **iii.** $C = \lfloor \frac{n}{6} \rfloor$

iv $\begin{cases} C = 25, & \text{for } 0 \le b \le 100 \\ C = 25 + .15b, & \text{for } b > 100 \end{cases}$

v. $M = 5.71n$

b. Choices will vary. Check students' graphs.

c. $E = 117.50 + 5.71n$; See below for graph.

d. Answers will vary. Sample: If the price of each bag is \$16, then $I = 16n$. The graph is below. One interpretation is that the business will make a profit in a month when at least 12 bags are sold.

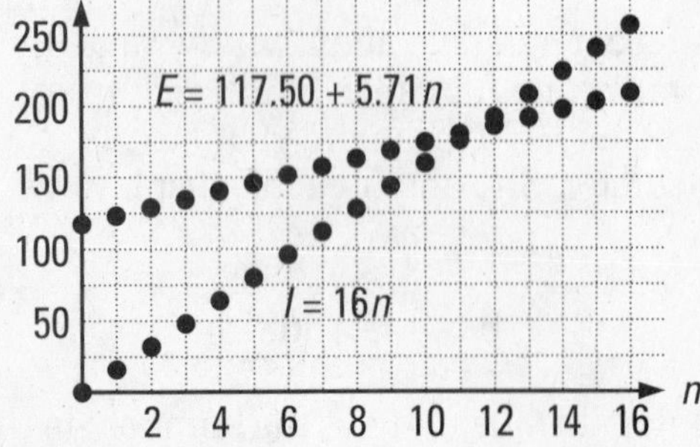

e. Check students' work.

Extension

Have students determine the effect on their business plans if incorporating the cost of shipping and packaging into the price of the item. Discuss with them the advantages and disadvantages of this practice.

Evaluation

Level	Standard to be achieved for performance at specified level
5	The student demonstrates an in-depth understanding of linear, piecewise, and step functions and their application to the given situations. Algebraic models and graphs are accurate and complete. The student prepares a thoughtful, well-organized report that outlines the business plan in detail.
4	The student demonstrates a clear understanding of linear, piecewise, and step functions. The student is able to devise appropriate algebraic models and graphs for the given situations, but they may contain minor errors. The report is well-organized but it may lack in clarity.
3	The student demonstrates an understanding of linear, piecewise, and step functions, but needs assistance in applying the concepts to the given situations. There are major errors or omissions in the student's algebraic models or graphs. The report is essentially complete, but it may be somewhat disorganized.
2	The student demonstrates some understanding of linear, piecewise, and step functions, but needs considerable assistance in understanding their application to the given situations. Even with help, the student makes several major errors in creating algebraic models or graphs, or omits one or more major steps of the process. The student attempts to prepare a report, but it is jumbled and incomplete.
1	The student demonstrates little if any understanding of linear, piecewise, and step functions and their application to the given situation. Even with assistance, any attempts to create algebraic models or graphs are superfluous or irrelevant. Instead of writing a report, the student may simply copy or restate the given information.

1. Let A be the matrix defined as follows.

$$A = \begin{bmatrix} 5 & -1 \\ -3 & 2 \\ -6 & -4 \end{bmatrix}$$

a. Choose any scalar k other than 0, 1, or -1. Find kA.

b. Create a matrix B in which no element is equal to 0 and for which $A + B$ exists. Find $A + B$.

c. Create a matrix C in which no element is equal to 0 and for which AC exists. Find AC.

Objectives A, B, D

- ☐ Is able to find scalar multiples of matrices.
- ☐ Is able to add matrices.
- ☐ Is able to multiply matrices.
- ☐ Recognizes properties of matrix operations.

2. Ms. Kouros owns a bakery that supplies bread to three markets. These slips of paper show last Monday's deliveries.

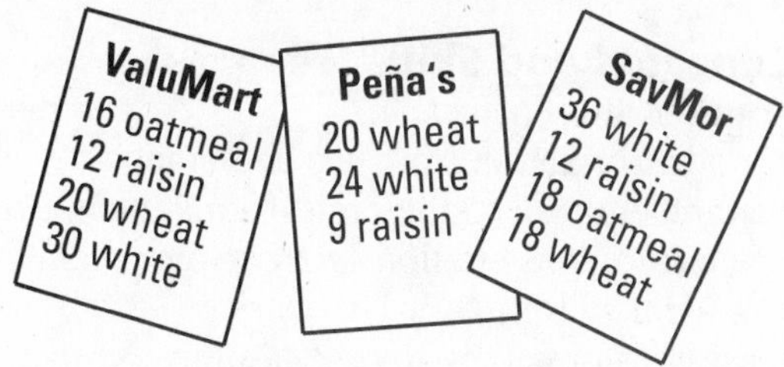

Show how Ms. Kouros could use a matrix to store these data. Then describe at least one way that she might use matrix operations to keep track of her sales.

Objectives G, H

- ☐ Is able to use matrices to store data.
- ☐ Is able to use matrix operations to solve real-world problems.
- ☐ Organizes the data into an appropriate matrix.
- ☐ Identifies one or more appropriate uses of matrix operations, such as: She can create a matrix for each day that deliveries are made, then add the matrices to find the total for a month.

3. Give equations for two lines that each pass through the point (1, -3) and are perpendicular to each other. How do you know that the lines are perpendicular?

Objective C

- ☐ Is able to determine equations of perpendicular lines.
- ☐ Gives equations for two appropriate lines, such as $y = x - 4$ and $y = -x - 2$.
- ☐ Gives a logical explanation, such as: The product of the slopes of the lines is -1.

4. While you are studying Chapter 4 together, a friend makes this statement.

For any two distinct transformations A and B, $A \circ B \neq B \circ A$.

Do you think this is true? Explain.

Objective F

- ☐ Understands composites of transformations.
- ☐ Recognizes that the statement is false.
- ☐ Gives an appropriate explanation, such as: If $A = R_{90}$ and $B = R_{180}$, then $A \circ B = B \circ A$.

5. Harry drew the graph at the right to illustrate a triangle and its image under the transformation R_{90}. Without performing any calculations, explain how you can tell that the image is incorrect. Now show how to correct the graph. Write a matrix multiplication to represent $R_{90}(\triangle ABC)$.

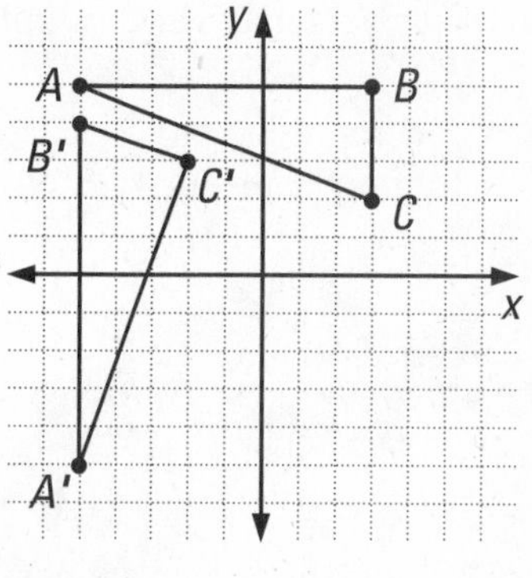

Objectives E, F, I

- ☐ Recognizes relationships between figures and their transformation images.
- ☐ Is able to relate transformations to matrices, and vice versa.
- ☐ Is able to graph figures and their transformation images.
- ☐ Recognizes that the graph is incorrect because the triangles are not congruent.
- ☐ Adjusts one or both triangles to illustrate a correct transformation under R_{90}.
- ☐ Gives a correct matrix multiplication for the transformation.

Teacher Notes

Objectives E, F

Concepts and Skills This activity requires students to:
- read information from text and graphs.
- graph figures and their transformation images, and recognize relationships between them.
- relate transformations to matrices.
- use transformations to create a simple animation.
- summarize results.

Materials
- graph paper, scissors, stapler or tape

Guiding Questions
- How would frame 3 be different if the instruction were simply "FRAME 2 under R_{90}"?
- Is there more than one transformation that you can use to obtain frame 4?

Answers

a. $\begin{bmatrix} -3 & 0 & 3 & 0 \\ -5 & 1 & -5 & -3 \end{bmatrix}$

b. $\begin{bmatrix} -3 & 0 & 3 & 0 \\ -5 & 1 & -5 & -3 \end{bmatrix} + \begin{bmatrix} 0 & 0 & 0 & 0 \\ 2 & 2 & 2 & 2 \end{bmatrix} =$

$\begin{bmatrix} -3 & 0 & 3 & 0 \\ -3 & 3 & -3 & -1 \end{bmatrix}$

c. Check students' graphs. The kite will appear to have moved two units up.

d. $\begin{bmatrix} 0 & -1 \\ 1 & 0 \end{bmatrix}\begin{bmatrix} -3 & 0 & 3 & 0 \\ -3 & 3 & -3 & -1 \end{bmatrix} +$

$\begin{bmatrix} -6 & -6 & -6 & -6 \\ 0 & 0 & 0 & 0 \end{bmatrix} = \begin{bmatrix} -3 & -9 & -3 & -5 \\ -3 & 0 & 3 & 0 \end{bmatrix}$;

Check students' graphs; the kite will appear to have rotated 90° around its lower-left vertex.

e. Answers may vary. Sample: FRAME 3 under R_{90}:

$\begin{bmatrix} 0 & -1 \\ 1 & 0 \end{bmatrix}\begin{bmatrix} -3 & -9 & -3 & -5 \\ -3 & 0 & 3 & 0 \end{bmatrix} =$

$\begin{bmatrix} 3 & 0 & -3 & 0 \\ -3 & -9 & -3 & -5 \end{bmatrix}$

f. Check students' work.

Extension
Have students create animations involving figures that are more complex than the kite, or that involve the kite and one or more additional figures.

Evaluation

Level	Standard to be achieved for performance at specified level
5	The student demonstrates an in-depth understanding of matrices and transformations. The student has a well-developed sense of the movements associated with given transformations, and vice versa. Matrix calculations are accurate and complete. The flip book presents an effective animation, and the accompanying instructions and calculations are thorough and well-organized.
4	The student demonstrates a clear understanding of matrices and transformations. The student associates appropriate movements with given transformations, and vice versa, but makes minor errors. The flip book is neat and accurate. The accompanying instructions lack in some detail.
3	The student demonstrates a fundamental understanding of matrices and transformations, but needs some assistance in relating appropriate movements to given transformations, and vice versa. Matrix calculations contain major errors or omissions. The flip book is done, but the accompanying instructions may be somewhat disorganized and contain some inaccuracies.
2	The student demonstrates understanding only of some matrices and transformations, and can only relate movements and transformations with considerable assistance. The student makes major errors in matrix calculations, or may omit one or more major steps. The student attempts to prepare a flip book and the accompanying instructions, but they are jumbled and incomplete.
1	The student demonstrates little or no understanding of matrices and transformations. The student is unable to relate movements and transformations or perform meaningful matrix calculations. The student may prepare a flip book of randomly drawn figures. Any written communication is superfluous or irrelevant.

1. a. Arrange -3, -2, 4, and 6 in a 2×2 matrix that does not have an inverse. Explain how you know that the inverse does not exist.

b. Arrange these same numbers in a 2×2 matrix that *does* have an inverse. Then find the inverse of your matrix.

Objective B

- ☐ Understands the meaning of the determinant of a square matrix.
- ☐ Is able to find the inverse of a square matrix.
- ☐ Creates a matrix that does not have an inverse and gives a logical explanation. SAMPLE: $\begin{bmatrix} -3 & -2 \\ 4 & 6 \end{bmatrix}$
- ☐ Creates a matrix that has an inverse and correctly determines that inverse. SAMPLE: $\begin{bmatrix} -3 & -2 \\ 6 & 4 \end{bmatrix}$

2. Explain how you know that these two systems are *not* equivalent.

$$\begin{cases} 2p + 5q = 10 \\ -3p - 2q = 7 \end{cases} \qquad \begin{cases} p = -5 \\ p + q = 6 \end{cases}$$

Make the systems equivalent by changing just one of the four equations.

Objectives A, D

- ☐ Is able to solve systems using the Linear Combination Method or substitution.
- ☐ Recognizes properties of systems of equations.
- ☐ Gives a logical explanation, such as: The solution of the first system is $p = -5$, $q = 4$; the solution of the second is $p = -5$, $q = 11$.
- ☐ Makes an appropriate change, such as: Change $p + q = 6$ to $p + q = -1$.

3. Siri wrote this matrix multiplication to solve a system of equations. If he wrote the correct matrices, what is the system?

$$\begin{bmatrix} 1 & 4 \\ 0.5 & -2 \end{bmatrix}\begin{bmatrix} a \\ b \end{bmatrix} = \begin{bmatrix} 40 \\ -36 \end{bmatrix}$$

He decided that the system has no solution. Do you agree? Explain. If you disagree, show how to use the matrices to solve the system.

Objective C

- ☐ Is able to use matrices to solve a system.
- ☐ Identifies the system as $\begin{cases} a + 4b = 40 \\ .5a - 2b = -36 \end{cases}$
- ☐ Notes the determinant of the coefficient matrix to be nonzero, so the system has one solution.
- ☐ Gives the correct solution, $a = -16$, $b = 14$.

4. How is graphing $x > -2$ on a coordinate plane different from graphing $x > -2$ on a number line? How is it similar?

Objectives H, J

- ☐ Is able to graph linear inequalities in one variable.
- ☐ Is able to graph linear inequalities in two variables.
- ☐ Recognizes one or more differences, such as: On a number line, the graph is part of a line; on the coordinate plane, the graph is part of a plane.
- ☐ Recognizes one or more similarities, such as: On a number line, an open circle indicates that -2 is not included in the graph; on the coordinate plane, a dashed line indicates that -2 is not included.

5. Write a real-world problem that can be solved using the following system.

$$\begin{cases} r + s + t = 78 \\ r = 2s \\ t = s - 6 \end{cases}$$

Show how to use the system to solve your problem.

Objective F

- ☐ Is able to use systems to solve real-world problems.
- ☐ Writes an appropriate problem.
- ☐ Gives a correct solution of the problem, $r = 42$, $s = 21$, $t = 15$.

6. State as many facts as you can about the graph at the right. Explain how you might use this graph in solving a problem.

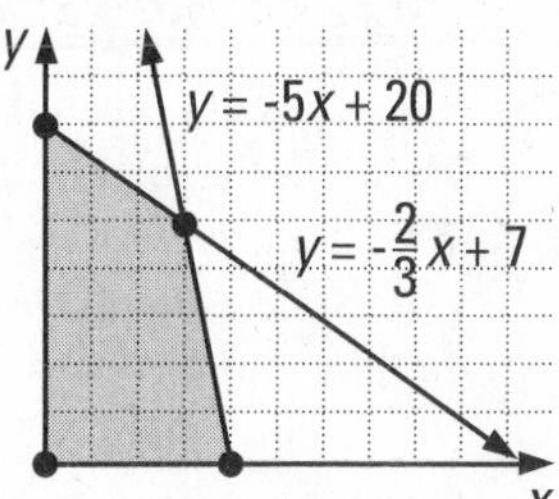

Objective G

- ☐ Understands linear programming.
- ☐ States several significant facts, such as identifying the constraints, the feasible region, and its vertices.
- ☐ Gives a logical explanation of how the graph might be used in a linear-programming situation.

Teacher Notes

Objectives E, G, H, J

Concepts and Skills This activity requires students to:
- read information from text and tables, and distinguish between necessary and extraneous information.
- graph linear inequalities in one and two variables.
- write and use a profit equation.
- use linear programming to solve problems.

Materials
- graph paper

Guiding Questions
- Which of the given facts must you consider in creating a profit equation?
- How do you interpret any negative values that arise when you evaluate a profit equation?

Answers
a. $10 \le t \le 20$, where t = total number of passengers

10 12 14 16 18 20

b. $x + y \ge 10$, $x + y \le 20$, $y \ge x$, $x \ge 0$, where x = number of adults and y = number of children

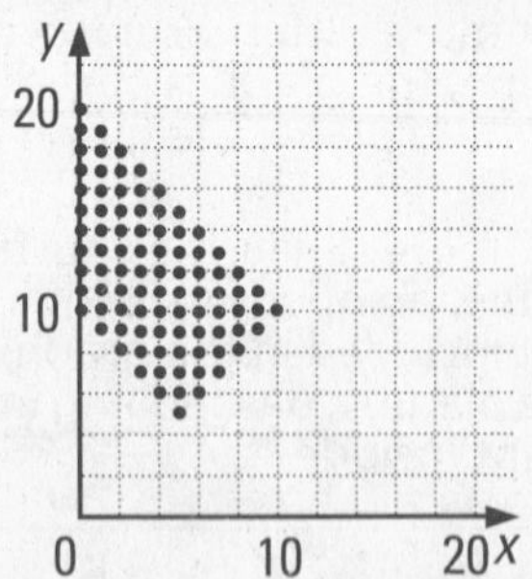

c. There are 91 possible combinations.
d. Part **b** is more helpful. Reasons may vary.
e. $P = .95x + .45y - 15$, where P = profit
f. No. Reasons may vary.
g. For 10 children and 10 adults, the company loses \$1. For all other combinations, the loss is greater.
h., i. Answers will vary. Check students' work.

Extension
Have students gather similar data about a local bus or train route and analyze its profitability. (If actual operating expenses are not obtained easily, assist students in making a reasonable estimate.)

Evaluation

Level	Standard to be achieved for performance at specified level
5	The student demonstrates an in-depth understanding of inequalities and linear programming. Graphs and calculations are accurate and complete; explanations are concise and insightful. The student prepares a thoughtful, well-organized report that reflects a firm grasp of the situation.
4	The student demonstrates clear understanding of inequalities and linear programming. Almost all graphs and calculations are appropriate, but they contain minor errors. The student prepares a well-organized report and makes suitable recommendations, but explanations or justifications have gaps.
3	The student demonstrates an understanding of inequalities and linear programming, but may need assistance in one or more steps of the programming process; graphs and calculations contain one or more major errors. The report is essentially complete, but may be disorganized. The student makes appropriate recommendations and attempts to justify them, but the logic behind the arguments is not cohesive.
2	The student demonstrates only a little understanding of inequalities and linear programming, and needs considerable assistance in setting up the programming process. Even with assistance, the graphs and calculations contain major errors; steps of the process are omitted. The student attempts to prepare an analysis and make recommendations, but the report is jumbled and incomplete.
1	The student demonstrates little if any understanding of inequalities and linear programming. Even with assistance, the student is unable to set up the programming process. Any attempts to prepare a report or make recommendations are superfluous. The student simply copies or restates given information.

1. Draw a geometric picture that illustrates why the following is *not* a true statement.

$$(k + 3)^2 = k^2 + 9$$

Write a brief paragraph that explains your picture.

Objective A

- ☐ Demonstrates an ability to expand squares of binomials.
- ☐ Draws an appropriate diagram. (Sample is at the right.)
- ☐ Writes an appropriate explanation.

	k	3
k	k^2	$3k$
3	$3k$	9

2. Give an example of a quadratic equation that you can solve by applying the Absolute Value-Square Root Theorem. Explain how to use the theorem to solve your equation.

Objectives C, E

- ☐ Is able to solve quadratic equations.
- ☐ Is able to apply the Absolute Value-Square Root Theorem.
- ☐ Gives an equation of the form $ax^2 + b = c$, where $a \neq 0$.
- ☐ Gives the correct solution of the equation.
- ☐ Gives a logical explanation.

3. Find two different sets of integers a and b that make the following a true statement.

$$\sqrt{a} \cdot \sqrt{b} = 6i$$

Then find two different sets of integers c and d that make the following a true statement.

$$\sqrt{c} - \sqrt{d} = 6i$$

Objective D

- ☐ Is able to perform operations with complex numbers.
- ☐ Gives appropriate values for a and b, such as: $a = -36$, $b = 1$; $a = -18$, $b = 2$.
- ☐ Gives appropriate values for c and d, such as: $c = -49$, $d = -1$; $c = -64$, $d = -4$.

4. Consider the set of all equations of the form $y = x^2 + 8x + a$, where a is a real number. How are the graphs of these equations related to the graph of $y = x^2$? State as many facts as you can.

Objectives I, J

- ☐ Demonstrates an understanding of the process of graphing quadratic equations.
- ☐ Demonstrates an understanding of the Graph-Translation Theorem.
- ☐ States several significant facts about the relationship to $y = x^2$, such as:
  All are congruent to the graph of $y = x^2$.
  All are parabolas that open upward.
  All are translated four units to the left of $y = x^2$ and some number of units up or down.

5. **a.** Write an equation in vertex form for a parabola with vertex (3, -2) that has no x-intercepts. Change it to standard form and show how to use the discriminant to verify the number of x-intercepts. What are the solutions to your equation?

   b. Repeat Part **a** for a parabola with vertex (3, -2) that has two x-intercepts.

Objectives B, C, F, K

- ☐ Is able to transform quadratic equations from vertex to standard form.
- ☐ Is able to solve quadratic equations.
- ☐ Understands the use of the discriminant.
- ☐ Writes two appropriate equations, such as:
  a. $y + 2 = -(x - 3)^2$, or $y = -x^2 + 6x - 11$
  b. $y + 2 = (x - 3)^2$, or $y = x^2 - 6x + 7$
- ☐ Gives correct solutions to the equations above: **a.** $3 \pm \sqrt{2}\,i$ **b.** $3 \pm \sqrt{2}$.

6. Suppose an object is thrown upward. What information do you need to know in order to determine when the object will hit the ground? Describe how you would use this information to find the answer.

Objective G

- ☐ Is able to use quadratic equations to solve problems dealing with velocity and acceleration.
- ☐ Correctly identifies a set of facts that would make it possible to calculate the time, such as: the initial upward velocity and the height from which the ball is thrown.
- ☐ Gives an appropriate description of how the information would be used, such as: If the given information is initial velocity v_0 and initial height h_0, substitute these values into the equation $h = -.5gt^2 + v_0t + h_0$. Replace g with the appropriate gravitational constant (32 ft/sec² or 9.8 m/sec²). Replace h with 0 and solve the resulting equation for t.

Teacher Notes

Objective H

Concepts and Skills This activity requires students to:

- fit linear and quadratic models to three-dimensional geometric patterns.
- create three-dimensional geometric patterns that can be modeled by linear and quadratic functions.
- summarize results.

Guiding Questions

- How is fitting a quadratic model to data different from fitting a linear model to data?
- What seems to be characteristic of a geometric pattern that is modeled by a linear function? by a quadratic function?

Answers

a. The number of boxes in the *n*th row can be modeled by the linear function $f(n) = 6n$.
b. The number of boxes in the *n*th row can be modeled by the quadratic function $g(n) = .5n^2 + .5n$.
c. Yes. When there are *n* rows, the number of boxes in the display can be modeled by the quadratic function $h(n) = 3n^2 + 3n$.
d. The number of boxes in the *n*th stack can be modeled by the function $s(n) = n^3$. Explanations may vary. Sample: A quadratic function is of the form $f(n) = ax^2 + bx + c = 0$, where $a \neq 0$; the exponent of *n* is 3, so *s* cannot be quadratic.
e. Yes. The number of boxes visible in the *n*th stack of the display can be modeled by the quadratic function $v(n) = 5n^2 - 8n + 4$.
f. Answers will vary. Check students' work.

Extension

Cassandra's display has its origins in this problem, some form of which may be familiar to your students.

> A cube with edge of length *n*, where *n* is a positive integer, is painted red. Then the painted cube is cut into cubes with edges of length 1. How many of these unit cubes have paint on exactly one face? two faces? three faces? no faces?

Have students write functions to model the answers to these questions. Have them use these functions to derive a function for the number of cubes that have paint on one or more faces. Then lead students to relate this new function to their response to Part **e**.

Evaluation

Level	Standard to be achieved for performance at specified level
5	The student demonstrates an in-depth understanding of linear and quadratic models for geometric patterns. Functions are identified accurately, and the student is able to articulate differences between the types of functions if asked. The student prepares an appropriate design and explains it correctly.
4	The student demonstrates a clear understanding of linear and quadratic models for geometric patterns. Correct procedures are used in deriving functions, but there may be minor errors in calculation. The original design is appropriate, and the report is well-organized, but one or both may have gaps.
3	The student demonstrates an understanding of linear and quadratic models for geometric patterns. The student recognizes correct procedures for deriving functions, but may make major errors in carrying them out. The design and report are completed, but they may be somewhat disorganized.
2	The student demonstrates only a little understanding of linear and quadratic models for geometric patterns, and needs considerable assistance in deriving appropriate functions. Even with assistance, the student makes major errors or may omit one or more major steps of a procedure. The student attempts to create original designs and prepare a report, but the presentation is jumbled and incomplete.
1	The student demonstrates little if any understanding of linear and quadratic models for geometric patterns. The student is unable to distinguish between the two types of models, and so cannot derive appropriate functions for the given patterns. Any attempt to create an original pattern or to prepare a report is superfluous or irrelevant. The student may simply draw random geometric figures.

1. a. Given that x, m, and n are integers greater than 1, and that $m \neq n$, find values of x, m, and n for which the value of $x^{\frac{m}{n}}$ is between 10 and 20. Show how to evaluate the expression for these values of x, m, and n.

   b. Repeat Part **a**, but this time find values of x, m, and n for which the value of $x^{\frac{m}{n}}$ is between 0 and 1.

Objective A

- ☐ Is able to evaluate b^n when $b > 0$ and n is a rational number.
- ☐ Gives appropriate values, such as: **a.** $x = 32$, $m = 4$, $n = 5$; **b.** $x = 32$, $m = -4$, $n = 5$.
- ☐ Correctly evaluates the expression; for the samples given, 16 and .0625.

2. Karl says the statements at the right are all true. So, he says, $x^4 = 1296$ has four real solutions.

$6^4 = 1296$
$(-6)^4 = 1296$
$(6i)^4 = 1296$
$(-6i)^4 = 1296$

Do you agree or disagree with Karl? Justify your response.

Objectives D, E

- ☐ Recognizes properties of nth powers and nth roots.
- ☐ Is able to solve equations of the form $x^n = b$.
- ☐ Recognizes that Karl's reasoning is incorrect.
- ☐ Gives a logical explanation, such as: The statements at the right above are all correct, so 6, -6, $6i$, and $-6i$ are the fourth roots of 1296. However, only 6 and -6 are real numbers, so $x^4 = 1296$ has only two real solutions.

3. Suppose that the following is a true statement:

$$\frac{2^a \cdot 5^b}{2^c \cdot 5^d} = (2 \cdot 5^{\frac{1}{2}})^4$$

What can you say about the relationship between a and c? What can you say about the relationship between b and d?

Objective B

- ☐ Is able to simplify expressions and solve equations using properties of exponents.
- ☐ Gives an appropriate description of the relationships, such as: $a - c = 4$; $b - d = 2$.

4. Create a geometric sequence whose first term is a positive integer and whose constant ratio is 0.5. Write an explicit formula and a recursive formula for this sequence. Describe a real-world situation that might be modeled by this sequence.

Objectives C, H

- ☐ Is able to describe geometric sequences explicitly and recursively.
- ☐ Is able to relate real-world problems to geometric sequences.
- ☐ Creates an appropriate sequence.
- ☐ Gives correct formulas for the sequence.
- ☐ Describes an appropriate situation.

5. Tamara wants to invest \$1000 for a period of six years. She saw a sign at a bank advertising one type of account that pays 4% interest and a second type that pays 4.03% interest. She thinks her \$1000 will definitely earn more interest if she chooses the second type of account, since 4.03% is more than 4%. Is her reasoning correct? Give examples to justify your answer.

Objective G

- ☐ Is able to apply compound-interest formulas.
- ☐ Recognizes that whether the second account pays more interest depends on how frequently the interest is compounded in each account.
- ☐ Gives appropriate examples.

6. Consider the function f with $f(x) = x^n$, where n is a positive integer. Compare the graph of f obtained when n is even to the graph of f when n is odd. How are they alike? How are they different? State as many similarities and differences as you can.

Objective I

- ☐ Is able to graph nth power functions.
- ☐ States several similarities, such as: The domain of each is all real numbers. The graph of each passes through the origin.
- ☐ States several differences, such as: The range is all real numbers when n is odd, but all nonnegative reals when n is even. The graph has reflection symmetry when n is even, but rotation symmetry when n is odd.

Teacher Notes

Objectives C, G, H

Concepts and Skills This activity requires students to:
- read information from text, a table, and a graphic.
- make decisions based on given information.
- apply the compound interest formulas.
- describe a geometric sequence explicitly and recursively.
- summarize results.

Guiding Questions
- How might you use a table or tables to organize your calculations?
- What is the least amount of time it would take to earn the amount of money that you need?

Answers
a. No. The new amount will be just $16,247.14.
b. Yes. The five-year CD will have $20,859.65. The three-year CD will have $17,934.27, which is very close to $18,000. No other CD will be close.
c. Estimates may vary. After 1.25 years, the total would be $18,031.50.
d. 1 year from now: $18,630; 2 years: $19.282.05; 3 years: $19,956.92; 4 years: $20,655.41; 5 years: $21,378.35; 6 years: $22,126.60; 7 years: $22,901.03; 8 years: $23,702.56; 9 years: $24,532.15; 10 years: $25,390.78
e. geometric; explicit: $g_n = 18{,}630(1.035)^{n-1}$;

recursive: $\begin{cases} g_1 = 18{,}630 \\ g_n = 1.035g_{n-1}, \end{cases}$

for integers $n \geq 2$

f. Answers will vary. Check students' work.

Extension
Have students consider obtaining a loan for the $3000 that is needed. Give them an appropriate annual interest rate, such as 6%, and have them choose a term, such as 2, 3, or 4 years. They can then use this formula to calculate each monthly payment.

$$M = \frac{Pr(1 + r)^n}{(1 + r)^n - 1}$$

In this formula, M is the amount of the monthly payment, P is the total amount of the loan, r is the *monthly* interest rate, and n is the number of *months* over which the loan will be repaid. Students can calculate the total amount that will be paid over the term of the loan and then discuss the advantages and disadvantages of this course.

Evaluation

Level	Standard to be achieved for performance at specified level
5	The student demonstrates an in-depth understanding of powers, geometric sequences, and their application to the given situation. All calculations are accurate and complete. The investment plan is appropriate, and the report presents an articulate rationale for all choices. The student may ask probing questions or offer additional insights.
4	The student demonstrates a clear understanding of powers and geometric sequences. The concepts and formulas are applied correctly to the given situation, but the student's calculations may contain minor errors. The investment plan is appropriate, and the student has a clear rationale for all choices, but the report may lack in some detail.
3	The student demonstrates a fundamental understanding of powers and geometric sequences. The student recognizes which concepts and formulas are appropriate to a given situation, but may make major errors in applying them, or may omit critical steps. The student prepares an investment plan, but the reasoning behind the choices may be flawed, and the report may be disorganized.
2	The student demonstrates little understanding of powers and geometric sequences, and needs assistance in applying the concepts and formulas to the given situation. Even with help, the student may make several major errors or may omit major steps of a procedure. The student attempts to devise an investment plan and prepare a report, but the reasoning is jumbled, and the presentation is incomplete.
1	The student is unable to apply powers and geometric sequences to the given situation. The student may attempt some calculations, but they are superfluous or irrelevant. There is no attempt to organize an investment plan. The student may simply copy or restate the given information.

1. Let $f(x) = 3x - 2$. Find a function g such that $g(f(4)) = 5$. Then use your function g to find $f(g(4))$.

Objective A

- ☐ Is able to find values and rules for composites of functions.
- ☐ Identifies an appropriate function g, such as: $g(x) = x - 5$.
- ☐ Gives a correct value for $f(g(4))$ for the function g given above, $f(g(4)) = -5$.

2. When $x \geq 0$, $f(x) = x^2$ and $g(x) = \sqrt{x}$ are inverse functions. So Peter reasons that, when $x \geq 0$, $h(x) = (5x)^2$ and $k(x) = \sqrt{5x}$ also are inverse functions. Do you agree or disagree? Justify your answer.

Objectives B, F

- ☐ Is able to find the inverse of a function.
- ☐ Is able to apply properties of the inverse.
- ☐ Recognizes that Peter's conclusion is false.
- ☐ Gives a logical justification.

3. How is solving $\sqrt[3]{m + 1} + 8 = 6$ similar to solving $\sqrt[4]{m + 1} + 8 = 6$? How is it different? Solve each equation.

Objective E

- ☐ Is able to solve equations with radicals.
- ☐ States one or more similarities, such as: The first step is to add -8 to each side.
- ☐ States one or more differences, such as: Solving the first equation involves cubing each side; solving the second involves raising each side to the fourth power.
- ☐ Gives correct solutions. For the first equation, $m = -9$; the second has no real solution.

4. Demonstrate the fact that $\frac{1}{2 - \sqrt{3}}$ is equal to $2 + \sqrt{3}$ by rationalizing the denominator. Then explain how you can use a calculator to verify the result.

Objective D

- ☐ Understands the process of rationalizing a denominator.
- ☐ Writes an appropriate demonstration of the fact that the expressions are equal.
- ☐ Gives a logical explanation of checking the result by using a calculator.

5. Rewrite the expression below, replacing each box with an integer greater than 1 to make a true statement.

$$\sqrt[3]{\blacksquare a^{\blacksquare} b^{\blacksquare}} \cdot \sqrt[3]{\blacksquare a^{\blacksquare} b^{\blacksquare}} = 4a^2b^2\sqrt[3]{a^2}$$

Is your statement true for all real numbers a and b, or must you restrict the values of a and b? Explain your answer.

Objectives C, D, G

- ☐ Is able to evaluate radicals.
- ☐ Is able to simplify expressions with radicals.
- ☐ Is able to apply properties of radicals.
- ☐ Gives an appropriate statement, such as: $\sqrt[3]{16a^3b^3} \cdot \sqrt[3]{4a^5b^3}$.
- ☐ Recognizes that the statement is true for all real numbers a and b, and gives a logical explanation.

6. On the coordinate axes below, graph a function other than $f(x) = x$ that is its own inverse. Justify your answer.

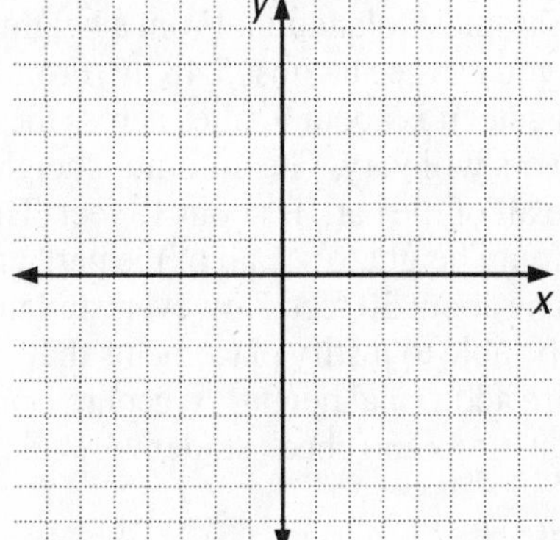

Objectives F, I

- ☐ Is able to make and interpret graphs of inverses.
- ☐ Is able to apply properties of the inverse.
- ☐ Sketches an appropriate graph, such as: $f(x) = \frac{1}{x}$ or $f(x) = -x + b$ for any real number b.
- ☐ Gives a logical justification.

Teacher Notes

Objectives A, B, C, H

Concepts and Skills This activity requires students to:

- read information from text and a map.
- evaluate formulas.
- find a rule for a composite of a function.
- find the inverse of a function.
- evaluate radicals.
- solve real world problems modeled by equations with radicals.
- make real world decisions based on given information and mathematical reasoning.
- summarize results in a written report.

Guiding Questions

- In the given situation, why does it make sense to find the composite function in Part **b**? to find the inverse function in Part **c**?
- What is the scale of the map? How do you use it?
- What factors should you consider when determining a reasonable location for the tower?

Answers

a. 125.86 miles
b. $d(c(h)) = \sqrt{1.5h}$ or $d(c(h)) \approx 1.22\sqrt{h}$; about 12.25 miles
c. $h = \frac{d^2}{1.5}$; about 16.67 feet
d. No. Sample explanation: From a height of 20 feet, you can see at most 5.48 mi. From the main gate, it is about 9 miles across the park.
e. Answers will vary. The minimum height to see all of the park is about 18 feet. The minimum height to see all of the park and forest is about 30 feet. However, students may be able to justify placements that require additional height. Accept reasonable explanations and check students' work.

Extension

Have students develop several questions that can be answered using both the given distance formula and the height formula that they derived from it. Then have them research any information necessary to answer their questions. Samples: How far can you see from the top of the Sears Tower in Chicago? How tall a tower would you have to build in order to see all of your city or county? If you build a tower twice as tall, can you see twice as far?

Evaluation

Level	Standard to be achieved for performance at specified level
5	The student demonstrates an in-depth understanding of composites, inverses, radicals, and their application to the given situation. All formulas and calculations are accurate and complete. The student prepares a thorough, well-organized report.
4	The student demonstrates a clear understanding of composites, inverses, radicals, and their application to the given situation. The student develops the required formulas, but may make errors in applying them. The report is well-organized and presents two sensible plans, but it may lack in some detail.
3	The student demonstrates an understanding of composites, inverses, and radicals, but may need some assistance in applying the concepts to the given situation. The student responds to all questions and performs almost all required tasks, but may make major errors or omit critical steps in developing and applying the formulas. The report is essentially complete, but it may be somewhat disorganized.
2	The student demonstrates only a little understanding of composites, inverses, and radicals, and has considerable difficulty in applying the concepts to the given situation. Even with assistance, the student makes several major errors in developing and applying the formulas. The student attempts to prepare a report, but it may be jumbled and incomplete.
1	The student demonstrates little if any understanding of composites, inverses, and radicals, and is unable to apply the concepts to the given situation. The student may attempt some calculations, but they are superfluous or irrelevant. There is no effort to develop meaningful formulas. Rather than prepare a report, the student may simply copy or restate the given information.

1. How are the following three equations alike? How are they different? What is the solution of each?

$\log x = 3 \qquad \log_4 x = 3 \qquad \ln x = 3$

Objective C

- ☐ Is able to solve logarithmic equations.
- ☐ States at least one similarity, such as: In each equation, x represents the result when a number is raised to the third power.
- ☐ States at least one difference, such as: Each involves a different number as the base.
- ☐ Gives correct solutions: 1000, 64, and $e^3 \approx 20.09$.

2. Name two properties of logarithms that you studied in this chapter. State each property in your own words. Then give an example to illustrate each property that you chose.

Objective E

- ☐ Demonstrates an understanding of logarithms.
- ☐ Is able to identify and apply properties of logarithms.
- ☐ Correctly names two properties.
- ☐ Gives an appropriate description of each property.
- ☐ Gives appropriate examples.

3. $\log_2 2^x = \log_2 10 \qquad \log 2^x = \log 10$

$\ln 2^x = \ln 10$

Which of the equations above could you use to solve $2^x = 10$? Explain your reasoning. Then show how to find the solution.

Objective B

- ☐ Is able to use logarithms to solve exponential equations.
- ☐ Recognizes that each is equivalent to $2^x = 10$.
- ☐ Makes a reasonable choice.
- ☐ Gives a logical explanation.
- ☐ Gives the correct solution, $x \approx 3.32$.

4. Do you agree or disagree with this statement?

> If successive units on a scale are unequally spaced, then the scale is logarithmic.

Justify your answer. Give an example of a logarithmic scale and describe how it illustrates your answer.

Objective H

- ☐ Understands logarithmic scales.
- ☐ Recognizes that the statement is false.
- ☐ Gives a logical explanation, such as: The criterion for a logarithmic scale is that the ratio between successive units is the same.
- ☐ Gives an appropriate example.

5. The size N of a certain population over t years is described by this formula.

$$N = 10{,}000e^{-.045t}$$

State as many facts as you can about the growth of this population. Then make a prediction about the future size of this population.

Objective F

- ☐ Is able to apply exponential-growth and exponential-decay models.
- ☐ States several significant facts about the population, such as:
  The situation is one of continuous decay.
  The initial population is 10,000.
  The growth factor is $e^{-.045} \approx .956$, so the population is decreasing by about 4.4% per year.
- ☐ Makes a significant prediction, such as: The population will be half its original size in about 15.4 years.

6. Suppose your friend was ill and missed some math classes. You offer to prepare a study sheet about exponential and logarithmic functions. Write a brief paragraph that could accompany this figure on your study sheet.

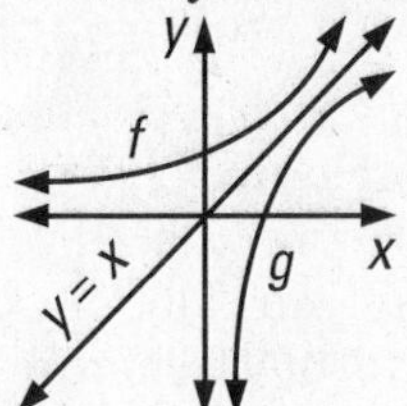

Objectives I, J

- ☐ Is able to interpret graphs of exponential and logarithmic functions.
- ☐ Writes a paragraph that includes several relevant observations, such as:
  f is an exponential function; g is logarithmic.
  The figure shows that the logarithmic and exponential functions with base b are inverses.

Teacher Notes

Objectives B, F, G

Concepts and Skills This activity requires students to:

- apply exponential and linear growth models.
- use logarithms to solve exponential equations.
- solve linear equations.
- fit algebraic models to data, and use the models to make predictions.
- summarize and justify results.

Guiding Questions

- How do you decide if a given model is a good model?
- How do you decide whether to consider an exponential model for a given set of data? a linear model? What other type of model might you consider? (quadratic)
- How do you decide whether to use more than one type of model for a given set of data?

Answers

a. Check students' work.
b. 4.4 million; 412.2 million
c. 1910
d. 1820: 4.4 million; 1990: 52.9 million; the population would reach 50 million in 1981.
e. Answers will vary. Sample: The model in Part **d** is better than the model in Part **b**, but neither is a good model. The model in Part **d** provides closer values for the data after 1850, but there still seems to be a considerable difference between the model values and the actual data. From examining the graph, it appears that perhaps yet another model is needed for the set of data that begins in 1970.
f. Answers will vary. Check students' work.

Extension

Have students research population data for the city or town in which they live and fit an algebraic model to the data. Have them compare the population growth of the city or town to the population growth of the entire region. Have students research the reasons for any significant differences.

Evaluation

Level	Standard to be achieved for performance at specified level
5	The student demonstrates an in-depth understanding of exponential and logarithmic functions and their application to the given situation. All calculations are accurate and complete with at most minor errors. The student creates an appropriate model for one of the regions and may offer significant insights in justifying the model. The report is neat, thorough, and easy to read.
4	The student demonstrates a clear understanding of exponential and logarithmic functions and their application to the given situation. Correct procedures are followed in working with the functions, but there may be several minor errors and a major error. The student creates a reasonable model for one of the regions and is able to justify it.
3	The student demonstrates some understanding of exponential and logarithmic functions. The student recognizes correct procedures for working with the functions, but makes major errors in carrying them out, or omits critical steps. Some assistance may be needed in developing a model for one of the regions. The report is essentially complete, but it may be somewhat disorganized.
2	The student demonstrates a little understanding of exponential and logarithmic functions, but needs help in applying them to the given situation. The student makes several major errors in working with the functions, and omits major steps of a procedure. The student attempts to develop a model and prepare a report, but the effort is jumbled and incomplete.
1	The student demonstrates no understanding of exponential and logarithmic functions. The student may attempt to perform some calculations, but they are superfluous or irrelevant. The student is unable to develop an algebraic model, and may simply copy or restate the given information.

1. Suppose the [COS] key on your calculator is broken, so the *cos* and cos^{-1} functions are not available to you. How could you use your calculator to find cos 37°? How could you find θ if you know cos θ = .25? (Assume θ is between 0° and 90°.)

Objectives A, C, E

- ☐ Is able to approximate values of trigonometric functions using a calculator.
- ☐ Is able to determine the measure of an angle given its sine or cosine.
- ☐ Can use theorems relating sines and cosines.
- ☐ Gives an appropriate method for finding cos 37°, such as: Find sin 53°, which is ≈ .799.
- ☐ Gives an appropriate method for finding θ, such as: Find 90° − $\sin^{-1}$ .25, which is ≈ 76°.

2. What is a *radian*? How can you convert back and forth between degrees and radians? Give an example of each kind of conversion.

Objective D

- ☐ Understands the relationship between radians and degrees.
- ☐ Gives an appropriate description of a radian, such as: A radian is the measure of an angle, arc, or rotation that π radians = 180°.
- ☐ Correctly identifies the conversion factors: To convert radians to degrees, multiply by 180 degrees/π radians; to convert degrees to radians, multiply by π radians/180 degrees.
- ☐ Gives appropriate examples.

3. Write a real-world problem that can be solved using either the Law of Sines or the Law of Cosines. Then show how to solve your problem.

Objective G

- ☐ Is able to solve real-world problems using the Law of Sines or Law of Cosines.
- ☐ Writes an appropriate problem.
- ☐ Writes a correct solution to the problem.

4. Dan was absent for a day in the middle of studying Chapter 10. On the day before his absence, the class was studying trigonometry and right triangles. When he returned, he was surprised that the class was discussing circles. How would you explain this to Dan?

Objective I

- ☐ Is able to use the properties of a unit circle to find trigonometric values.
- ☐ Gives a logical explanation, such as: With the right triangle, sine and cosine are defined only for 0° ≤ θ ≤ 90°. The unit circle extends the definition over the domain of all real numbers.

5. Identify the trigonometric function that is graphed below. Then state as many facts as you can about the function.

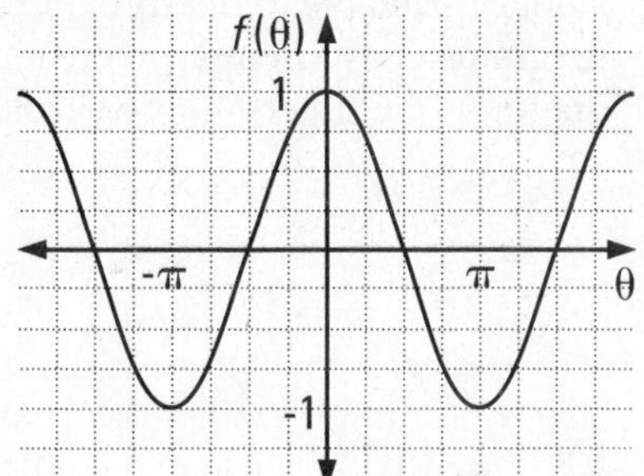

Objective J

- ☐ Correctly identifies the graph as being the graph of the cosine function.
- ☐ Is able to use the graph to identify several properties of the cosine function.

6. Add one reasonable measure to the triangle below that would enable you to solve the triangle. Then show how to find all the missing measures.

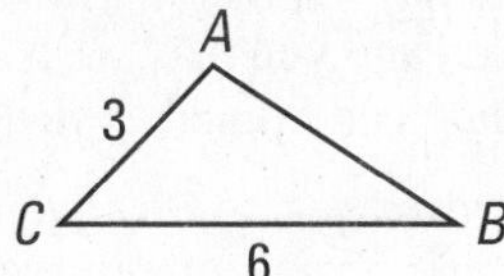

Objective H

- ☐ Is able to find missing parts of a triangle using the Law of Sines or the Law of Cosines.
- ☐ Adds a reasonable measure, such as: m∠C = 45° or AB = 4.
- ☐ Gives all missing measures: If m∠C = 45°, AB ≈ 4.4, m∠A ≈ 104°, and m∠B ≈ 31°.

Teacher Notes

Objectives B, D, E, H, I, J

Concepts and Skills This activity requires students to:

- read and interpret given diagrams related to trigonometry.
- create original diagrams to illustrate trigonometric concepts.
- identify the key concepts of the chapter and demonstrate an understanding of them.
- prepare a visual summary of the key concepts.

Guiding Questions

- What are the basic types of diagrams that you have seen in this chapter? (*triangle, unit circle, sine curve*) How can you decide what type of diagram to use for a given concept?
- How do you think you might identify the most important concepts in the chapter?

Answers

a. The basic fact is $\sin 45° = \cos 45° = \frac{\sqrt{2}}{2}$. Explanations may vary. Sample: The diagram helps him derive the fact by using the Pythagorean Theorem and the unit circle.

b. The relationship is π radians = 180 degrees; diagrams will vary.

c. The concepts are the unit circle and the sine curve. Explanations may vary. Sample: The diagram shows how the y-coordinate of each point on the unit circle is related to the range of the sine function.

d. Answers will vary. Check students' work.

Extension

Have students design a second poster that highlights real-world applications of the trigonometry that they studied in this chapter. They may feature applications that they studied in this chapter, and you may wish to encourage them to research additional applications.

Evaluation

Level	Standard to be achieved for performance at specified level
5	The student demonstrates an in-depth understanding of the basic concepts of trigonometry. The student offers logical interpretations of the given diagrams, and may display significant insights. The student's original diagrams are appropriate, accurate, and complete.
4	The student demonstrates a clear understanding of the basic concepts of trigonometry. The interpretations of the given diagrams are clear and coherent, but the student's original diagrams may contain minor errors and one major error.
3	The student demonstrates some understanding of the basic concepts of trigonometry. The student's interpretations of the given diagrams are reasonable, and the original diagrams are essentially complete, but overall the work may reflect some confusion or minor misconceptions, and one or more major concepts are omitted or misrepresented.
2	The student demonstrates only a little understanding of the basic concepts of trigonometry, but needs considerable assistance in interpreting the given diagrams and in creating original diagrams. Even with help, the student's work may contain several misstatements and reflect major misconceptions.
1	The student demonstrates no understanding of the basic concepts of trigonometry. Even with assistance, the student is unable to interpret the given diagrams. Any attempts to create original diagrams are superfluous or irrelevant.

1. Consider the trinomial $x^2 + bx + 16$.

a. Name a value of b for which the trinomial is factorable into linear factors with integer coefficients. Give the factorization.

b. Name a value of b for which the trinomial is prime over the set of rational numbers. Justify your answer.

Objective B

- ☐ Demonstrates an ability to factor polynomials.
- ☐ Gives an appropriate value of b for Part **a**, such as: $b = 8$.
- ☐ Gives the correct factorization for the sample above: If $b = 8$, then $x^2 + 8x + 16 = (x + 4)^2$.
- ☐ Gives an appropriate value of b for Part **b**, such as: $b = 9$.
- ☐ Gives a logical explanation.

2. Let $f(x) = 6x^3 - 9x^2 - 6x$. Give an equation for a polynomial function g having the same zeros as f, plus one additional zero. Your equation should *not* have any double roots. Write your polynomial in standard form and identify the zeros of your function.

Objectives A, C

- ☐ Demonstrates an ability to find zeros of polynomial functions by factoring.
- ☐ Demonstrates an ability to use the Extended Distributive Property to multiply polynomials.
- ☐ Gives an appropriate function g, such as: $g(x) = x(2x + 1)(x - 2)(x + 1)$.
- ☐ Gives the correct standard form of the polynomial above: $x(2x + 1)(x - 2)(x + 1) = 2x^4 - x^3 - 5x^2 - 2x$.
- ☐ Correctly identifies the zeros of the new function above: 0, -.5, 2, -1.

3. Complete the table below so the set of data can be modeled by a polynomial function of degree two or higher. Identify your function. Then explain how, given this set of data, a person could work backward from the table to determine your function.

x	1	2	3	4	5	6
y	6	13	32	69	130	221

Objective D

- ☐ Gives an appropriate set of data. See table for sample.
- ☐ Is able to determine the equation for a polynomial function from data points. For the data above, $y = x^3 + 5$.
- ☐ Gives a logical explanation.

4. The diagram at the right shows a pattern for a cardboard box. Explain how the surface area and volume of the box are related to polynomial functions.

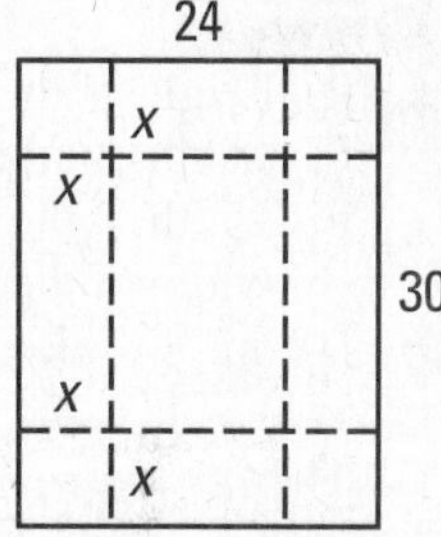

Objective I

- ☐ Demonstrates an ability to use polynomials to model geometric situations.
- ☐ Gives a logical explanation, such as: Assume the four "corners" are discarded and an open box is formed by folding along the dashed lines. The volume of the box is $V(x) = x(30 - 2x)(24 - 2x)$; the surface area is $S(x) = (30 - 2x)(24 - 2x) + 2x(30 - 2x) + 2x(24 - 2x)$.

5. Andi graphed $y = x^4 - 9x^3 - 37x^2 + 9x + 36$ on an automatic grapher and obtained the display shown at the right. She concluded that the equation has exactly three rational roots: -3, -1, and 1.

Do you agree or disagree? If you agree, justify your answer. If you disagree, explain how you would correct Andi's work.

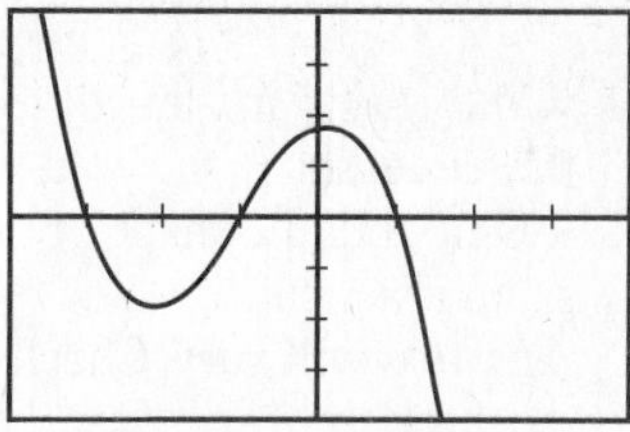

$-4 \le x \le 4$, x-scale = 1
$-80 \le y \le 80$, y-scale = 20

Objectives G, J

- ☐ Demonstrates an understanding of the Rational-Zero Theorem.
- ☐ Demonstrates an ability to graph polynomial functions.
- ☐ Recognizes that Andi's conclusion is incorrect.
- ☐ Gives a logical explanation, such as: By the Rational-Zero Theorem, both -36 and 36 could be zeros, so Andi should graph the function over the domain $-36 \le x \le 36$; she would find that 12 is another rational zero.

Teacher Notes

Objectives A, C, I, J

Concepts and Skills This activity requires students to:
- read and interpret information from a diagram.
- use polynomials to describe geometric situations.
- find zeros of polynomial functions by factoring.
- graph polynomial functions.
- summarize results.

Materials
- automatic grapher

Guiding Questions
- If you are having difficulty visualizing the box, what can you do? (*Make a model.*)
- How do you know if the shape of a carton is reasonable?

Answers
a. **i.** height of the box
ii. width of all the top and bottom flaps
iii. width of the gluing flap
iv. width of the front of the box

b. **i.** x in. **ii.** $(23 - x)$ in.

c. $V(x) = 12x(23 - x)$, or $V(x) = -12x^2 + 276x$

d. The zeros are 0 and 23. Explanations may vary. Sample: The zeros represent values of x that give a volume of 0; this occurs if the width of both front and back is 0 in.; it also occurs if the width of both front and back is 23 in., leaving 0 in. for the lengths of the sides.

e. The graph is at the right. Explanations will vary. Sample: From the graph, the maximum volume is less than 1600 in^3.

f. $x \approx 4.5$ and $x \approx 18.5$; height: 12 in., width: $\approx$ 4.5 in., length: $\approx$ 18.5 in.; with these measures, the volume is approximately 999 in^3, but the shape of the box does not seem practical.

g. Answers will vary. Check students' work.

Extension
Have students identify a type of carton or box that requires a different type of pattern. Have them create a pattern for the carton or box and determine how they might use polynomial functions in describing and analyzing the volume of the box obtained from that pattern.

Evaluation

Level	Standard to be achieved for performance at specified level
5	The student demonstrates an in-depth understanding of polynomial functions and their application to the given situation. All graphs, calculations, and other responses are accurate and complete with at most minor errors. The set of patterns is neat, precise, and easy to read, and they indicate a considerable amount of reflection.
4	The student demonstrates a clear understanding of polynomial functions and their application to the given situation. The student makes articulate responses and uses appropriate graphs or tables, but makes minor errors in calculations and one major error. The set of patterns is reasonable and neat, but they may lack in some detail.
3	The student demonstrates some understanding of polynomial functions, but may need some assistance in applying them to the given situation. Graphs and calculations may contain major errors, and responses in general may reflect a major misconception. The set of patterns is essentially complete, but they are somewhat disorganized and contain some inaccuracies.
2	The student demonstrates a little understanding of polynomial functions, but needs considerable assistance in applying them to the given situation. The student may need prompting in order to respond to the questions posed, and graphs and calculations contain major errors.
1	The student demonstrates no understanding of polynomial functions and their application to the given situation. Even when prompted, the student is unable to create or graph appropriate polynomial functions. Any calculations are superfluous or irrelevant. The student may simply copy the given pattern.

1. On the coordinate axes at the right, sketch two different ellipses that each have an area of 12π square units. Then give an equation for each ellipse.

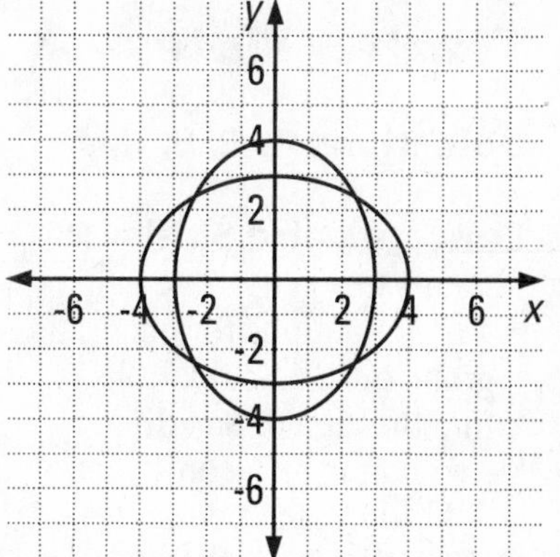

Objectives C, J

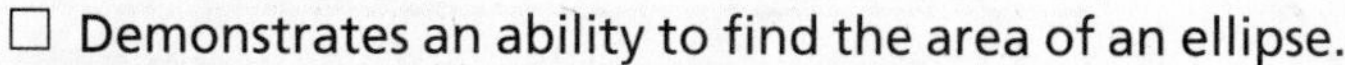

☐ Demonstrates an ability to find the area of an ellipse.
☐ Demonstrates an ability to give an equation for an ellipse.
☐ Sketches two appropriate ellipses, such as: the ellipse with vertices (4, 0), (-4,0), (0, 3) and (0, -3); the ellipse with vertices (3, 0), (-3, 0), (0, 4), and (0, -4). See grid for graphs.
☐ Gives a correct equation for each ellipse. For the ellipses graphed, the equations are $\frac{x^2}{9} + \frac{y^2}{16} = 1$ and $\frac{x^2}{16} + \frac{y^2}{9} = 1$.

2. Explain how you can describe the parabola shown at the right without giving its equation and without naming any points that it contains.

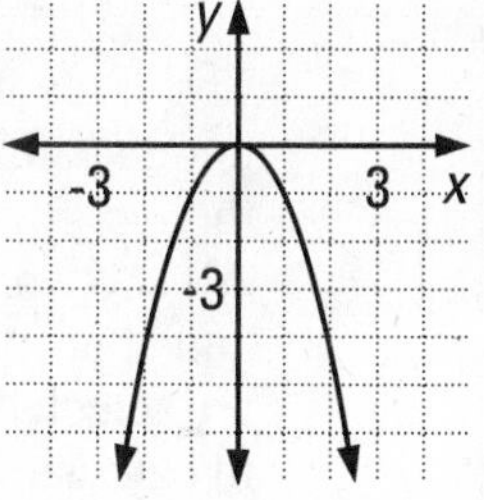

Objective B

☐ Demonstrates an understanding of sufficient conditions for generating an equation or inequality for a quadratic relation.
☐ Gives an appropriate method for describing the curve, such as: The curve is a parabola with focus $(0, -\frac{1}{4})$ and directrix $y = \frac{1}{4}$.

3. How are a hyperbola and an ellipse alike? How are they different? State as many likenesses and differences as you can.

Objectives F, G

☐ Demonstrates an understanding of the characteristics of hyperbolas and ellipses.
☐ Is able to classify curves as hyperbolas and ellipses using algebraic or geometric properties.
☐ States one or more significant likenesses, such as: Each represents a quadratic relation. Each has two foci.
☐ States one or more significant differences, such as: Given foci F_1 and F_2 and focal constant $2a$, a hyperbola is the set of points P such that $|PF_1 - PF_2| = 2a$; an ellipse is the set of points P such that $PF_1 + PF_2 = 2a$.

4. Choose from the following equations.

i. $(x-2)^2 + (y+3)^2 = 16$ **ii.** $xy = 8$
iii. $\frac{x^2}{4} + \frac{y^2}{36} = 1$ **iv.** $y = \frac{1}{4}x + 4$
v. $y = -\frac{1}{4}x^2$

a. Find two equations that form a system with exactly two solutions.
b. Find two equations that form a system with exactly one solution.
c. Find two equations that form an inconsistent system.

Justify your answers.

Objectives D, K

☐ Demonstrates an ability to solve systems involving quadratic relations.
☐ Chooses an appropriate pair of equations to satisfy each condition. For **a**, i and v, i and iii, ii and iv, iii and iv, iii and v; for **b**, ii and v; for c, i and ii, i and iv, ii and iii, iv and v.
☐ Gives a logical explanation.

5. The curve in the figure below is a semicircle. Describe a real-world situation that this figure might represent. Write a problem about the situation that you could solve by using the equation of the semicircle. Then show how to solve your problem.

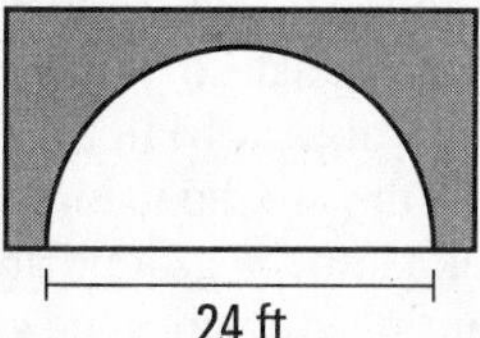

Objective H

☐ Demonstrates an ability to use circles and semicircles to solve real-world problems.
☐ Writes an appropriate problem, such as: Can a truck that is 11 ft high and 8 ft wide pass through the opening above without crossing the center line?
☐ Gives a correct solution to the problem, no.

Teacher Notes

Objectives B, C, E, H, J

Concepts and Skills This activity requires students to:

- write equations for quadratic relations.
- graph quadratic relations.
- find the area of an ellipse.
- find points on a conic section using the definition of the conic.
- use conic sections to solve real-world problems.
- summarize results.

Guiding Questions

- What is the scale of the sketch? How can you use that to find a reasonable size for the rose bed?
- Why can't you give an equation for the ellipse using just the sketch as it is given?

Answers

a.-e. Answers may vary. Sample responses:

a. 16 feet; 6 feet

b. Set up a coordinate system with the center of the ellipse at the origin. An equation of the ellipse might be $\frac{x^2}{64} + \frac{y^2}{9} = 1$; check students' graphs.

c. For the ellipse in Part **b**: $(\sqrt{55}, 0)$, $(-\sqrt{55}, 0)$

d. Sample: 1) Locate the center of each side of the garden. 2) Connect the centers of opposite sides with string. 3) On the longer string, find the two points that are $\sqrt{55}$ ($\approx$ 7 ft. 5 in.) from the point where the strings intersect. 4) Drive a stake into the ground at each point found in step 3. 5) Tie one end of a string to each stake so the amount of string between the stakes is 16 ft. 6) Pull the string tight against the ground using one finger. Drive a stake into the ground at the point where your finger touches the ground. 7) Move a small distance and repeat step 6. 8) Repeat step 7 until you are back where you began in step 6. 9) Use the stakes from steps 6 through 8 as a guide to digging the border.

e. 16 or 17 rose bushes

f. Answers will vary. Check students' work.

Extension

Have students brainstorm other conic-shaped features that they might add to the garden. Have them determine equations that can guide the landscaper in locating these additional features.

Evaluation

Level	Standard to be achieved for performance at specified level
5	The student demonstrates an in-depth understanding of quadratic relations and their application to the given situation. Chosen measures are reasonable, and equations and graphs are accurate and complete. The written instructions are precise and easy to read, and they may be presented imaginatively. Any errors are minor.
4	The student demonstrates a good understanding of quadratic relations and their application to the given situation. All chosen measures are reasonable, and appropriate equations and graphs are selected, but the student makes errors in calculation or in rendering the graphs. The written instructions are sound and easy to read, but they may lack in some detail and have some errors.
3	The student demonstrates some understanding of quadratic relations and their application to the given situation. The student is able to choose reasonable measures, perhaps with some assistance, but may make major errors in writing appropriate equations or in rendering suitable graphs. The written instructions may be somewhat disorganized, and one or more critical steps may be omitted.
2	The student demonstrates a little understanding of quadratic relations, but needs considerable assistance in applying them to the given situation. Even with assistance, the student makes major errors in writing appropriate equations and in rendering suitable graphs. The student attempts to develop a set of instructions, but the effort is jumbled, and major steps are omitted.
1	The student demonstrates very little understanding of quadratic relations and their application to the given situation. The student may attempt to write some equations or prepare some graphs, but they are superfluous or irrelevant. The student makes no effort to develop a cohesive set of instructions, and may simply copy or restate the given information.

1. Pat wrote the following statement on a homework assignment.

$$\sum_{i=1}^{10} (2i + 3) = 23$$

Do you agree or disagree with Pat's statement? If you agree, justify your answer. If you disagree, explain how you would correct the statement.

Objectives A, C

- ☐ Understands summation notation.
- ☐ Is able to calculate values of finite arithmetic series.
- ☐ Recognizes that the given statement is false.
- ☐ Gives the correct sum, 140.

2. Give both a mathematical explanation and a real-world explanation to demonstrate why the expression $\binom{5}{7}$ is not meaningful.

Objectives D, H

- ☐ Demonstrates an understanding of the process of calculating combinations.
- ☐ Demonstrates an understanding of using combinations to solve real-world problems.
- ☐ Gives a logical mathematical explanation, such as: $\binom{5}{7} = \frac{5!}{7!(-2)!}$; however, the factorial function is not defined for negative integers.
- ☐ Gives an appropriate real-world explanation, such as: In a real-world problem, it makes no sense to speak of the number of combinations of 7 objects from 5 objects.

3. State two important properties of Pascal's Triangle. Demonstrate how these properties apply to row 6 of the triangle.

Objective F

- ☐ Recognizes properties of Pascal's Triangle.
- ☐ Correctly identifies two properties, such as: The sum of the elements of row n is 2^n. The elements in row n are the coefficients in the expansion of $(a + b)^n$.
- ☐ Correctly applies the properties to row 6. For the properties given above: The sum of the elements of row 6 is $2^6 = 64$. The expansion of $(a + b)^6$ is $a^6 + 6a^5b + 15a^4b^2 + 20a^3b^3 + 15a^2b^4 + 6ab^5 + b^6$.

4. Create a set of seven test scores that satisfies all the following conditions.

The mean is 75.
The median is 77.
The mode is 78.

Find the standard deviation of your scores.

Objective I

- ☐ Is able to use measures of central tendency and dispersion to describe data.
- ☐ Gives an appropriate set of seven test scores, such as: 69, 70, 73, 77, 78, 78, 80.
- ☐ Gives the standard deviation of the scores. For the scores above, the standard deviation is 4.

5. Describe a real-world situation that the function at the right might represent. Then graph the function.

$$P(n) = \frac{\binom{8}{n}}{2^8}$$

Objectives J, L

- ☐ Is able to solve problems using probability.
- ☐ Is able to graph binomial distributions.
- ☐ Describes an appropriate real-world situation, such as: For integers n from 0 through 8, the function gives the probability of getting n heads when a fair coin is tossed 8 times.
- ☐ Correctly graphs the function. The graph is given above.

6. Use the Binomial Theorem to show that $(a - b)^4 = (b - a)^4$. Do you think it follows that $(a - b)^n = (b - a)^n$ for all nonnegative integers n? Explain your reasoning.

Objective E

- ☐ Demonstrates an ability to expand binomials.
- ☐ Applies the Binomial Theorem correctly to each of the given expressions to show that they are equivalent, such as: $(a - b)^4 = a^4 - 4a^3b + 6a^2b^2 - 4ab^3 + b^4 = b^4 - 4b^3a + 6b^2a^2 - 4ba^3 + a^4 = (b - a)^4$.
- ☐ Recognizes that $(a - b)^n$ is *not* equivalent to $(b - a)^n$ when n is odd.
- ☐ Gives an appropriate explanation.

Teacher Notes

Objectives C, D, J

Concepts and Skills This activity requires students to:

- read information from text.
- calculate combinations.
- use factorial notation.
- solve real-world problems using probability.
- summarize results in a written report.

Guiding Questions

- How can you translate the probability of winning into an expected number of winners?
- For a given number of balls, how does changing the number of balls that must match affect the probability of winning?

Answers

a. 120; $\frac{1}{120}$

b. – e. Answers will vary. Sample responses are given.

b. Since the probability of winning is $\frac{1}{120}$, one of every 120 people might be a winner; $4000 \div 120 \approx 33$. About 33 winners are expected.

c. You might expect to win about \$240. With a \$2 admission, and 4000 adult entries, the amount of money in the lottery "pool" is \$8000. If there are 33 winners, each receives $\$8000 \div 33 \approx \$240$.

d. If there are as few as eight winners, each will receive at least \$1000. However, it is likely that there will be many more than two or three winners, and each would receive far less than \$1000.

e. With ten balls, the lowest probability of winning occurs in matching five balls. This probability $\left(\frac{1}{252}\right)$ is still high. If the cost of adult admission is \$2, and 5000 adults enter, there would be about twenty winners, each receiving about \$500.

f. Answers will vary. Check students' work.

Extension

Have students adjust their lotteries so that a smaller prize is awarded to someone who picks almost all the winning numbers. Have them calculate the probability of winning a smaller prize, choose an amount of money to [illegible] awarded as this prize, and determine what [illegible]t the smaller prizes will have on the [illegible] of the "grand prize."

Evaluation

Level	Standard to be achieved for performance at specified level
5	The student demonstrates an in-depth understanding of combinations and probability and their application to the given situation. Calculations are accurate and complete, and the student's explanations reflect considerable insight. The plan for conducting the lottery is presented in a well-organized and thoughtful report that may be rendered imaginatively. Any errors are minor.
4	The student demonstrates a good understanding of combinations and probability and their application to the given situation. The student sets up appropriate calculations and provides reasonable responses to the questions posed, but the calculations contain minor errors, and the responses may reflect some misconceptions. The report is well-organized and easy to read, but may lack in some detail.
3	The student demonstrates some understanding of combinations and probability, but needs assistance in applying the concepts to the given situation. Calculations contain major errors and responses to questions posed may indicate some flaws in reasoning. The report is essentially complete, but may be somewhat disorganized.
2	The student demonstrates a little understanding of combinations and probability, but needs considerable assistance in understanding their application to the given situation. Even with help, the student makes several major errors in calculations and omits major steps of the process. The student attempts to prepare a report, but it is jumbled and incomplete.
1	The student demonstrates very little if any understanding of combinations and probability and their application to the given situation. Some calculations may be attempted, but they are superfluous or irrelevant. There are no coherent responses to the questions posed. Instead of writing a report, the student may simply copy or restate the given information.